# A Practical Guide to
# Autodesk Civil 3D® 2020

**Rick Ellis**

A CADapult Press Publication

## Copyright

Published in the United States of America by:
CADapult Press, Inc.
(503) 829-8929
books@cadapult-software.com

Printed and manufactured in the United States of America

## About the Author

**Rick Ellis** has worked with and taught Autodesk Civil 3D, along with Map 3D and other Autodesk products since the mid-90s. He is the Author of several critically acclaimed books on Autodesk Civil 3D, Map 3D and Land Desktop.

Rick continues to use Autodesk Civil 3D on projects in a production environment, in addition to teaching classes to organizations both large and small.

This practical background and approach has made him an award winning speaker at Autodesk University, a member of the national speaker team for the AUGI CAD Camps and a sought after instructor by organizations around the world.

Rick can be reached at: rick@cadapult-software.com

## About the Technical Editor

**Russell Martin** is an independent consultant who has worked with AutoCAD since 1985. He pioneered the position of Staff Geographer, and later served as CAD/GIS Manager at a multi-disciplinary engineering consulting firm. Russell has served as technical editor for many of Cadapult Press training books, and has co-authored and contributed to several other books on CAD, GIS and technical graphics software.

Russell can be reached at: russell@cadapult-software.com

## Exercise Data

I would like to thank the City of Springfield, Oregon for providing the data for this book. The dataset provided is for illustration purposes only. While it is based on real world information to add relevance to the exercises, it has been altered and modified to more effectively demonstrate certain features as well as to protect all parties involved. The data should not be used for any project work and may not represent actual places or things. It is prohibited to redistribute this data beyond your personal use as a component of training.

# A Practical Guide to Autodesk Civil 3D 2020

## Introduction

Congratulations on choosing this course to help you learn how to use Autodesk Civil 3D 2020. The term "practical" is used in the title because this course focuses on what you need to effectively use Autodesk Civil 3D 2020 and does not complicate your learning experience with unnecessary details of every feature in the product. Should you want to pursue aspects of features and functionality in greater detail than provided in this course, you are directed and guided to that information.

Each lesson contains the concepts and principles of each feature to provide you with the background and foundation of knowledge that you need to complete the lesson. You then work through real world exercises to reinforce your understanding and provide you with practice on common tasks that other professionals are performing with Autodesk Civil 3D 2020 in the workplace every day.

You can take the lessons in this course in whatever order is appropriate for your personal needs. If you want to concentrate on specific features, the lesson for those features does not require that you complete prior lessons. With this course organization, you can customize your own individual approach to learning Autodesk Civil 3D.

When you complete this course, you will be armed with the background and knowledge to apply Autodesk Civil 3D to your job tasks, and become more effective and productive in your job.


## Course Objectives

The objectives of this course are performance based. In other words, once you have completed the course, you will be able to perform each objective listed. If you are already familiar with Autodesk Civil 3D, you will be able to analyze your existing workflows, and make changes to improve your performance based on the tools and features that you learn and practice in this course.

After completing this course, you will be able to:

- Understand and work with Object Styles.
- Create, manage and apply Label Styles.
- Import and manage Points, and work with Point Groups.
- Create and edit Alignments.
- Define Parcels.
- Create and edit Profiles and Profile Views.
- Create Corridors and extract information from them.
- Sample Sections and plot Section Views.
- Import and leverage GIS Data in your Civil 3D projects.
- Use Queries to manage and share data.
- Layout Pipe Networks and edit them in plan and profile.
- Layout Pressure Networks and edit them in plan and profile.
- Create Sheets with the Plan Production tools.
- Work with the Grading tools.
- Create reports for Civil 3D objects.
- Calculate Volumes.
- Share project data with Data Shortcuts.

## Prerequisites

Before starting this course, you should have a basic working knowledge of AutoCAD. A deep understanding of AutoCAD is not required, but you should be able to:

- Pan and Zoom in the AutoCAD drawing screen.
- Describe what layers are in AutoCAD, and change the current layer.
- Create basic CAD geometry, such as lines, polylines and circles.
- Use Object Snaps.
- Describe what blocks are, and how to insert them.
- Perform basic CAD editing functions such as Erase, Copy, and Move.

If you are not familiar with these functions, you can refer to the AutoCAD Help system throughout the course to gain the fundamental skills needed to complete the exercises.

## Conventions

The course uses the following icons and formatting to draw your attention to guidelines that increase your effectiveness in Autodesk Civil 3D, or provide deeper insight into a subject.

 The magnifying glass indicates that this text provides deeper insights into the subject.

 The compass indicates that this text provides guidance that is based on the experience of other users of Autodesk Civil 3D. This guidance is often in the form of how to perform a task more efficiently.

# Downloading and Installing the Datasets

In order to perform the exercises in this book, you must download a zip file and install the datasets.

Type the address below into your web browser to load the page where you can download the dataset.
**www.cadapult-software.com/data**

If you are using a previous version of Civil 3D you can download previous versions of the dataset to use with this book.

## Unzip the Files

Unzip the file **APG_C3D2020.zip** directly to the C drive. The zip file will create the following folder structure:

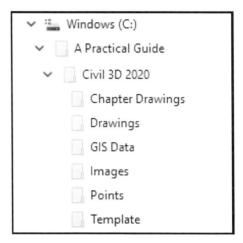

A folder called *Chapter Drawings* is created that contains a drawing that can be used to begin each exercise. This will allow you to jump in at the beginning of any exercise in the book, and do just the specific exercises that you want, if you do not have time to work through the book from cover to cover. The drawings in the Chapter Drawings folder are not necessary and only need to be used if you want to start in the middle of the book, or if you want to overwrite any mistakes that you may have made in previous chapters.

Three drawing templates called *_Practical Guide Training by Style.dwt*, *_Practical Guide Plan & Profile.dwt* and *_Practical Guide Section.dwt* are also available in the template folder.

## Exercises

The exercises in this course have been designed to represent common tasks that are performed by civil engineers, surveyors, designers and drafters. The data included in the exercises are typical drawings, point files and other data used by professionals like you. You work with drawings, point files, aerial photos, GIS data, and much more; as you work through a road design project that also includes a sewer extension and detention pond.

Exercises provide higher level process information throughout the exercise tasks. You are given information about not only what to do, but why you are doing it. In most cases, an image is included to help guide you.

# Table of Contents

# 1 - Autodesk Civil 3D User Interface

In this chapter, you will learn to navigate through the Civil 3D user interface. You will also learn about settings that can help you configure the Civil 3D environment to work more efficiently for you. Two drawing templates are included with the dataset and you will copy those to your template folder. Finally, you will learn how project data is saved in Civil 3D and get an overview of the project used in this book.

## Lesson: Navigating the Autodesk Civil 3D User Interface

In this lesson, you learn how to effectively navigate and use the Autodesk Civil 3D user interface. You learn the basics of how to work with ribbons, set options that make Autodesk Civil 3D work best for you, and set workspaces.

## Lesson: Project Overview

In this lesson, you learn how project data is managed in Civil 3D. You will also get an overview of the project used for the examples in this book.

## 1.1 Lesson: Navigating the Autodesk Civil 3D User Interface

### Introduction

In this lesson, you learn how to effectively navigate and use the Autodesk Civil 3D user interface. You learn the basics of how to work with ribbons, set options that make Autodesk Civil 3D work best for you, and set workspaces.

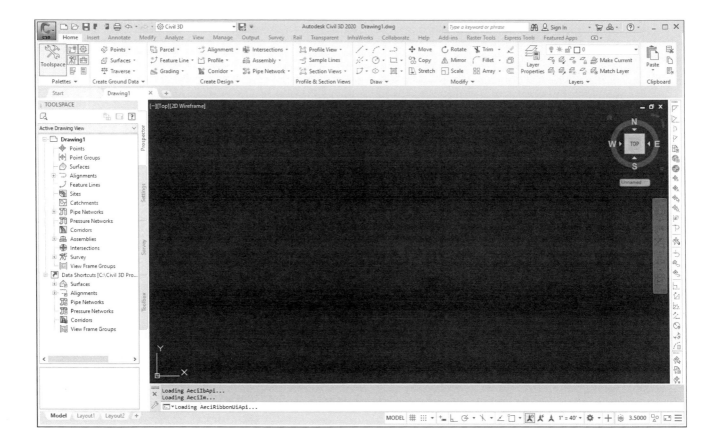

### Key Concepts

Concepts and key terms covered in this lesson are:

- Interface
- Objects
- Ribbons
- Toolspace
- Task Pane
- Workspaces

### Objectives

After completing this lesson, you will be able to:

- Describe the high-level design approach of the Autodesk Civil 3D user interface.
- Describe ribbons and their components.
- Explain the Toolspace and how it is organized.
- Navigate the Autodesk Civil 3D interface and make settings.

## About the Autodesk Civil 3D Interface

The Autodesk Civil 3D interface is similar to AutoCAD in terms of the components used. The ribbons and menus are specific to Autodesk Civil 3D, but you can configure the ribbons and menus to be organized in any way you like. There are three main components to the Autodesk Civil 3D interface:

- Ribbons
- Toolspace
- Task Pane

Nearly all commands have multiple methods for access. It is not the intent of this course to describe each method of command access. For more information on command access alternatives, refer to the Autodesk Civil 3D help system.

## About Ribbons

Ribbons are the primary interface for Autodesk Civil 3D. Ribbons are similar to menus but with more direct access to the most common commands you use. The following illustration provides definitions for the ribbon components.

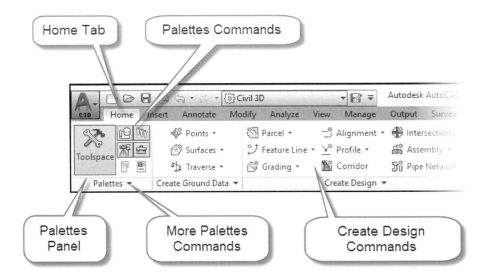

## Contextual Ribbons

When working with Autodesk Civil 3D, depending on your activity, if there is a context ribbon available, Autodesk Civil 3D automatically displays that ribbon. In the following example, the surface EG is selected, and Autodesk Civil 3D displays the **Tin Surface: EG** context ribbon with panels and commands that are used to work with surfaces.

## About the Toolspace

The Toolspace, where you manage civil objects, control settings and styles, generate reports and work with survey data. You can access many common Civil 3D command through the Toolspace. There are four tabs in the Toolspace:

- Prospector
- Settings
- Survey
- Toolbox

## Prospector

The Prospector tab displays and allows access to all of the civil objects in the drawing. You can expand the object collections to view information about individual objects. Here you can right-click on the object to access many common commands.

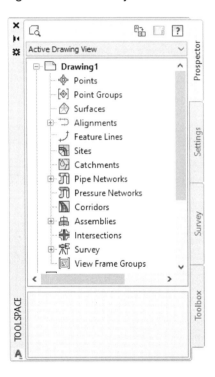

## Settings

The Settings tab manages object styles for the display of civil objects and label styles for annotating them. You can also specify drawing settings and command defaults on this tab.

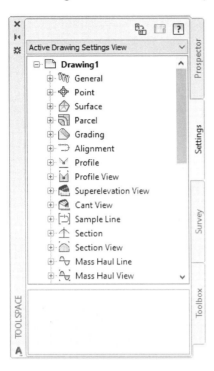

## Survey

The Survey tab is used to manage survey data.

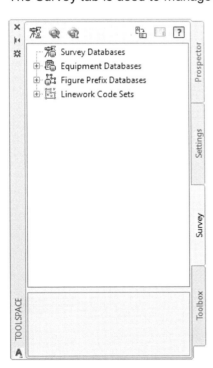

## Toolbox

The Toolbox tab contains the Report Manager as well as third party tools that you may acquire over time.

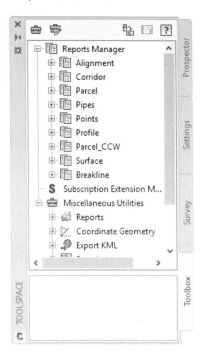

## About the Task Pane

The Task Pane displays many of the data connections, attached drawing files, feature layers, and much more. Along with these lists is access to the most common commands used. There are four tabs in the Task Pane:

- Display Manager
- Map Explorer
- Map Book
- Survey

Each tab has a toolstrip menu along the top with command buttons that are specific to the elements in that tab.

## Display Manager

You use the Display Manager to manage display maps. The layers in the Display Manager can be both features as well as drawing layers. By default, when features are added to a map, the layers are displayed in the Display Manager rather than as a traditional layer in AutoCAD.

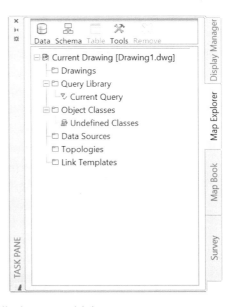

## Map Explorer

The Map Explorer displays all drawings that are attached and all data sources that are connected. In addition, the Map Explorer displays additional definitions in the drawing such as Queries, Object Classes, Topologies, and Link Templates.

## Map Book

The Map Book tab displays Map Book pages. Map books are a series of tiled maps which can cover a large area of interest. Each page, or tile, can be plotted at a larger scale.

## Survey

The Survey tab displays any survey data that is connected to the drawing. This tab is a feature of AutoCAD Map and is different than the Civil 3D survey tools. Civil 3D handles survey data differently through the Toolspace.

## The Autodesk Civil 3D Workspaces

Autodesk Civil 3D is installed with four workspaces that you can begin work with. Each workspace is organized so that you can work in a custom, task-oriented environment. You can also customize the workspaces, or create your own, to better suit your specific job tasks and style of working with Autodesk Civil 3D. The primary change in the interface when you select a workspace is the way the ribbon is organized.

The workspaces provided in Autodesk Civil 3D are:

- Civil 3D
- Drafting & Annotation
- 3D Modeling
- Planning and Analysis

# Civil 3D

The Civil 3D ribbon displays commands related to civil engineering and surveying features.

# Drafting & Annotation

The Drafting & Annotation ribbon is customized for those who are familiar with the AutoCAD ribbon and work primarily with general drafting tasks. The civil engineering and surveying features that are unique to Civil 3D are hidden in this workspace.

# 3D Modeling

The 3D Modeling ribbon displays commands related to the 3D modeling features in AutoCAD.

# Planning and Analysis

The Planning & Analysis ribbon displays commands related to the AutoCAD Map 3D features available in Civil 3D. It attempts to organize commands in a way that combines object and feature commands in each panel based on tasks related to setting up a GIS, and performing spatial analysis tasks.

## Setting Options
Autodesk Civil 3D is built on top of a full version of AutoCAD®. While the Autodesk Civil 3D designers have setup the default configurations to maximize the effectiveness of your work in a civil environment, there are some settings you can make to fine-tune how Autodesk Civil 3D behaves. Many of these settings are meant to limit the tools that appear while performing tasks and other settings are to display certain components that assist in engineering and surveying tasks.

## Drafting Settings
AutoCAD is often used in an architectural or mechanical environment. In these cases, objects in the drawings are often orthogonal, while in civil engineering, surveying and mapping, this is rarely the case. You can disable these drafting tools and minimize the behavior to better represent drawing tasks for your workflow.

## Command Line
Autodesk Civil 3D by default is configured to use Dynamic Input. This is a method of heads-up command entry which does not require that you look at the command line to enter commands and options. However, in Autodesk Civil 3D the command line reports the status of several commands that otherwise are not reported.

## GIS tools in Civil 3D

In addition to all of the tools built into Civil 3D for civil engineering workflows, the software also includes many powerful tools for creating, editing, importing, displaying and utilizing a wide range of GIS and mapping data. For instance, aerial and satellite imagery can be displayed, geometric data that includes corresponding tabular data can be attached to existing AutoCAD objects, such as lines representing pipes and polygons representing tax lots. Geometry with corresponding tabular data can also be attached to, or displayed in Civil 3D drawing files, from a variety of GIS sources, such as ESRI Shapefiles and Autodesk SDF.

Many of these additional tools can be used alone, or in various combinations, and are not necessarily limited to GIS and mapping projects, or even civil design projects. Unlike most Civil 3D workflow processes, these tasks are typically not linear. For instance, for any given project you may use different combinations of these tools or processes, in different sequences.

*Autodesk Civil 3D* is built on top of *AutoCAD Map 3D*, which is built on top of standard *AutoCAD*. Using the many tools found in *Civil 3D*, you can work with three types of objects: standard *AutoCAD* objects, (such as lines, arcs, circles, polylines and blocks); *Map 3D* objects, (such as *Object Data*, *Topologies* and connected *Features*); and *Civil 3D* objects, (such as alignments, profiles, parcels, surfaces, and pipe networks).

| Autodesk Product: | Tools work on: |
|---|---|
| **AutoCAD Civil 3D** | **Civil 3D Objects, (such as Alignments, Surfaces, Profiles, Parcels, etc.), plus everything below.** |
| **AutoCAD Map 3D** | **Map 3D Objects, (such as Object Data, Topologies, Connected Features, etc.), plus everything below.** |
| **AutoCAD** | **Standard AutoCAD Objects, (such as Lines, Circles, Polygons and Blocks).** |

Some commands are designed to only work with standard AutoCAD objects, while other commands are designed to work specifically with Map 3D or Civil 3D objects. This chapter will give you an introduction to a few of these GIS tools. While they are not a required part of the Civil 3D workflow, you may find they can save you a tremendous amount of time on typical Civil 3D projects. If you would like to learn even more about the GIS tools in Civil 3D check out our book *A Practical Guide to GIS in Autodesk Civil 3D*.

## Exercise: Navigate the Autodesk Civil 3D Interface

In this exercise, you start Autodesk Civil 3D for the first time. You choose the Civil 3D Workspace and examine the ribbons and commands. You then set options that make Autodesk Civil 3D behave in a more efficient manner.

You do the following:

- Start Autodesk Civil 3D and set a workspace.
- Examine tabs and ribbons.
- Examine the Toolspace.
- Set Options

### 1.1.1 Navigating the Autodesk Civil 3D Interface

In the first series of steps, you start Autodesk Civil 3D, and choose a Workspace.

NOTE: Instructions for Downloading and Installing the Datasets can be found on page vi.

1. Start Autodesk Civil 3D.

2. In the upper-left corner of the screen, click on select the **Workspace Picker** and notice the various workspace options available.

3. Select the **Civil 3D Workspace**.

Note: Autodesk Civil 3D may have started with this workspace already set.

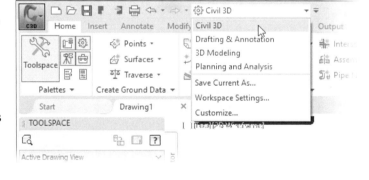

4. Examine the tabs in the *Civil 3D* workspace.

5. Select the **Modify** tab and review the commands.

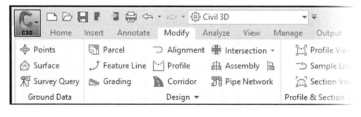

6. Select the **Analyze** tab and review the commands.

Exercises in this book will use the following format to access *Ribbon* commands:

Select **Ribbon: Analyze ⇒ Ground Data ⇒ Contour Check.**

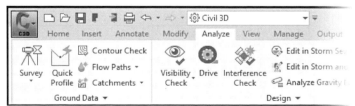

7. In the **Toolspace**, select the **Prospector** tab and examine the layout.

You will be using the *Toolspace* for many of the exercises in this book.

8. Right-click the **Surfaces** object.

9. Examine the commands available in the context menu.

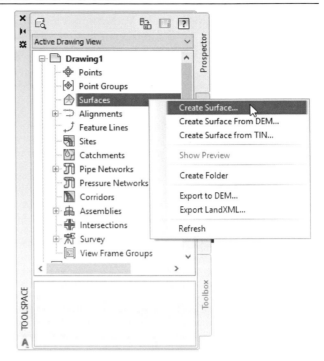

Most nodes and objects in the *Toolspace* tabs have right-click menus you can work from.

Exercises in this book will use the following format to access *Toolspace* commands:

In the *Prospector*, right-click **Surfaces** and select ⇒ **Create Surface.**

10. Continue to explore the tabs and tools on the *Toolspace*, and leave it open.

Like many other Autodesk interface palettes, it can be docked, float over the drawing editor and made to Auto-Hide when not needed. You will be using the Toolspace for a lot of exercises in this book, so it is good practice to leave it available.

11. On the Status bar, deselect:
   • Dynamic Input
   • Polar Tracking
   • Object Snap Tracking
   • 3D Object Snap
   • Allow/Disallow Dynamic UCS

Each of these options can be turned back on at any time and are really personal preferences that are up to you. Generally, they are not needed in a civil engineering and surveying environment. If any of these options are not visible on the status bar you can add them by

clicking the customization button ≡ .

Next you will copy two drawing templates from the dataset provided to your default template folder in Civil 3D.

12. Right-click anywhere in the drawing editor, and select ⇒ **Options.**

13. In the *Options* dialog box, select the **Files** tab.

14. Expand **Template Settings**.

15. Expand **Drawing Template File Location**.

16. Take note of the path.

This path may be different on your system than the one shown to the right.

17. Click **<<Cancel>>** to exit the dialog box without making any changes.

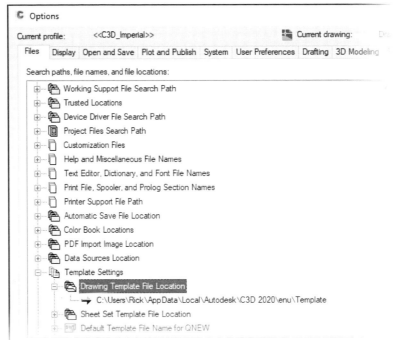

18. Open Windows Explorer and browse to the dataset.
    **C:\A Practical Guide\Civil 3D 2020\Template\**

19. Copy the three templates:
    **_Practical Guide Plan & Profile.dwt**
    **_Practical Guide Section.dwt**
    **_Practical Guide Training by Style.dwt**

20. Paste these three templates into the folder you identified as the *Drawing Template File Location* earlier in the exercise.

These templates will be used in later exercises and contain many default styles and settings.

## Lesson Review

In this lesson, you became familiar with the basics of the Autodesk Civil 3D interface and set options that provide an efficient behavior in a civil engineering and surveying environment. You also saved three drawing templates to your template folder fur use in later lessons. The settings in this exercise represent the interface used in this course.

# 1.2 Lesson: Project Overview

## Introduction

In this lesson, you learn how project data is managed in Civil 3D. You will also get an overview of the project used for the examples in this book.

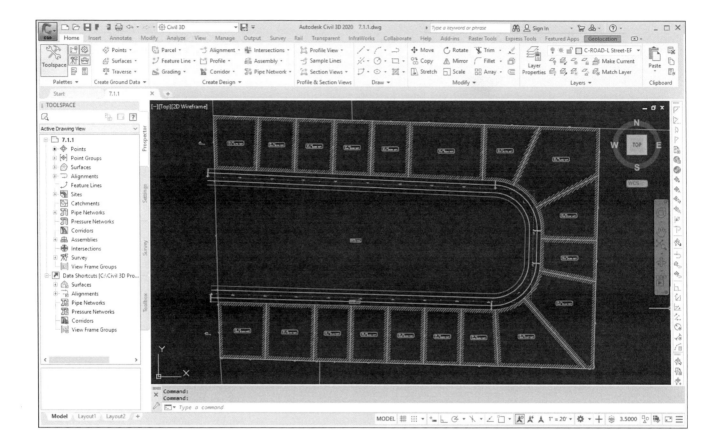

## Key Concepts

Concepts and key terms covered in this lesson are:

- Styles
- Data Shortcuts
- Vault

## Objectives

After completing this lesson, you will be able to:

- Describe different ways data is stored in Civil 3D.
- List items that can be saved in a Civil 3D template.
- Describe the project you will be working with in this book.

## Data Management

*Civil 3D* is a drawing based program and the majority of this book will cover working with *Civil 3D* in a standalone manner. However, *Civil 3D* does include an option to install *Autodesk Vault*. *Vault* is a powerful document management tool, and you should give your implementation of *Vault* careful consideration.

As an alternative to using *Vault* you can also share *Civil 3D* data between drawings with *Data Shortcuts*. Both *Vault* and *Data Shortcuts* are optional features and are not a required part of a *Civil 3D* project. This is a big change if you are a *Land Desktop* user who learned to leverage its project to share data and reduce drawing size. Since the data is stored in the *Civil 3D* drawing, it is important to **save often**. It also means that all of your settings and styles are saved in the drawing, and should also be saved in a drawing template, so they are available when you create new drawings.

Using *Data Shortcuts* will be covered in Chapter 11 of this book.

## Styles

One of the most important features in *Civil 3D* is *Styles*. *Styles* control the display, labeling, and in some cases the geometric properties of *Civil 3D* objects. This book will expose you to many different object and label styles, as you work through the project. You will find that in many cases the interface to create and edit these styles is similar from object to object. This consistency will help as you learn to work with styles because, for example, creating an alignment style is not that different than creating a profile style.

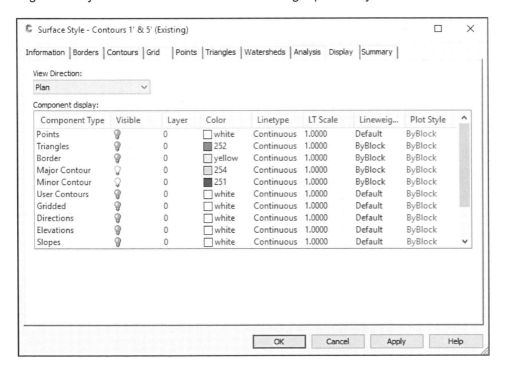

*Styles* control the display of the components that make up an object. For example, a *Surface Style* has components that control the display of that surface as triangles, contours, points, elevation bands, slope arrows, and much more. The style controls the visibility, color, layer, linetype, linetype scale, lineweight, and plot style of these components. One of the choices that you will need to make as you set up your own styles is if the styles will be configured to place each component on a different layer so that you can manage the display of the components with standard layer commands; or, if the styles will be configured to manage the display of the components themselves, independent of layers. This book will use styles to manage the display of the components, independent of layers, to expose you to these new options and limit the number of layers in the drawing.

## Project Overview

The exercises in this book lead you through a basic road design project from beginning to end. The project begins by importing data from a variety of sources. You will learn how Civil 3D can leverage existing GIS data, aerial photography, and aerial survey data to efficiently add information to your project and manage it with one program.

The project continues with preliminary layout and design by building a surface from the aerial survey data, laying out a preliminary alignment, and exporting points for field verification.

Next you will add survey data to the project and learn to manage points through the use of description keys, point groups, point styles, and point label styles. The survey points will be used to create a more accurate surface and that new surface will be merged with the aerial surface to give you more accurate surface data on the site while using the aerial survey information around the edge of the site where you do not have survey data. Parcels will also be defined based on the survey points.

You will continue on to alignment design where you will lay out and edit the horizontal alignment. You will learn how alignments interact with parcels and you will subdivide and layout new parcels based on several criteria. You will also create and edit existing and finished grade profiles.

The road design will be completed as you create a corridor that combines the alignment, profile, surface, and assembly into a model of the road design. The corridor model is used to create surfaces and sections that you will plot as well as use for quantity takeoffs.

After completing the road design you will move on to pipe networks where you learn to lay out a pipe network, edit and label it in both plan and profile.

Next you move on to the grading tools. You will create a grading group to grade a pond and automatically generate a surface. The pond surface will be compared with the existing surface to create a volume surface and calculate cut and fill quantities.

The book concludes with a look at managing and sharing project data with Data Shortcuts. You will learn about the different methods of managing project data in Civil 3D and how to share and reference objects with Data Shortcuts.

## Lesson Review

In this lesson, you learned how project data is managed in Civil 3D. You also explored an overview of the project used for the examples in this book.

# 2 - Data Collection and Base Map Preparation

One of the strengths of *Civil 3D* is its ability to bring together data from a variety of sources for use in your project. This chapter shows several ways to bring data from different sources together to build base maps with existing map information. It covers importing GIS data, inserting registered ortho photography, as well as attaching and querying specific layers from planimetric map sheets and *Digital Terrain Model (DTM)* source sheets. Several of the tools covered in this chapter are part of *AutoCAD Map 3D*, which is the foundation for *Civil 3D*.

There are many other powerful Map 3D tools built in to Civil 3D, which can substantially increase your productivity.

### Lesson: Importing GIS Data

In this lesson, you begin by learning the formats and types of data that can be imported into Autodesk Civil 3D, and guidelines around integrating other mapping data into your mapping system. You then import ArcView Shapefile files representing streets and parcels and examine the associated data.

### Lesson: Using Queries to Manage and Share Data

In this lesson, you learn the basic concepts of attaching source drawings and using queries to manage, edit, and extract drawing objects.

## 2.1    Lesson:  Importing GIS Data

### Introduction

Importing GIS file formats into Autodesk Civil 3D opens the door to a tremendous amount of data. Much of this data is free, and can be integrated into your mapping system. In this lesson, you begin by learning the formats and types of data that can be imported into Autodesk Civil 3D, and guidelines around integrating other mapping data into your mapping system. You then import an ArcView SHP file into Autodesk Civil 3D.

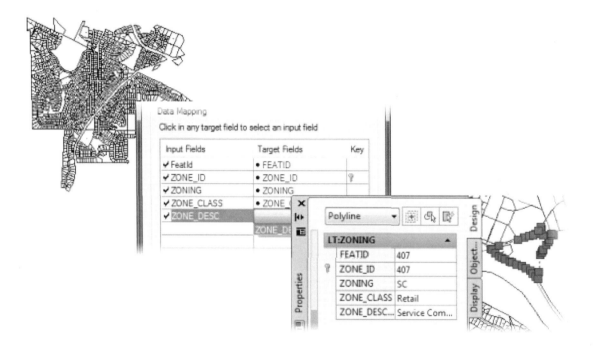

### Key Concepts

Concepts and key terms covered in this lesson are:

- Import
- Geometry
- Attributes
- Coordinate Systems
- Import dialog box

### Objectives

After completing this lesson, you will be able to:

- Describe what Map Import is.
- List the components that can be imported, and how Autodesk Civil 3D interprets incoming data.
- Identify and explain the tools used to import GIS data.
- Import street segments and parcels with Object Data.
- Review the data attached to the imported objects and describe its uses.

## About Importing GIS Data into Autodesk Civil 3D

GIS Data generally contains three types of data: geometry, attributes, and coordinate system data. Using the map import tools, you can define how Autodesk Civil 3D interprets and imports all three types of data.

The Map Import commands are used to convert other GIS formats into Autodesk Civil 3D geometry and attributes with the intent to retain them in the Autodesk Civil 3D format, with no need to maintain them in their original GIS format.

 Autodesk Civil 3D can also connect to data as a feature source and work with these files in their native format.

### Geometry

All GIS formats are different. Autodesk Civil 3D imports the data in such a way as to represent the native format as closely as possible. An example of this functionality is when importing line data from an ArcView shape file, any segments in the incoming file that have vertexes are imported as polylines, while those that are simple lines with a start and endpoint are imported as lines.

Points can be imported and mapped to either AutoCAD points, or blocks that are defined in the drawing.

### Attributes

Attributes are any data attached to an object. In *AutoCAD* you may be familiar with block attributes, which is a way to attach data to an *AutoCAD* block. *AutoCAD Map 3D* expands your ability to attach data to any object, not just a block, with object data and external database links. This means that in *AutoCAD Map 3D* the term *Attribute Data* applies not only to blocks but also to object data and external database links.

Attributes that are associated with incoming data can be mapped to Object Data, or can be imported to an attached data source, such as a Microsoft Access database table, and linked to the objects at the same time.

### Coordinate Systems

If the incoming file has coordinate system information associated with it, either within the file itself, or a companion file, Autodesk Civil 3D will read this information and convert the coordinates to the target drawing file. If there is no coordinate system information in the incoming file, you can assign a coordinate system to it during the import procedure.

### Spatial Filters

Some GIS applications can manage larger data sets than can be reasonably managed within Autodesk Civil 3D. Spatial filters enable you to limit the amount of data that you import based on a location in the current map.

## Guidelines for Preparing for Map Import

You can start a new drawing and simply import data. In most cases, you want to prepare a target drawing with layers, Object Data tables, or attached data sources that will receive the incoming data. This is especially true if your office has mapping standards that must be adhered to, or if you are importing into an existing drawing that already has all the layers, Object Data tables, or attached data sources present.

Another important point when preparing for an import is to have some familiarity with the incoming data. This may come from metadata or documentation of some kind. The best way to qualify the incoming data is to use the native application to review. However, this is not always possible, in which case the import process might be a trial and error process until you can make the correct settings for the final import.

If you perform the same type of import regularly, you can save a profile of the settings and load the profile each time you perform an import. You can also create a drawing template that has all of the definitions such as Object Data tables, layers, blocks and so on.

## The Import Interface

Once the target file is prepared, and the incoming data is qualified, the entire import procedure is performed in a single interface with various dialog boxes for the settings.

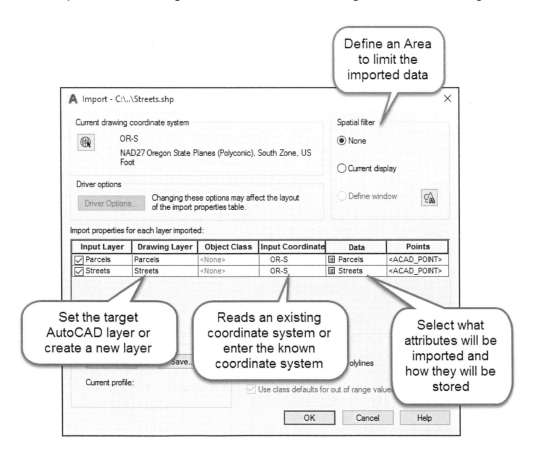

## Uses for Attached Attribute Data

Attribute data may be attached to objects in Civil 3D by importing GIS files that already contain data or by manually adding it in Civil 3D. Regardless of how the data is created once is it attached to objects in your drawing there are many ways it can be used. The following list contains some common examples, most likely, you can think of more that would apply to your project.

- Labeling Objects
- Quantity Takeoffs
- Creating Thematic Maps
- Mailing Lists
- Adding General Intelligence to the Drawing

## Exercises: Import Data from Other GIS Formats

In these exercises, you will add parcel and street data from the GIS department as well as an aerial photo of the project area. You will also insert an AutoCAD block that represents the extents of our project.

The use of the import command is very similar for all the different types of supported GIS data file formats. However, there are some differences depending on the type of geometry that is contained in those files (points, lines, or polygons).

You do the following:

- Import parcels and streets from ArcView shape files.
- View the data associated with the imported objects.
- Attach and Aerial Photo.
- Insert an AutoCAD block representing the project boundary.

### 2.1.1    Importing ESRI Shapefiles

*ArcView Shapefiles* are among the most common types of GIS data files that you will encounter. In this exercise, you will add parcel and street information from the city, which is in a *Shapefile* format, to your drawing for use as background information. This is an example of how you can use *Civil 3D* to bring data together from a variety of sources to meet the needs of your project.

1. Press **Ctrl + N** and select the template **_Practical Guide Training by Style.dwt** to start a new drawing.

NOTE: Instructions for Downloading and Installing the Datasets can be found on page vi.

*Civil 3D* makes extensive use of styles to control the display and properties of *Civil Objects*. These styles are saved in the drawing and default styles can be saved in a drawing template. You will probably create many customized styles for your organization and should add them to your standard drawing template file, so that all users have access to them in each new drawing they create. However, when you first start out with *Civil 3D* you will want to start with an existing template like the one provided with this book, *_Practical Guide Training By Style.dwt,* so that you can see some example styles and modify them to fit your needs. If you start with a blank template like acad.dwt you will only have the *standard* style available for all objects.

2. Click the Workspace button  on the status bar and set the current workspace to **Planning and Analysis**.

2638.9396, 7306.6591, 0.0000   MODEL   ⊞  ⋮⋮  ▾  +  L  ⟲  ▾  ⅄  ▾  ∠  ▯  ▾  🗚  🗚  🗚  1" = 40' ▾  ⚙  ▾  ╋  🌐  3.5000  ⊡  ⊡  ≡

3. Select **Ribbon: Insert ⇒ Import ⇒ Map Import**.

The *Import Location* dialog box opens.

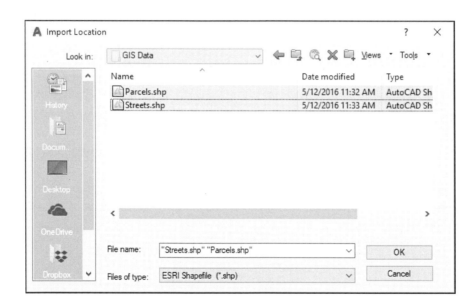

4. Browse to:

   **C:\A Practical Guide\Civil 3D 2020\GIS Data**

5. Set the Files of type to **ESRI Shapefile (*.shp)**.

6. Select the files **Parcels.shp** and **Streets.shp**.

7. Click **<<OK>>** to continue.

In the *Import* dialog box you can configure the *Layer, Coordinate Conversion*, and *Data* options that you wish to use to Import each of these two *Shapefiles* into *Civil 3D*.

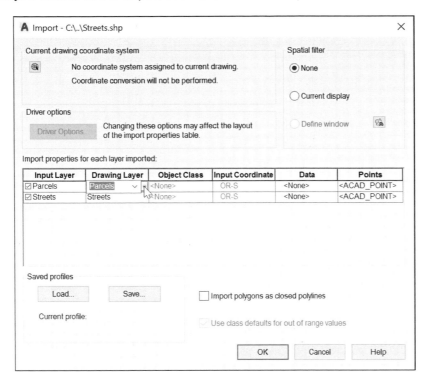

8.  Click on the **Drawing Layer** field in the *Parcels* row to activate the **more <<...>>** button.  Click this button to bring up the *Layer Mapping* dialog box.

Here you can choose to import the drawing objects onto an existing layer, create a new layer, or select a column of data from the file that you are importing to determine the layer names.  This last option will allow you to do some basic thematic mapping during the import of the objects.  For example, if you were importing parcel data and that data set had a column for zoning, you could have the import command create a new layer for each zoning type and place each parcel on the appropriate layer for its zoning designation.  However, in this exercise you will simply import all of the parcels onto one layer.

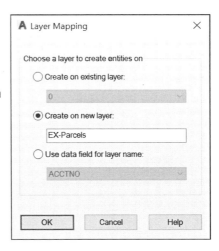

9.  Choose **Create on new layer** and name it **EX-Parcels**.

10. Click **<<OK>>**.

11. Repeat the process for the *Streets ShapeFile*, creating it on a new layer named **EX-Streets**.

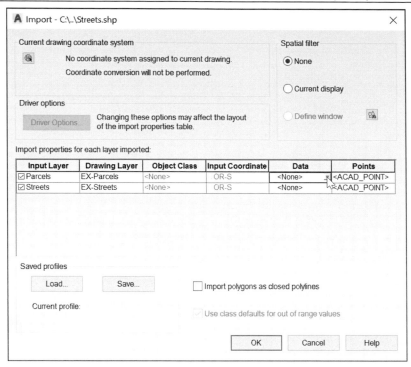

12. Back in the *Import* dialog box, click on the **Data** field in the *Parcels* row to activate the **more <<…>>** button.

13. Click the **more <<…>>** button to bring up the *Attribute Data* dialog box.

Here you will create *Object Data* from the shapefile's attribute data. You can enter the desired name for the *Object Data Table* and select the desired fields to import. This is the step that allows you to bring the intelligence of the GIS file along with the geometry into *AutoCAD*. By creating the object data table and populating it with the information provided in the shape file you will be able to click on a parcel and find the owner name, address, zoning, and any other information that was added by the GIS department. This will also allow you to edit the geometry and data from the GIS file in *AutoCAD* and then export it back to any of the supported GIS formats without losing any of the attached data. If you leave the *Data* option set to *None* or *Do not import attribute data*, then you will only import the geometry of the file and you will lose all of the attached information. The ability to convert the attribute data to object data is one reason the *Map Import* feature so powerful.

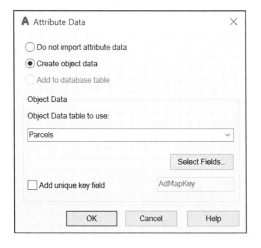

14. Choose **Create object data**.

15. Enter **Parcels** for the name of the **Object Data table to use**.

This will create a new *Object Data Table* in the drawing to store the parcel attribute data. You can name this *Object Data Table* anything you like, but it is recommended to keep the name simple and descriptive to avoid confusion. The name must be in alphanumeric characters with a maximum length of 25 characters. The name cannot contain spaces or symbols.

16. Click **<<OK>>** to return to the *Import* dialog box.

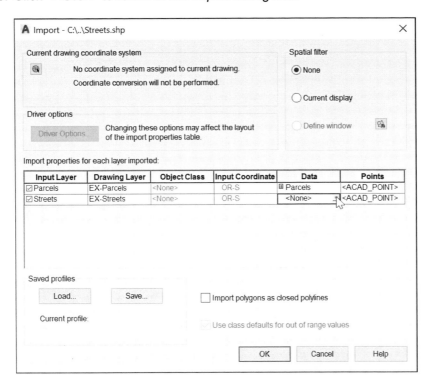

17. Click on the **Data** field in the *Streets* row to activate the **more <<…>>** button. Click this button to bring up the *Attribute Data* dialog box.

18. Choose **Create object data**.

19. Enter **Streets** for the name of the *Object Data table to use*.

20. This time, click the **<<Select Fields>>** button.

This will allow you to select only the attribute data you wish to import rather than the entire database.

21. Deselect all fields except **NAME_FULL**, **SPEED**, and **TYPE**.

This option allows you to be selective about what information you import into *AutoCAD*. If you don't want to import all of the attached data, you have control over the columns of information that you import from the shape file.

22. Click **<<OK>>** to return to the *Import* dialog box.

The completed dialog box should look like the one below. If you have assigned a coordinate system to the drawing it will display at the top of the Import dialog box. You can also assign a coordinate system to the drawing at this time by selecting the *Assign Global Coordinate System* button. If a coordinate system has been assigned to the drawing the *Input Coordinate System* column will be activated. This allows you to assign a coordinate system to the files that you are importing. If the input coordinate system is different than the current drawing coordinate system the geometry will be converted to the current drawing coordinate system as it is imported.

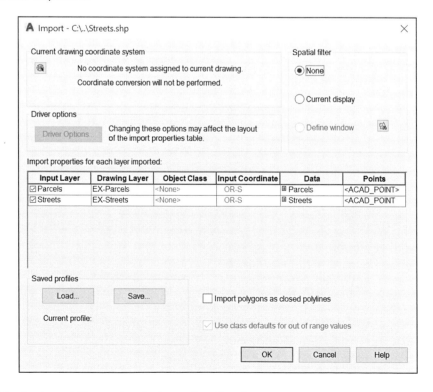

23. Click **<<OK>>** to begin importing the data.

24. **Zoom to Extents** to view the imported objects.

### 2.1.2 Controlling the Display of Polygons

Notice that the polygons are all displayed with a solid hatch fill. This display option is a feature of the *MPOLYGON* object. To display just the edges of the polygons you need to set the polygon display mode.

1. At the command line enter:
   Command: **POLYDISPLAY**

2. Type **E** to display only the edges of the polygons.

3. **Regen** to redisplay the Polygons.

4. Change the color of the layer **EX-Parcels** to **Yellow** and the layer **EX-Streets** to **Red**.

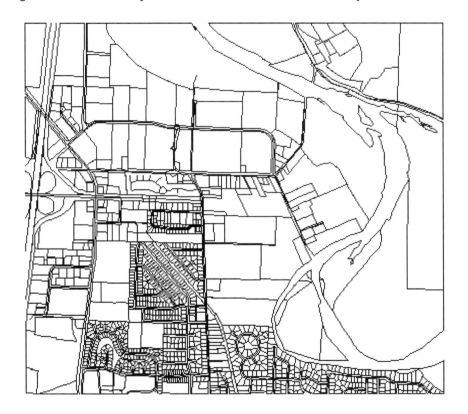

### 2.1.3 Viewing GIS Attributes in AutoCAD

When talking about GIS data the term *attributes* refers to any type of attached data, not just block attributes as in *AutoCAD* terminology. In *AutoCAD Map 3D*, attribute data can be object data, external database data, or block attributes. *Civil 3D* is built on and includes *AutoCAD Map 3D* which enables you to view and edit this attribute data, including attributes imported from GIS files, as well as attributes created as object data in *Map 3D*. To view the attributes imported above follow these steps.

1. Pick one of the new parcels, then right-click and select ⇒ **Properties**.

2. In the *Properties* palette, scroll to the bottom and notice the attribute data from the SHP file is now attached to the parcel.

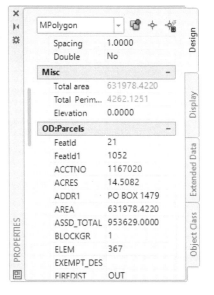

You can view and edit any of the object data here as needed.

3. Save the drawing as **Design.dwg**, in the folder **C:\A Practical Guide\Civil 3D 2020\**

### 2.1.4 Inserting a Registered Image (Rectified Aerial Photography)

It is important to use the **Ribbon: Insert ⇒ Image ⇒ Image** command when inserting a registered image, rather than the standard *AutoCAD* commands. This is because the Map command utilizes correlation information, in our example World Files (.tfw), to automatically place your image correctly in your coordinate system. Otherwise you would need to register each image manually.

1. Continue working in the drawing **Design.dwg**.

2. Create a layer called **Image** and set it **Current**.

3. Select **Ribbon: Insert ⇒ Image ⇒ Image.**

This opens the *Insert Image* dialog box where you can browse to and select the image that you want to insert into the drawing.

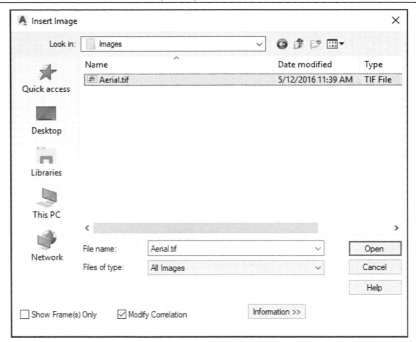

4. Browse to:
   **C:\A Practical Guide\ Civil 3D 2020\Images\**.

5. Confirm that the *Files of type:* is set to **All Images**.

6. Select the file **Aerial.tif**.

7. Click **<<Open>>**.

You will see that *Civil 3D* has automatically found the *World File* and set the *Correlation Source* and *Insertion Values*. You will also see a frame in your *AutoCAD* drawing editor showing the proposed location of the image.

8. Click **<<OK>>** to insert the image.

By default, the image will cover everything in your drawing. To correct this you will need to change the *display order* and move the image behind other drawing entities.

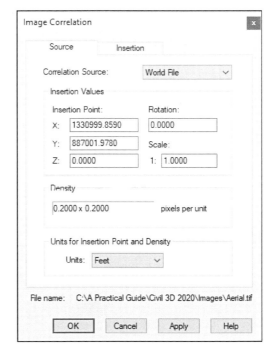

9. Select the Image by its frame, right-click and select **Display Order ⇒ Send to Back**.

You will now see the parcel and road centerlines displayed on top of the image. However, the image is still rather bright, making the linework somewhat difficult to see. This can be improved by adjusting the display properties of the image.

10. While holding the **[Shift]** key, **left-click** anywhere on the image to select it to display the context sensitive ribbon.

Alternatively, you could select the image by picking the frame. However, if you are zoomed into an area where you cannot see the frame, the *Shift Left-Click* method can be very useful.

11. Notice the context sensitive **Ribbon: Image** ⇒ **Adjust** panel has Brightness, Contrast and Fade controls.

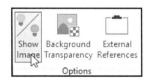

Here you can modify the brightness, contrast and fade of the image. Brightness and contrast adjustments can be helpful if the exposures differ somewhat on adjacent images, when inserting several.

12. Slide the **Fade** control to **40**.

Notice how much easier it is to see the parcel lines against a slightly faded image. No changes are made to the actual raster image file, only to the way it is displayed.

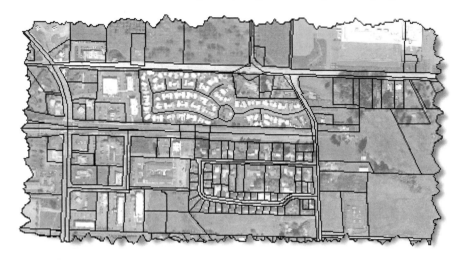

The aerial photographs provide useful background information, however they do take a lot of system resources to process and regenerate. So, when you are not using them it is best to turn them off.

13. While the image is still selected, on the context sensitive *Image* tab of the ribbon, select **Ribbon: Image** ⇒ **Options** ⇒ **Show Image**.

This is a toggle and can be used to turn the image on and off.

Now only the frame of the image is shown and regenerated.

You may elect to *Freeze* this layer as a valid alternative. The image is still attached and will be displayed again when the layer is thawed.

14. **[Esc]** to clear the selection and dismiss the context sensitive ribbon.

### 2.1.5    Assigning a Coordinate System to the Drawing

Coordinate systems can and should be assigned to drawings in *Civil 3D* whenever they are known.  Once assigned, the coordinate system is saved with the drawing, but only as a tag - no conversion occurs.

Assigning a Coordinate System will allow you to use the Online Map feature as well as preform coordinate tracking and coordinate conversions in the future.

The method of assigning a coordinate system used in this exercise is available in the *Planning and Analysis* workspace.  If you are in the *Civil 3D* workspace you can assign a coordinate system in the *Drawing Settings* command found on the *Settings* tab of the *ToolSpace*.

1.   Select **Ribbon: Map Setup ⇒ Coordinate System ⇒ Assign.**

The *Coordinate System - Assign* dialog box opens.

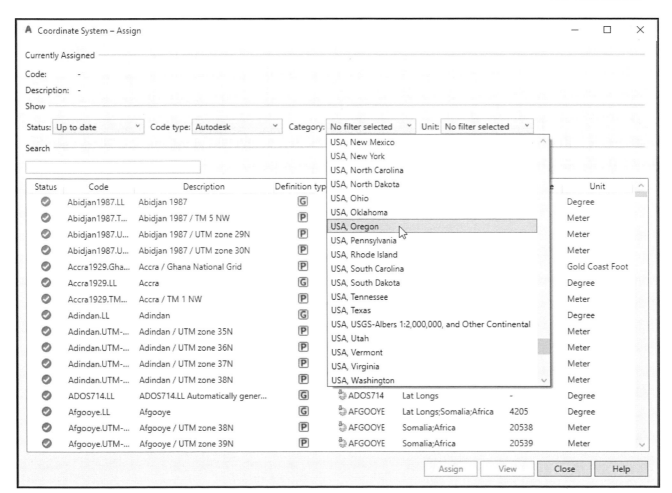

2.   From *Category* list, select **USA, Oregon**.

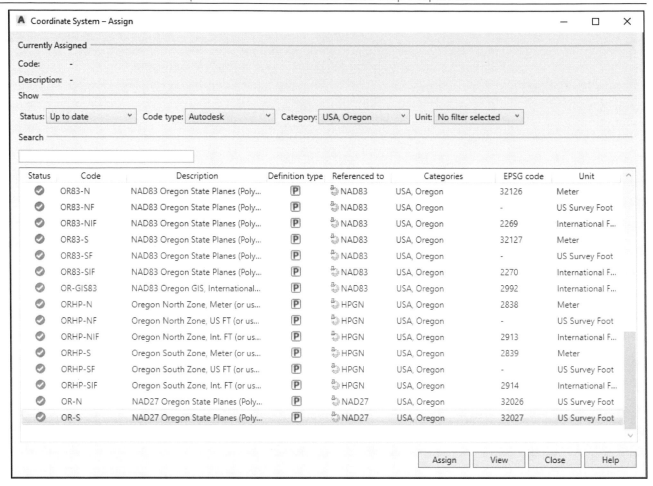

3. From list, select **OR-S   NAD27 Oregon State Planes (Polyconic), South Zone, US Foot**.

4. Click **<<Assign>>**.

The dialog box closes, and the *Ribbon* now displays the *Geolocation* tab.  Your drawing is now identified with the NAD 27 State Plane coordinate system - no conversion has occurred; you have a simply assigned that coordinate system to the drawing.  This will allow you to use the Online Map feature as well as preform coordinate tracking and coordinate conversions in the future.

Now that a coordinate system is assigned to the drawing you can add an Online Map.

## 2.1.6   Adding an Online Map

An alternative way to bring aerial imagery into your drawing is to us the online map service.
When signed in to *Autodesk A360*, you can turn on a map from an online maps service,
which displays as a background.  To use the *Online Map* you must have a coordinate system
assigned to your drawing.

1. If you are not signed into your Autodesk A360
   account, you must do so before you can use the
   Online Map feature.

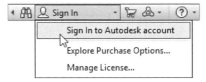

2. If you receive the prompt asking if you want to use
   Online Map Data click **<<Yes>>**.

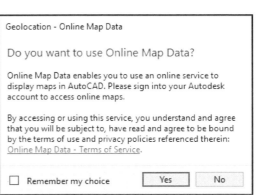

If you have already used online map data in Civil 3D you may not
get this prompt.

3. Select **Ribbon: Home ⇒ Online Map ⇒ Map Aerial**.

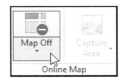

An aerial photo will now fill the background of your drawing area.  If you zoom out Civil 3D will
automatically stream a larger area of the map to fill the displayed area.  You also have
options to display a map of the roads or a hybrid map showing the roads on top of the aerial.

4. Select **Ribbon: Home ⇒ Online Map ⇒ Map Hybrid**.

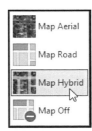

Street names and other feature labels are added to the background map data.

To plot the *Online Map, or to share the drawing with others who may not have an A360
account,* you will need to capture it first.

5. Select **Ribbon: Home ⇒ Online Map ⇒ Map Aerial**.

6. Zoom out and pan within the drawing editor.

Notice the online map adjust to always fill the editor screen with background map imagery.

7.  Zoom in to an area of your drawing similar to the image below.

Notice the resolution of the image adjusts to provide more detail at the higher resolution.

8.  Select **Ribbon: Home ⇒ Online Map ⇒ Capture Area**.

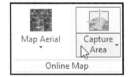

The command line prompts you to specify the first corner of a rectangular area, or a [Viewport].

  You can also capture a viewport area, if you have a layout tab set up with a viewport, and are on the layout tab with the viewport selected.

9.  Pick two opposing corners of a rectangular area.

10. Select **Ribbon: Home ⇒ Online Map ⇒ Map Off**.

11. The online map that filled the drawing editor is no longer displayed, except in the area you selected.

12. Select the edge of the image, then drag a corner grip to expand the rectangular area.

Notice that the online map data fills the newly defined area. This can only occur if you are signed in to an A360 account.

When you save the drawing, the image is embedded into the DWG file, and is saved with it, allowing other users to see the image without having to have, or be signed in to an account.

The imbedded image is permanently set behind all other drawing elements in *Display Order*.

13. Select the image by picking the frame.

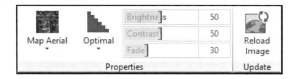

Once an online image area has been captured, selecting it provides access to tools in the context sensitive ribbon to adjust the display of the image, similar to the tools available when an image has been inserted into the drawing.

For this exercise, we will not use the online map and you will delete the capture in the next step.

14. Use the AutoCAD Erase command to delete the capture of the Online Map.

## 2.1.7   Adding the Project Area

You will now insert a block that contains a polyline defining our project area. This way you all are working with the same data, in a normal project you would just draw this line in the appropriate area.

1.   Select **Ribbon: Insert ⇒ Block ⇒ Insert ⇒ Blocks from Other Drawings**.

This opens the *Blocks* palette.

2.   Select the ⟨...⟩ button to load a drawing into the **Blocks Palette**.

The **Select Drawing File...** dialog box appears.

3.   Browse to **C:\A Practical Guide\Civil 3D 2020\Drawings\project boundary.dwg**

4.   Click **<<Open>>**.

The drawing appears in the **Blocks** palette.

5. Disable the option for **Insertion Point** and confirm it is set to 0,0,0.

6. Enable the option to **Explode** the block.

7. Right-click on the drawing Project Boundary and select **Insert**.

A polyline representing the project boundary will be inserted into the drawing.

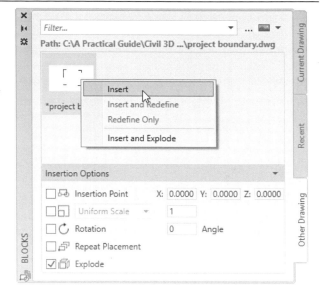

8. Set layer **0** current.

9. Freeze the **Image** and **Project Boundary** layers.

10. Save the drawing.

11. When finished, the drawing should look like the graphic below.

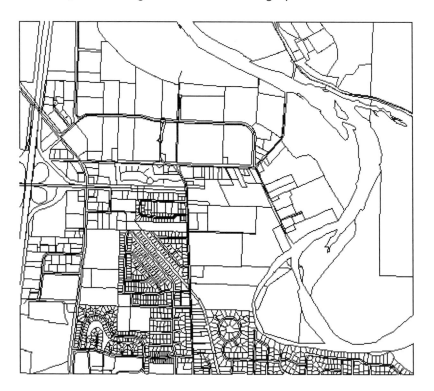

## 2.2    Lesson:  Using Queries to Manage and Share Data

### Introduction

In this lesson, you learn about the basics of queries. You start by learning the concepts, and the general process for defining queries, together with using the location and property conditions specifically.  You then define and execute a location and property query, and combine them into a compound query.

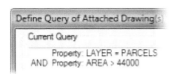

### Key Concepts

Concepts and key terms covered in this lesson are:

- Source drawing queries
- Query tools
- Query options

### Objectives

After completing this lesson, you will be able to:

- Create a Drive Alias.
- Attach source drawings to a current drawing.
- Describe the concept of queries and source drawings.
- List common purposes of queries.
- Describe the query tools.
- Explain the options for location and property queries.
- Explain the implications of saving drawings with queried objects.
- Execute a location and property query.

## About Source Drawing Queries

Once a current drawing has source drawings attached, all of the objects in the source drawings are available for query into the current drawing.

When you access drawing objects using queries, you are fundamentally changing the way you work with drawings and objects. The idea of opening drawings to access objects and work with them is no longer required. Instead of opening a drawing to work with the objects, you access multiple drawings at the object level. Once you incorporate this way of thinking, and method of working, you might never directly open a source drawing again, but rather access the objects in your drawings.

 You do open the current drawing, but all source drawings attached to the current drawing are not actually opened. However, the objects in the source drawings are *available* for query.

There are many methods to define conditions for queries. Queries are organized into four main types:

- Location
- Property
- Data
- SQL

The following is an example of a query that returns only city parcels that have specific area values. On the left, are all of the objects available in attached source drawings. These objects include creeks, sewer, storm, parcels, roads, and water systems. On the right, are the objects in the current drawing that were returned as a result of the query conditions.

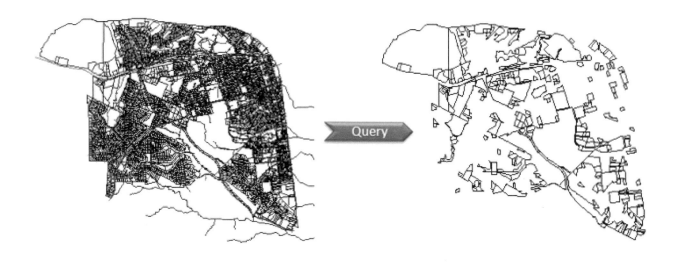

## Query Purposes

There are many reasons to query objects from source drawings. Most queries fall within five main categories of purpose:

- Create new maps, extract objects.
- Limit the amount of data you work with.
- Organize data.
- Analyze data.
- Edit objects in a multi user environment.

## Create New Maps

When you work with multiple drawings attached to a current drawing, you can combine the objects in those drawings in ways that were difficult, if not impossible to manage before using the query tools. In this way, you can create specialized maps that are designed for a specific purpose. For example, you can create a map that combines parcels from one drawing with storm drain inlets from another drawing. This map could be used for a crew in the field to locate the inlets easily.

## Limit the Amount of Data you Work With

In most cases, mapping systems contain an enormous amount of data. Some systems have so much data that it would be impossible to actually open the drawings. This scenario can only occur when AutoCAD Map 3D is used to produce the maps through source drawings, and done so purposely as part of the mapping system. Even in smaller files, it doesn't make much sense to open an entire drawing when you can access small portions of that drawing.

## Organize Data

You can use queries to return objects from multiple drawings that you want to save into a single drawing. For example, if you have several drawings that have objects on the same layer, and you want to combine those objects into a single drawing, you can query all of the drawings for that specific layer, and then save the current drawing as the new drawing. This process is a very efficient way to take drawings that are not well organized, and establish new source drawings that are better organized, or convert tiled maps into layered maps.

## Analysis

Using the query tools, you can combine queries to produce sophisticated analyses of maps. An example of this approach is to use queries to return only sewer maintenance holes that are located within a flood zone, and have inverts below a certain elevation. This query could be executed as both a map and a report. The Public Works department would then know how many sealed covers they need, and have a map to locate where they need to be installed.

## Edit Objects in a Multiple User Environment

When source drawings are attached to a current drawing, those same source drawings can be attached and active in another current drawing simultaneously. Each user can access the objects in the same drawing, and edit the same drawing at the same time. AutoCAD Map 3D has an editing transaction model that enables objects to be locked rather than locking an entire drawings. This functionality is an aspect of working with source drawings in AutoCAD Map 3D that profoundly changes the way you work with drawings. This functionality is covered in another lesson.

## Query Tools

All queries are created and executed from the Define Query of Attached Drawing(s) dialog.

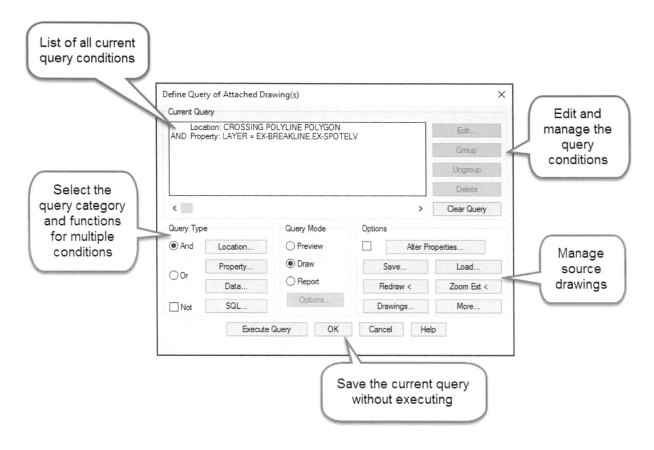

## Location Queries

Location queries are exactly what the name describes, queries based on the location of objects in the source drawings. There are several location conditions that you can use when defining a location query.

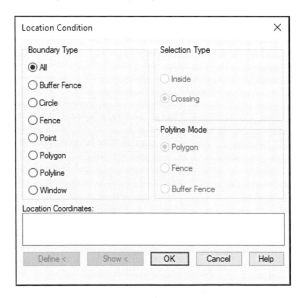

| Option | Description |
| --- | --- |
| All | Return all objects in all attached and active drawings. |
| Buffer Fence | Draw a fence, and enter the distance from the fence that objects are to be returned. |
| Circle | Define a circle in the drawing to return objects inside, or crossing. |
| Fence | Draw a fence and return objects that cross the fence. |
| Point | Define a point and return all closed objects that surround the point. |
| Polygon | Define a polygon and return all objects within or crossing the polygon. |
| Polyline | Select an existing polyline and select a mode for the selected polyline as Polygon, Fence, or Buffer Fence. |
| Window | Define a window as either inside or crossing. |

## Property Queries

Property conditions query objects based on the properties of the objects themselves. You select the property you want to use and an operator. The Values button retrieves all definitions from the source drawings and presents a list that you can choose from. For example, if creating a Layer query, when you click Values, a list is displayed that contains all of the layers in all the attached drawings.

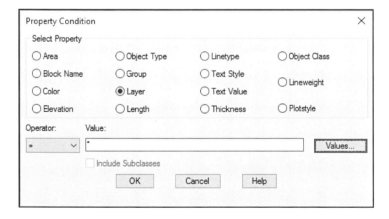

Most of the options in the Property Condition dialog are self-explanatory. Following is a list of options that deserve further explanation.

| Option | Description |
|--------|-------------|
| Color | Returns all objects with specific colors. This does not recognize bylayer colors. This is a good tool to use to identify which objects in source drawings that do not conform to bylayer colors. |
| Elevation | Returns objects that reside at specific Z values. You can create multiple query conditions to return a range of elevations. This is a good tool to use to return contour lines in source drawings. |
| Text Value | Returns text with specific values. This is a good tool to locate text with values such as parcel numbers or sewer line numbers. |
| Thickness | Returns objects based on the thickness of objects. (Applies to only extruded objects) |

## Compound Queries

You can create queries that contain multiple conditions. Each condition is separated by Boolean functions. You can select And, or Or, and then select the Not checkbox to produce And Not and Or Not functions. The conditions are listed in the Current Query window where they can be grouped if needed.

By using several query types together you can limit the objects that are queried into your drawing giving you a very specific selection set and keeping your drawing sizes smaller. This is typically referred to as a *Compound Query*.

In the following example, parcels with an area of less than 20,000sq ft are returned within a specified polygon, and all roads are returned, ignoring the polygon condition boundaries.

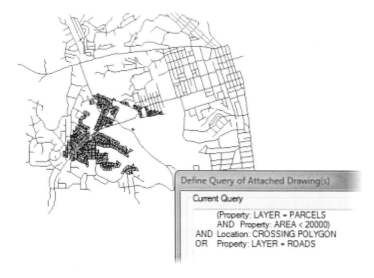

Define Query of Attached Drawing(s)

Current Query

```
    (Property: LAYER = PARCELS
     AND  Property: AREA < 20000)
AND  Location: CROSSING POLYGON
OR   Property: LAYER = ROADS
```

You can use Preview mode as you build the query to see the results of each condition before committing to a Draw query.

## Saved Queries

Sometimes you want to save a query so that you can run the same query multiple times. This process is an effective way of producing a map using the same conditions, and each time you create the map, it represents the current state of the data. For example, at the end of every month, you produce a map and report of all the maintenance holes that have been serviced during that month. You can use attribute information in a query to produce these results.

## Saving Drawings with Queried Objects

When you Draw query objects from source drawings, you create a copy of the objects that reside in the source drawings. They are not "moved" from the source drawings to the current drawing, simply copied. Once objects are draw queried, AutoCAD Map 3D keeps track of these objects for any changes that are made to them for the purpose of adding them to a Save Set if you want to save them back to the source drawing. This process is covered in detail in another lesson, but this scenario has implications when saving drawings with queried objects as well.

When you save a drawing with queried objects, AutoCAD Map 3D considers the queried objects to be new objects that no longer have a connection with the objects they were created from in the source drawings. This is a desired behavior if you are creating a new map from source drawings. But if you save the drawing with the queried objects, breaking the connection with the objects in the source drawing, and then query the same objects from this drawing, they will be duplicated in the current drawing. The danger is that the objects are coincident, and there is no visible indication that you have duplicated the objects in your current drawing.

You can query the same objects multiple times in the same drawing session and AutoCAD Map 3D will not duplicate them in the current drawing.

The following warning is presented to you before AutoCAD Map 3D breaks connections between objects in a current drawing and those in the source drawings.

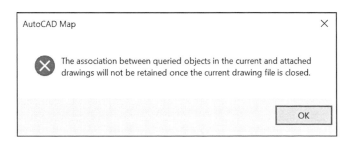

When you save a drawing with queried objects for the purpose of creating a new map, always save it as another drawing, detach the source drawings from the new drawing, and then resave. This eliminates the possibility of duplicating objects.

Before querying objects into a current drawing, turn off the Auto Save options.

## Exercises: Executing Location and Property Queries

In many cases, the drawings that cover an entire town or city are too large to reasonably work with. In addition, each of the attached maps by themselves would not provide the ability to work with the entire infrastructure in one drawing.

You will use *AutoCAD Map 3D's* ability to query information from other drawings to import, edit, and save back specific sanitary sewer information. This gives you the ability to work with small, specific, pieces of larger data sets as well as allowing you to share the data with others that may need to be using it at the same time. You will also use queries to extract spot elevation and breakline data for a specific area from a large citywide data set.

You do the following:

- Attach source drawings.
- Quick View source drawings.
- Define an area to query all objects from.
- Execute a Location Query.
- Edit a Sewer Line and Manhole and save them back to the source drawing.
- Detach source drawings.
- Execute a Compound Query by area and layer to extract points and breaklines for later use.

### 2.2.1 Attaching Source Drawings

Before you can perform a query, you must attach at least one source drawing to the current drawing. This will become the source of the information you find with the query.

1. Continue working in the drawing **Design.dwg**.

*Reminder:* You can also open the drawing with this exercise number in the *Chapter Drawings* folder of the dataset if you prefer a fresh start at this point.

2. If the *Task Pane* is not visible on your screen, at the command line enter:

   Command: **MAPWSPACE**

3. Type **ON** to display the *Task Pane,* which includes the *Map Explorer* tab.

4. Select the **Map Explorer** tab of the *Task Pane*.

5. In the **Map Explorer** right-click on the **Drawings** folder and select ⇒ **Attach** from the fly-out menu.

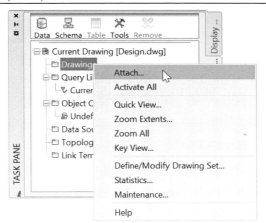

To attach source drawings in *Autodesk Civil 3D*, you need to use a drive alias. A drive alias is simply a named shortcut to a drive or directory on your local machine or network. Its purpose is to aid in sharing data with others whose directory structure may be different from yours. When multiple users share a named drive alias, each user has their own specific paths to the data.

*Autodesk Civil 3D* includes a default alias defined for the C: drive, which you could use for the exercises in this book, if the dataset is installed on your C: drive. However, we include an exercise in defining an alias because it is standard procedure when sharing drawings across a network and between organizations.

6. Click the **Create/Edit Aliases** button at the top of the dialog box to create a drive alias.

7. In the *Drive Alias Administration* dialog box enter **Civil3D_2020_APG** for the alias name.

Aliases cannot contain any spaces.

8. Click **<<Browse>>** to add the *Actual Path*. For all the exercises in this book the path will be: **C:\A Practical Guide\Civil 3D 2020\Drawings\.**

9. Click **<<Add>>** and this alias will appear in the *Drive List*.

If you click **<<Close>>** before you click **<<Add>>**, the alias will not be saved.

10. After you have added the alias, click **<<Close>>**.

11. Back in the *Select Drawing* dialog box select the **Civil3D_2020_APG alias** from the drop-down list.

12. Double-click on the **Sanitary Sewer** drawing file, to add it to the *Selected drawings* list.

13. Click **<<OK>>**.

You will now see the drawing listed in the *Map Explorer*. *Active drawings* will be used for all *Query* and *Quick View* commands. Right-clicking on attached drawings in the *Map Explorer* and choosing deactivate can deactivate them. *Deactivated drawings* are still attached to the drawing but will not be used in *Queries* or *Quick Views*.

14. Right-click on **Drawings** and select ⇒ **Quick View**.

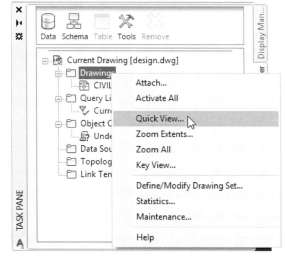

15. Confirm that the option to **Zoom to the Extents of Selected Drawings** is Enabled.

This will zoom your current drawing to the extents of the attached drawings. If you don't do this the quick view image may appear in an area that is not shown on your screen.

16. Click **<<OK>>** to display the Quick View of the drawing.

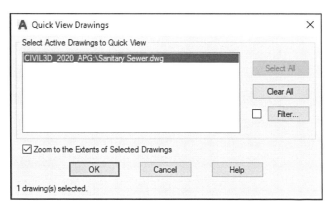

A *Quick View* will show you a preview image of what is contained in any attached and active drawings, in this case the sanitary sewer lines. The quick view image will go away when you use a Redraw or during an AutoSave. If you lose the quick view just run the quick view command again to redisplay it.

## 2.2.2   Defining a Query

You can use any combination of four different *Query Types* to create your query and filter through the attached, active, drawings to select the exact objects that you want to bring into your drawing. The four types are Location, Property, Data, and SQL.

- **Location** allows you to limit your Query to a specific area which you define within the source drawings.
- **Property** allows you to select the object to be queried by any AutoCAD property such as Layer, Linetype, Color, etc.
- The **Data** and **SQL** options allow you to select options for your Query according to their attached data; both object data and external database data.

By using the above query types together you can limit the objects that are queried into your drawing giving you a very specific selection set and keeping your drawing sizes smaller.

1. On the *Map Explorer* tab of the *Task Pane*, right-click on **Current Query** under the *Query Library*, and select ⇒ **Define** to open the *Define Query* dialog box.

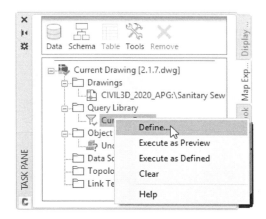

Here, you set up the parameters of your query.

2. Click **<<Location>>** in the **Query Type** section.

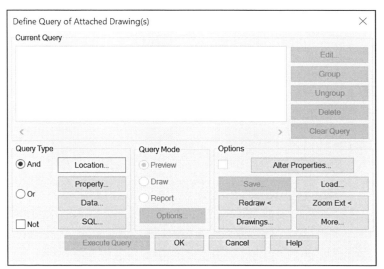

3. Choose a **Boundary Type** of **Circle**.

4. Confirm the **Selection Type** is set to **Crossing**.

5. Click **<<Define>>**.

6. At the command line enter **1335500,890800** for the center of the circle.

7. Enter **2500** for the **radius**.

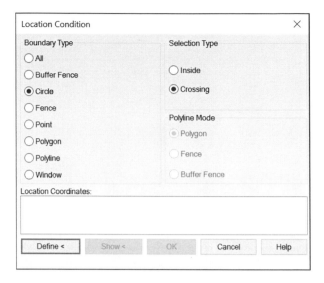

8. Back in the *Define Query* dialog box; change the **Query Mode** to **Draw**.

9. Click **<<Execute Query>>**.

This will bring all of the objects in the attached drawing or drawings that meet the query criteria into the current Drawing. They are brought in as regular *AutoCAD* objects so you can edit them using any of your *AutoCAD* commands. Any changes can be saved back to the source drawings.

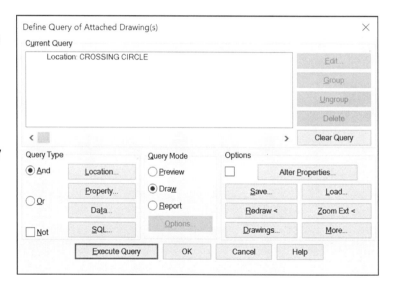

You will now see the sewer lines displayed in the area of the circle you defined for the query.

10. **Save** the drawing.

When saving after querying objects into the drawing you will get a warning message. This is not an error.  It is only informing you that if you close the drawing the link to the queried objects will be lost.  Those objects will remain in this drawing as stand-alone copies and will no longer have a link to the original objects in the source drawing.

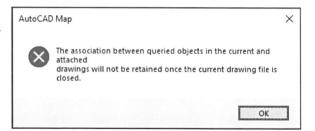

### 2.2.3    Saving Changes Back To the Source Drawings

Any changes made to a queried object can be saved back to the source drawing that the object was queried from.  This is a very powerful feature but also one that you need to be very careful with.  Using the Save Back command when it is not appropriate can edit base data and cause you to lose valuable information.  Be aware, the Undo command does not work with the Save Back command.

1.  **Freeze** the layer **EX-Streets**.

2.  Zoom or pan to the vicinity of the project area, similar to the example below to locate the manhole at the end of the sewer line.

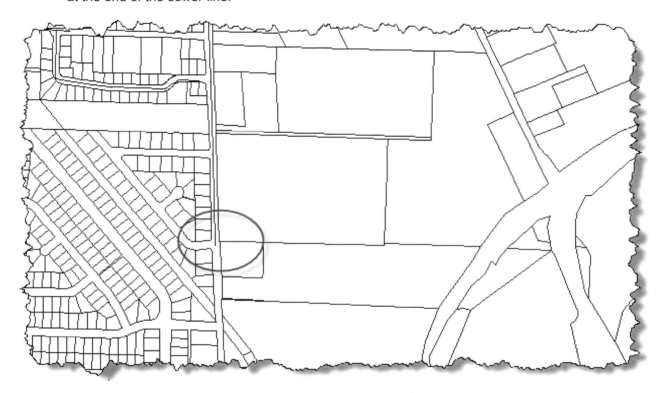

We have information from our surveyors that the manhole and pipe in this location are incorrect in the as built drawing and need to be updated.

3.  Stretch the manhole and connecting pipe to the coordinate **1334859.85,889467.12**

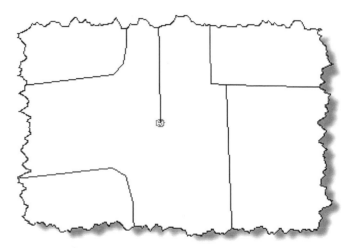

4.  Once you finish the edit you will be asked if you want to add object(s) to the save Set.

5.  Click **<<Yes>>** to add the object(s) that you just edited to the save set.

This has not saved the edited objects back to the source drawing yet. It has only added them to a group of objects that can be saved back when you are ready.

6.  Select **Ribbon: Home ⇒ Data ⇒ Save to Source.**

You will need to expand the Data panel to display this command.

This opens the Save Objects to Sources Drawings dialog box where you confirm the number of objects in the save set and how they will be saved back to the source drawing(s).

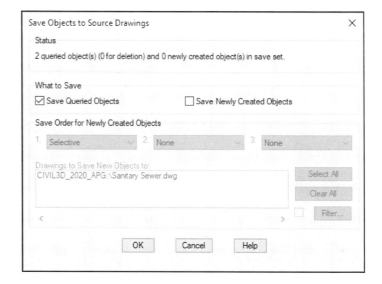

7.  Click **<<OK>>** to save the object in the save set back to the source drawings.

Notice that the object(s) that you saved back have disappeared from your drawing. To bring them back you can just run the query again.

8.  On the *Map Explorer* tab of the *Task Pane*, right-click on **Current Query** under the *Query Library,* and select ⇒ **Define** to open the *Define Query* dialog box.

9.  In the *Define Query* dialog box; notice the properties of the last query have been saved.

10. Click **<<Execute Query>>**.

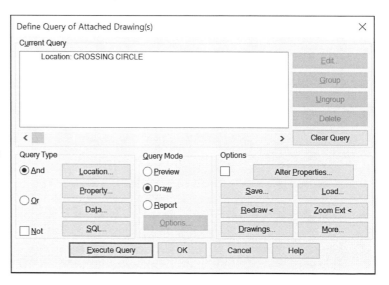

This will bring all of the objects in the attached drawing or drawings that meet the query criteria into the current Drawing. Since most of these objects have already been queried into the drawing it will replace them rather than creating duplicates.

11. Review the new objects that have been queried into the drawing and you will find the changes that were saved back in the previous steps are now displayed.

There are no more changes to be saved back to the original drawing. You will now detach the Sanitary Sewer drawing. This will create a stand-alone copy of the queried objects and prevent any future save backs to this source drawing.

12. Right-click on the **Sanitary Sewer** drawing in the *Map Explorer* and select ⇒ **Detach**.

When you detach the source drawing the objects that you have queried will no longer know that they were queried from a source drawing. If you make any additional edits to these objects the program will not prompt you to add them to the save set. You can always erase these objects, attach the source drawing again, and rerun the query to get a current copy of the object in the drawing so you will be able to save edits to the source drawing.

## 2.2.4 Defining a Compound Query

In this exercise, you will use *AutoCAD Map's* ability to query information from multiple drawings to bring in spot elevation and breakline data. The breakline and point data is stored in a tiled format to maintain smaller drawing sizes. This project, like many others, does not fit neatly inside of one of these tiles, so we will bring data together from several drawings to fit our project area. *AutoCAD Map 3D* allows you to attach multiple drawings and perform simple or very complex queries across tiled drawings.

You can use any combination of four different query types to create your query. The query types are *Location, Property, Data*, and *SQL*.

By using several query types together you can limit the objects that are queried into your drawing giving you a very specific selection set and keeping your drawing sizes smaller. This is typically referred to as a *Compound Query*.

In this exercise you will attach four source drawings containing aerial survey data and use a compound query to select just the points and breaklines

This is just one way to bring data into your drawing and is not a required step when using Civil 3D. You could also WBLOCK the needed objects out of the other drawings and insert it into this drawing. However, once you use the method in this exercise you may find it easier and faster than other methods.

1. **Freeze** the layers **EX-Parcels, EX-Sewer-Line** and **EX-Sewer-MH**.

2. **Thaw** the layer **Project Boundary**.

3. Select the **Map Explorer** tab of the *Task Pane*.

4. Right-click on **Drawings** and select ⇒ **Attach**.

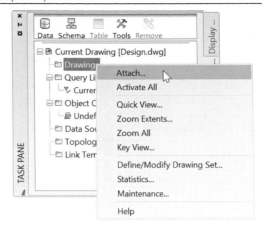

5. In the *Select Drawing* dialog box, select the **CIVIL3D_2020_APG** alias at the top of the dialog box.

6. Hold down the **[Ctrl] key**, select **D03-dtm, D04-dtm, E03-dtm** and **E04-dtm,** and then click **<<Add>>**.

7. Click **<<OK>>**.

You will now see the four drawings listed in the *Map Explorer*.

8. Right-click on the **Drawings** folder and select ⇒ **Quick View**.

9. Click **<<Select All>>**.

10. Click **<<OK>>** to display the *Quick View* of all the attached drawings.

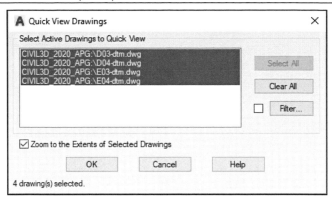

This will show you a preview image of what is contained in the attached drawings. The Quick View image will go away when you use a Redraw.

11. After you finish reviewing the contents of the attached drawings enter **R** at the command line to Redraw the display and clear the *Quick View*.

12. On the *Map Explorer* tab of the *Task Pane*, right-click on **Current Query** and select ⇒ **Define** to open the *Define Query* dialog box.

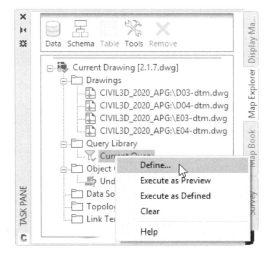

13. The previous query is still saved in the query dialog box. Click **<<Clear Query>>** to clear the previous query criteria and start a new one.

14. Click **<<Location>>** in the Query Type section.

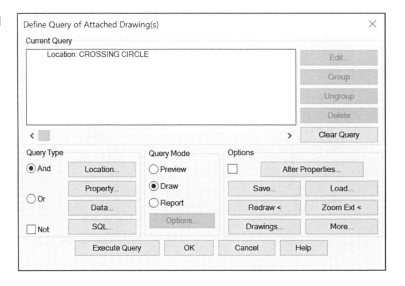

15. Choose a **Boundary Type** of **Polyline**.

16. Verify the **Selection Type** is set to **Crossing**.

17. Verify the **Polyline Mode** is set to **Polygon**.

18. Click **<<Define>>**.

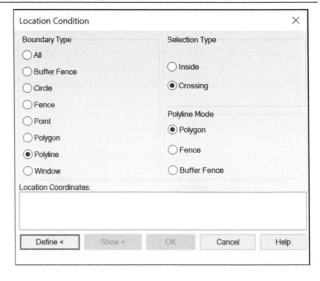

19. When asked to select the polyline, pick the magenta site boundary that you inserted on the layer *Project Boundary*. You will see a preview of the boundary you selected on the screen.

20. Back in the *Define Query* dialog box, in the **Query Type** section click **<<Property>>**.

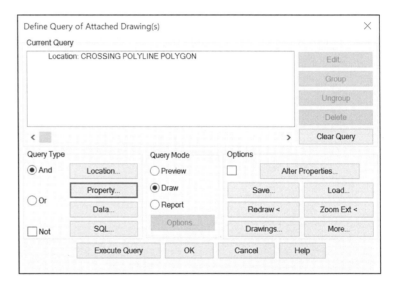

21. Select the **Property** of **Layer**.

22. Click **<<Values>>**.

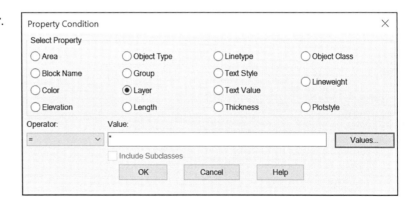

You will see a list of all of the layers in all of the active attached drawings.

23. Hold down the control key, and select the layers:
**EX-BRKLINE, EX-SPOTELV**.

24. Click **<<OK>>**.

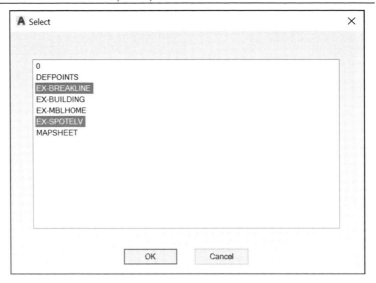

25. Click **<<OK>>** to save your changes to the **Property Condition** dialog box.

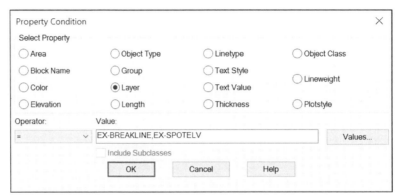

26. Back in the *Define Query* dialog box, Set the **Query Mode** to **Preview** and click **<<Execute Query>>**.

Preview mode will display a *Quick View* of the objects that meet the criteria you set in the *Query*. This gives you a chance to confirm that you have defined the query correctly and it is selecting the objects that you expected it to. You can clear that display with a redraw. If you do not see the points and breaklines displayed, or if you see too much information, you will need to check the definition of the query before you proceed.

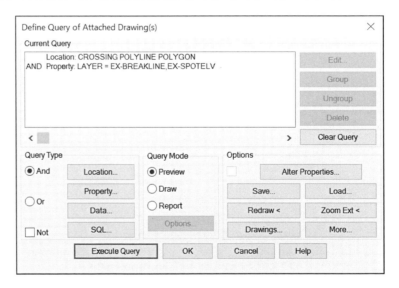

The preview query results should look like the graphic below.

27. Right-click on the **Current Query** in *Map Explorer* and select ⇒ **Define**.

All of the information from the previous query is retained.

28. Change the **Query Mode** to **Draw**.

29. Click **<<Execute Query>>**.

This will bring all of the objects that you saw in the preview into the drawing. They are brought in as regular *AutoCAD* objects so you can edit them using any of your *AutoCAD* commands. Any changes can be saved back to the source drawings. Be careful with *Savebacks*. In many situations, like this one, you would never want to save changes back to the source data. That would change and corrupt the information from your aerial survey.

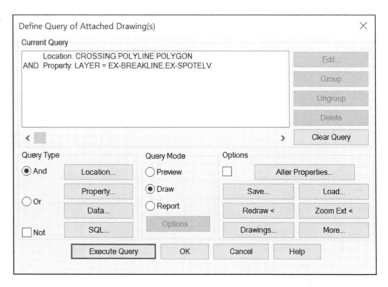

30. To prevent any changes from being saved to the source drawing select **all four of the source drawings** in the *Map Explorer* while holding down the **[Shift]** key, then **right-click** on the selected source drawings and select ⇒ **Detach**.

When you detach the source drawing the objects that you have queried will no longer know that they were queried from a source drawing. If you make any additional edits to these objects the program will not prompt you to add them to the save set. You can always erase these objects, attach the source drawing again, and rerun the query to get a current copy of the object in the drawing so you will be able to save edits to the source drawing.

31. At the command line, type **PDMODE**.

32. Set the point mode to **3**, then **[Enter]** to end the command.

The spot elevations will now be displayed with an X rather than just dots. The size is relative to the screen so as you zoom in and out they will change size after a *Regen*.

33. **Save** the drawing.

34. When finished, the drawing should look like the graphic below.

# 3 - Preliminary Layout

In this chapter you will be introduced to several concepts that will be covered in more detail in later chapters of this book. You will learn how to create surfaces from *AutoCAD* objects and control surface display. You will use transparent commands to layout a preliminary alignment and you will create points based on that alignment. In later chapters *Points*, *Surfaces*, and *Alignments*; and the *Styles* that control them, will be covered in much greater detail with specific examples. In this chapter, your main goal is to become comfortable working with these objects.

### Lesson: Creating a Preliminary Existing Ground Surface
In this lesson, you will learn to build a surface from AutoCAD objects. You will also learn to control the display of surfaces with styles.

### Lesson: Creating a Preliminary Alignment
In this lesson, you will learn the concepts and process of creating an alignment.

### Lesson: Creating Points from an Alignment
In this lesson, you will learn to create points from horizontal alignment geometry and export points to an ASCII file for use by a survey crew.

# 3.1    Lesson:  Creating a Preliminary Existing Ground Surface

## Introduction

A *Surface* in *Civil 3D* is an *Object*.  This surface object contains the surface definition and is saved in the drawing on a layer just like any other *AutoCAD* object.  The surface object can be displayed many different ways by changing the surface style.  As an example, the surface can be displayed as triangles, contours, or elevation bands.

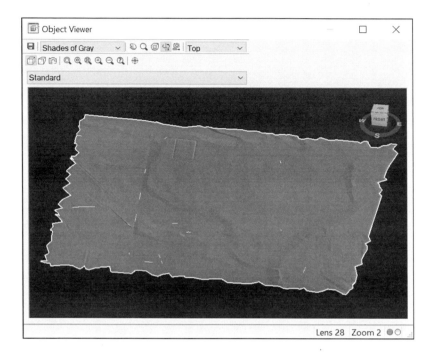

## Key Concepts

Concepts and key terms covered in this lesson are:

- Surface
- Points
- Breaklines
- Surface Boundary
- Surface Styles

## Objectives

After completing this lesson, you will be able to:

- Describe what a Surface is.
- List the types of data that can be used to build a Surface.
- Build a surface from AutoCAD Objects.
- Change Surface Styles.

## Introduction to Surfaces

This lesson is an introduction to surfaces in Civil 3D.  Surfaces are covered in detail in Chapter 5, however, some basic concepts of surfaces that you should begin to become familiar with are:

- A Surface in Civil 3D is an object that is stored in the drawing
- A Surface can be built from many different types of data
- Civil 3D Surfaces are dynamically linked to the surface data
- The display of a surface is controlled by the Surface Style

## A Surface in Civil 3D is an object that is stored in the drawing

- AutoCAD commands like move, copy, and rotate can be used to edit a surface
- The Undo command works with surfaces
- If you erase or explode a surface the surface is gone

 Surfaces can be locked to prevent accidental editing.

## A Surface can be built from many different types of data

- Boundaries
- Breaklines
- Contours
- DEM files (Digital Elevation Models)
- Drawing Objects
- Point Files
- Point Groups
- Point Survey Queries
- Figure Survey Queries

## Civil 3D Surfaces are dynamically linked to the surface data

If you edit a point, breakline, or any other surface data the surface is updated when it is rebuilt.

## The display of a surface is controlled by the Surface Style

Surface styles can display the surface as:

- Points
- Triangles
- Contours
- A Grid
- Directions
- Elevation Bands
- Slopes
- Slope Arrows
- Watersheds

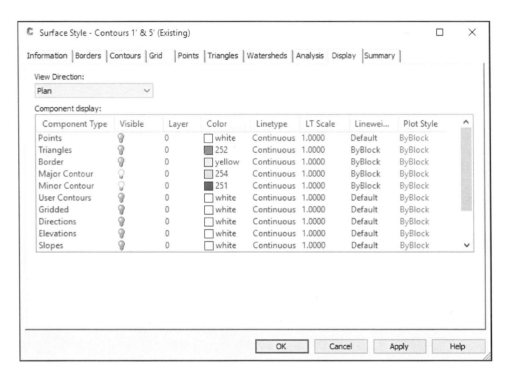

The surface style allows you to control the layer, color, linetype and other standard properties of the different surface components.

 If styles are set up correctly they can make complying with standards almost automatic.

## Exercises: Create and View a Surface

In these exercises, you will create a preliminary surface of the existing ground from the *AutoCAD* objects that you queried into the drawing in the previous chapter. In later chapters, you will build a surface from survey data and merge it with the preliminary surface, using the preliminary surface to add buffer data around your survey.

You do the following:

- Create a new Surface.
- Add Surface Data including AutoCAD points, breaklines, and a boundary.
- Change the Surface Style to control the display.
- Use the Object Viewer to view the Surface in 3D.

### 3.1.1 Creating a Surface

In this exercise you will create a surface. When first created this surface object will not be displayed on the screen because it is simply an empty container waiting for you to add surface data in later exercises.

1. Continue working in the drawing **Design.dwg**.

*Reminder:* You can also open the drawing with this exercise number in the *Chapter Drawings* folder of the dataset if you prefer a fresh start at this point.

NOTE: Instructions for Downloading and Installing the Datasets can be found on page vi.

2. Click the Workspace button ⚙ ▼ on the status bar and set the current workspace to **Civil 3D**.

3. If the *Toolspace* is not visible, turn it on by selecting **Ribbon: Home ⇒ Palettes ⇒ Toolspace**.

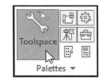

4. On the *Prospector* tab of the *Toolspace*, right-click on **Surfaces** and select ⇒ **Create Surface**.

5. Confirm that **TIN surface** is selected as the **Type**.

The *TIN Surface* type is the most common type of surface. It can be created from many different types of data that form a triangulated irregular network.

You can also create *Grid Surfaces* that are optimized for data on a regularly spaced grid. A common use of the Grid Surface is for building a surface from DEM (Digital Elevation Model) data.

*TIN Volume* and *Grid Volume* surfaces can also be created for volume calculations between two surfaces. These are similar to the Composite Volume and Grid Volume calculations in *Land Desktop*.

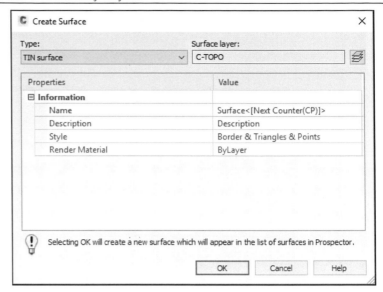

6. Click the **Surface Layer** 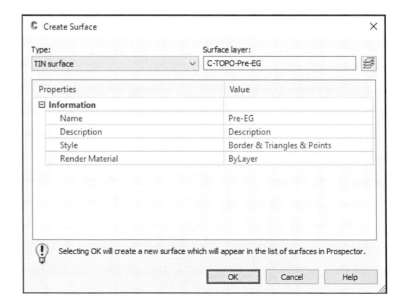 button to open the *Object Layer* dialog box.

7. Set the **Modifier** to **Suffix**.

8. Enter -* as the **Modifier value.**

This will add the surface name as a suffix to the surface layer.

9. Click **<<OK>>** to close the **Object Layer** dialog box.

This setting can be set as a default in your drawing, or better in your drawing template, so the layer modifier and values are automatically set each time you create a surface.

10. Enter **Pre-EG** for the *Surface Name*.

11. Confirm the **Style** field is set to **Border & Triangles & Points.**

This will set your surface to display a standard looking TIN as soon as surface data is added.

12. Click **<<OK>>** to close the **Create Surface** dialog box.

The surface is now created and can be found in the *Prospector*. At this point the surface does not have any data so it is not displayed in the drawing editor.

## 3.1.2   Adding Surface Data

Once a surface is created you can add many different types of data to construct the model. The first step in this process is to find out what type of data you have available. You may want to List the properties of objects that you intend to use in the surface to find out what type of an object they are and if they have an elevation assigned to them. For example, it is important to know if your spot elevations are *AutoCAD* points, blocks, or text. If they have elevations you can use any of these but you need to know what they are so that you can use the appropriate command.

1. Turn off the layers **EX-BREAKLINE** and **Project Boundary** to isolate the spot elevations layer.

2. On the *Prospector* tab of the *Toolspace*, expand the **Surfaces** node.

3. Expand the *Surface* **Pre-EG**.

4. Expand the **Definition** node under *Pre-EG*.

5. Right-click on **Drawing Objects** under the *Definition* node and select ⇒ **Add**.

6. Confirm the **Object type** is set to **Points**.

7. Click **<<OK>>**.

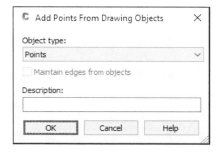

8. Select all the points with a crossing window, then **[Enter]** to end the command.

The spot elevations are added to the surface and the surface is updated. The surface will display on your screen as triangles according to the surface style. If the surface is not visible on your screen, then check to see if the layer *C-TOPO-Pre-EG* is off or frozen. If it is, turn it on to display the surface. You may need to Regen the drawing after changing the layer state to see the surface.

When finished, the drawing should look like the graphic below.

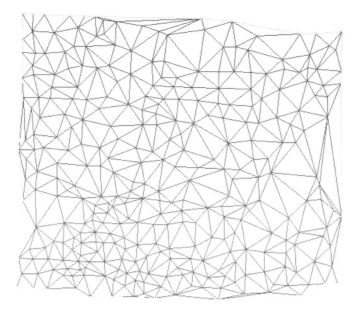

9.  Turn off the layer **EX-SPOTELEV**.

10. Turn on the layer **EX-BREAKLINE**.

11. Confirm that the **Definition** node under the *Surface* **Pre-EG** is expanded on the *Prospector* tab of the *Toolspace*.

12. Right-click on **Breaklines** under the **Definition** and select ⇒ **Add**.

13. Enter **Aerial Survey** for the **Description**.

14. Confirm that the **Type** is set to **Standard**.

You will not use any *Weeding* or *Supplementing factors* in this exercise.   These options allow you to remove or add vertices to breaklines respectively.  These are useful options if you have breaklines that have been over digitized and may have thousands of extra vertices very close together or if you need to add vertices to a breakline that has long distances between vertices.

15. Click **<<OK>>**.

16. Pick the **breaklines** with a crossing window.

The breaklines are added to the surface and the surface is updated.

When finished the drawing should look like the graphic below.

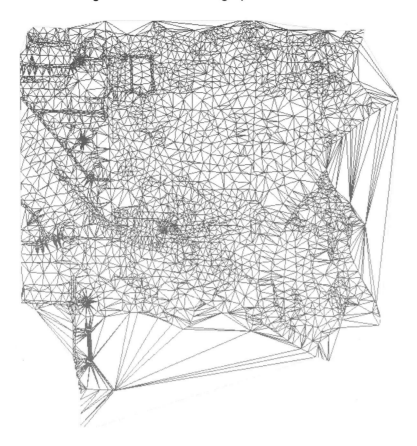

17. Turn **on** the layer **Project Boundary**.

18. Confirm that the **Definition** node under the *Surface* **Pre-EG** is expanded on the *Prospector* tab of the *Toolspace*.

19. Right-click on **Boundaries** under the **Definition** and select ⇒ **Add**.

20. Enter **Project Limits** for the **Name**.

21. Confirm that the **Type** is set to **Outer**.

22. **Disable** the option for **Non-destructive breaklines**.

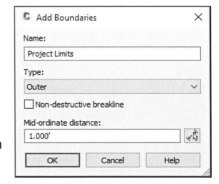

Enabling the *Non-destructive breaklines* option trims the surface at the boundary while disabling it erases any surface lines that cross the boundary. This option is useful when you have good surface data on both sides of the boundary and are using the boundary to limit the extents of the surface. It is typically not used for outer boundaries.

23. Click **<<OK>>**.

24. Pick the magenta boundary line.

The boundary is added to the surface and the surface is updated. The surface is dynamically linked to all of its surface data. So if you edit a point, breakline, or boundary the surface and the corresponding node under the surface definition will display as Out of date in the *Prospector*. If you right-click on the surface name in the *Prospector* and select *Rebuild* the surface will be updated to reflect the changes in the surface data. The undo command can be used to undo any changes to the surface or the surface data.

    25. Save the drawing.

When finished, the drawing should look like the graphic below.

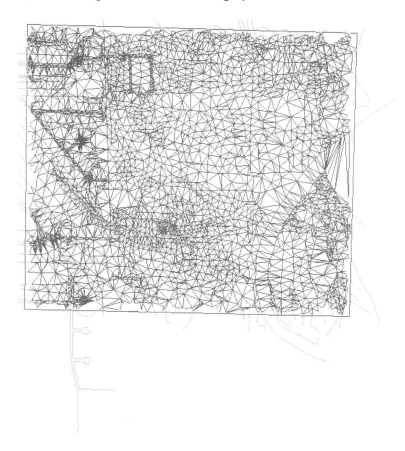

### 3.1.3    Changing the Surface Style to Control Display

The surface style controls the display of the surface. By changing the surface style you can display the surface in many different ways. Creating and editing surface styles will be covered in detail in *Chapter 5*. For now you should just get comfortable with the concept that surfaces can be displayed many different ways and that the display is controlled by the surface style.

    1.    Turn **off** the layers **EX-BREAKLINE** and **Project Boundary.**

You should now see the surface, displayed as triangles, by itself without the breaklines or boundary.

2. On the *Prospector* tab of the *Toolspace*, right-click on **Surface Pre-EG** and select ⇒ **Surface Properties**.

3. Select **Border & Contours** from the **Object style** list.

4. Click **<<OK>>**.

The surface is now displayed showing contours. The contour interval, color, smoothing, and much more are all part of the surface style.

When finished, the drawing should look like the graphic below.

### 3.1.4    Managing Drawing Settings

In previous exercises you set the layer for the Surface object to be created on during the process of creating the new Surface.  This can become tedious to do each time you create a new Surface.  In this exercise you will learn to set the default layer for surfaces as well as other objects so you don't have to set them each time.

1.  On the *Settings* tab of the *Toolspace*, right-click on the drawing **Design** at the top of the *Toolspace* and select ⇒ **Edit Drawing Settings**.

2.  In the *Drawing Settings* dialog box select the **Object Layers** tab.

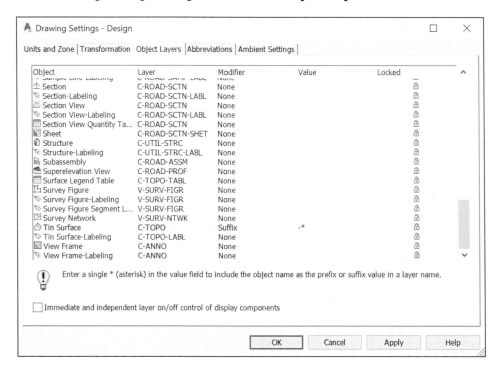

Here you can set the default layer that all Civil 3D objects will be created on.

3.  Notice the columns for Object and Layer.  You can change the layer name to match any organizational standards that you may have.  For this exercise you will leave the layer names as the defaults.

4.  For the **Tin Surface** *Object* set the *Modifier* to **Suffix**.

5.  For the **Tin Surface** *Object* set the *Value* to **-\***.

This will add the surface name as a suffix to the surface layer.

6.  For the **Alignment** *Object* set the *Modifier* to **Suffix**.

7.  For the **Alignment** *Object* set the *Value* to **-\***.

This will add the alignment name as a suffix to the alignment layer.

8.  Click **<<OK>>** to save these changes in this drawing.

The new layer settings are only for the current drawing. To set layer standards for all future drawing you can open your drawing template and make the changes to the layer, modifier and value there. Then any drawing you start using that template will have those layer settings.

### 3.1.5    Using the Object Viewer

The *Object Viewer* is a separate window that will allow you to view a selected object or objects in 3D and rotate them in real-time.

1. Pick one of the **contours** to highlight the entire surface and display the context sensitive ribbon.

2. Select **Ribbon: Tin Surface: Pre-EG ⇒ General Tools ⇒ Object Viewer.**

3. In the **Object Viewer**, click and drag while holding down the left mouse button to rotate the surface in 3D.

Once you rotate to a 3D view the contours will change to 3D faces. This is controlled by the surface object style.

4. In the *Object Viewer*, right-click and select ⇒ **Visual Styles ⇒ 3D Wireframe**.

You will now see the wireframe triangles representing the surface.

5. In the *Object Viewer*, right-click and select ⇒ **Visual Styles ⇒ Shades of Gray**.

You will now see shaded triangles representing the surface.

6. Continue to rotate the surface to examine it from different angles.

7. When you are finished viewing the surface, close the object viewer window to return to the drawing editor.

## 3.2 Lesson: Creating a Preliminary Alignment

### Introduction

An *Alignment* in *Civil 3D* is an *Object*. This alignment object contains the alignment information and parameters like stationing, design speed, and superelevation information. The alignment is saved in the drawing on a layer just like any other *AutoCAD* object. The display of the alignment object is controlled by the alignment style and the labeling is controlled by the alignment label set.

### Key Concepts

Concepts and key terms covered in this lesson are:

- Alignments
- Alignment Styles
- Transparent Commands

### Objectives

After completing this lesson, you will be able to:

- Describe what an Alignment is.
- Create an Alignment.
- Use Transparent Commands to enter coordinates.

## Introduction to Alignments

This lesson is an introduction to alignments in Civil 3D. Alignments are covered in detail in Chapter 6, however, some basic concepts of alignments that you should begin to become familiar with are:

- Alignments are Civil 3D objects that are stored in the drawing
- They represent road centerlines, pipes, ditches, streams, and any other lineal feature
- The display of an alignment is controlled by the Alignment Style
- An alignment label set is assigned to the alignment when it is created
  - This assigns a group of label styles that control the default labeling

## Alignments are Civil 3D objects that are stored in the drawing

- AutoCAD commands like move, copy, and rotate can be used to edit an alignment
- The Undo command works with alignments
- If you erase or explode an alignment the alignment is gone

## Alignments can be laid out in a number of ways:

- Graphically sketching
- Typing in exact coordinates
- Using object snaps
- Using Transparent Commands

## Transparent commands

The transparent commands in Civil 3D allow you to specify locations using methods of coordinate entry that are more common to civil engineers and surveyors, like bearing and distance, or angle and distance. The transparent commands must be run once you have started another command, and after it has prompted you for a location.

The toolbar below contains the Civil 3D transparent commands, they can also be entered manually at the command line.

Transparent commands are covered in detail in Chapter 4.

## Exercise: Create a Preliminary Alignment

In this exercise, you will lay out a preliminary version of the horizontal alignment for the road in our project. This will be based on our aerial survey data and will need to be checked, and most likely modified, by the survey crew when they go on site and conduct their survey.

You do the following:

- Create a new Alignment.
- Use transparent commands to locate PIs.

### 3.2.1   Drafting the Preliminary Alignment Using Transparent Commands

1.   Continue working in the drawing **Design.dwg**.

*Reminder:* You can also open the drawing with this exercise number in the *Chapter Drawings* folder of the dataset if you prefer a fresh start at this point.

2.   Confirm that **Dynamic Input** is turned off.

If it is on, Click the  button on the *Status Bar* to disable it.

If you are not familiar with using *Dynamic Input* with the *Transparent Commands* can be confusing and cause unexpected results.

3.   Select **Ribbon: Home ⇒ Create Design ⇒ Alignment ⇒ Alignment Creation Tools**.

This opens the *Create Alignment - Layout* dialog box where you can name and setup your alignment.

4.   Change the default **Name** to **Pre L Street**.

Alignment types automatically categorize alignments in the *Prospector* according to their properties and use, and enable you to create alignments with specialized behavior, like offsets, curb returns and rail.  In this exercise you will be using a *Centerline* alignment.

5.   Confirm the *Alignment Type* is set to **Centerline**.

In *Civil 3D* a *Site* is a collection of objects that relate to and interact with each other.  *Alignments, Parcels*, and *Grading Groups* can all be contained in a *Site*.  By using multiple *Sites* in your drawing you can control which of these objects interact with each other.  You may want to use different sites for different phases of a project or for different design alternatives.

In this example you do not want the alignment to interact with other alignments or parcels, so you will not add the alignment to a *Site*.

6.   Confirm the **Site** is set to **None**.

7.   Confirm that the **Alignment Style** is set to **Design Style**.

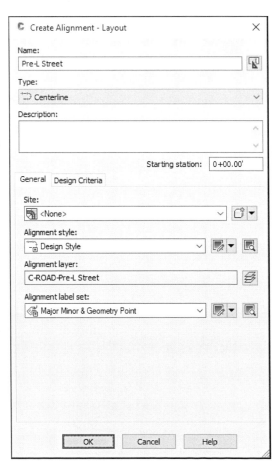

The alignment style controls the display of the alignment geometry. This particular style will use continuous lines with the tangents colored red and the curves colored blue. This may be helpful during the design process because you can easily identify where the tangents and curves begin and end. However, it may not work well for plotting. In that case you can change the alignment style when you are ready to plot to display the colors and linetypes that you prefer to see on your plots.

8. Confirm the **Alignment Layer** is set to **C-ROAD-Pre L Street**.

This layer setting, including the suffix using the alignment name, was set in the *Drawing Settings* during a previous exercise.

9. Confirm that the **Alignment label set** is set to **Major Minor & Geometry Point**.

The alignment label set controls the group of styles used to label the alignment. This includes displaying stationing, ticks, geometry information, and much more. Alignment Labels will be discussed in more detail in *Chapter 6*.

The *Design Criteria Tab* allows you to select design criteria based on minimum design standards. AASHTO standards in both imperial and metric units are included with *Civil 3D*. You also have the option to modify and create your own design standards. Using design criteria is optional and you will not be using it in this exercise.

10. Click **<<OK>>** to create the alignment and open the *Alignment Layout* toolbar.

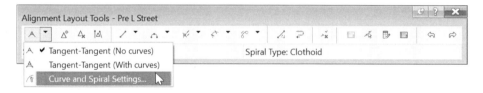

11. Click the down arrow ⌐A ▾⌐ next to the **Tangent-Tangent (No curves)** button on the *Alignment Layout* toolbar, to display the other creation commands.

12. Select ⇒ **Curve and Spiral Settings** to display the *Curve and Spiral Settings* dialog box.

13. Set the default Curve **Radius** to **150**.

This will set the default radius for all the curves you are about to create in the alignment to 150'. This allows you to quickly lay out the entire alignment using the default curve and spiral settings rather than adding each curve individually. You can go back and edit individual curves as needed.

14. Click **<<OK>>**.

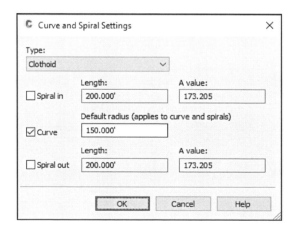

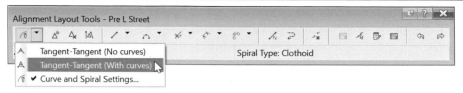

15. Click the down arrow [icon] next to the **Curve and Spiral Settings** button on the *Alignment Layout* toolbar to display the other creation commands.

16. Select ⇒ **Tangent-Tangent (With curves)**.

17. Enter **1334862.1,890056.7** for the start point.

18. Enter **'BD** to start the bearing and distance transparent command.

You can also click the *Bearing and Distance* [icon] button from the *Transparent Commands* toolbar.

19. Follow the prompts at the command line to create the next 3 PIs by entering the following information.

| Quadrant | Bearing | Distance |
|----------|---------|----------|
| 2 | 88.2435 | 995 |
| 3 | 03.5411 | 410 |
| 4 | 88.0843 | 955 |

20. Now when asked for a Quadrant, **[Enter]** to end the line, and **[Enter]** again to end the command.

21. Close the **Alignment Layout Tools** toolbar.

If you make a mistake you can erase the alignment with the *AutoCAD* erase command or by right-clicking on it in the *Prospector*.  You can also grip edit the alignment or edit it with the edit alignment command.  All of these options will be covered in detail in Chapter 6.

22. Save the drawing.

When finished, the alignment should look like the graphic below.

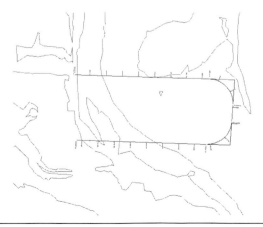

## 3.3    Lesson:  Creating Points from an Alignment

### Introduction

Points can be created based on the alignment geometry.  These points can be used to field check the preliminary layout of the alignment.  This lesson will explore working with default settings for creating points and creating points based on an alignment.

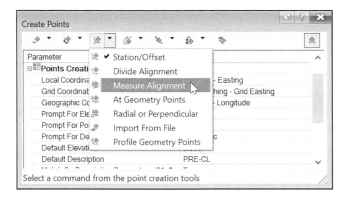

### Key Concepts

Concepts and key terms covered in this lesson are:

- Point Settings
- Creating Points based on Alignment Geometry
- Point Groups
- Point Import/Export Formats
- Exporting Points to an ASCII File

### Objectives

After completing this lesson, you will be able to:

- Control Point Settings.
- Create an Alignment.
- Create a Point Group.
- Create a Point Import/Export format.
- Export Points to an ASCII File.

**Introduction to Points**

Points can be created in Civil 3D many different ways. In this lesson you will create points based on the geometry of an alignment. Those points will not be linked to the alignment, only based on its geometry at the time the points were created. If the alignment changes, the points will not be moved.

This lesson is an introduction to Points in Civil 3D. Points are covered in detail in Chapter 4, however, some basic concepts of surfaces that you should begin to become familiar with are:

- A Point in Civil 3D is an object that is stored in the drawing
- The display of a point is controlled by the Point Style and Point Label Style
- Points can be organized and managed with Point Groups

**A Point in Civil 3D is an object that is stored in the drawing**

- AutoCAD commands like move, copy, and rotate can be used to edit a point
- The Undo command works with points
- If you erase or explode a point the point is gone

 Points can be locked to prevent accidental editing.

**The display of a point is controlled by the Point Style and Point Label Style**

The Point Style controls the display of the Point Marker, while the Point Label Style controls the display of the text associated with the point. These styles can be assigned to individual point or to Point Groups.

## Points can be organized and managed with Point Groups

Point Groups are selection sets of points that are saved with the drawing. Once you define a Point Group you can then select points by that group while using any point related command. Point Groups can also control the display of the points by assigning a Point Style and a Point Label Style to the group.

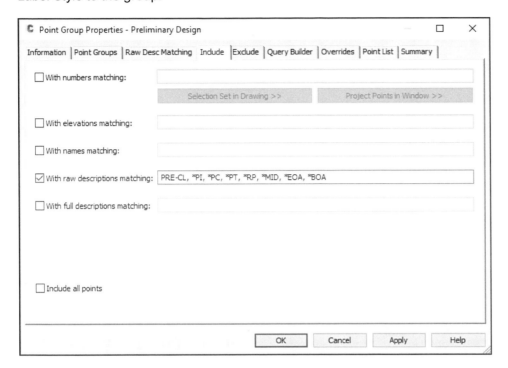

## Point Settings

The Create Points toolbar contains all of the commands for creating points as well as an area to control all of the point settings. You may need to change the point settings often depending on the command that you are using and the type of points that you are creating. Point settings include the default point layer, default elevation, default description, and current point number.

If the point settings are configured properly they can drastically reduce the number of steps involved in creating points.

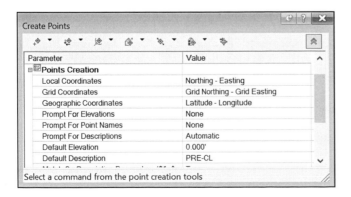

## Point Import/Export formats

Civil 3D comes with many standard import/export formats predefined. However, at some point you may need to define a new format for a specific project need.

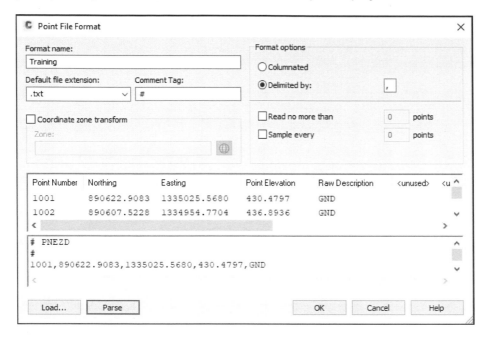

## Exercises: Create Points on an Alignment

In these exercises, you will create points based on the geometry of an alignment. Once the points are created you will add them to a point group and finally, export the points to an ASCII file that you could provide to the survey crew for field verification.

You do the following:

- Establish Point Settings.
- Create Points on an Alignment.
- Create a Point Group.
- Define a Point Import/Export Format.
- Export Points to an ASCII File.

### 3.3.1    Establishing the Point Settings

1.  Continue working in the drawing **Design.dwg**.

*Reminder:* You can also open the drawing with this exercise number in the *Chapter Drawings* folder of the dataset if you prefer a fresh start at this point.

2. Select **Ribbon: Home** ⇒ **Create Ground Data** ⇒ **Points** ⇒ **Point Creation Tools**.

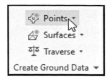

This will display the *Create Points* toolbar where you can find all the point creation commands as well as point settings.

3. Select the **chevron** button on the right of the *Create Points* toolbar to expand it and show the point settings.

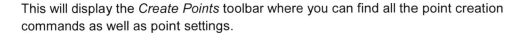

4. Expand the **Default Layer** parameters.

5. Select the **Layer** value field and click the **more <<…>>** button.

6. In the *Layer Selection* dialog box click **<<New>>**.

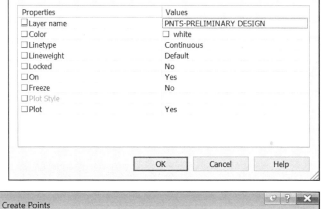

7. Enter **PNTS-PRELIMINARY DESIGN** for the new **Layer name**.

8. Click **<<OK>>** to create the new layer.

9. Click **<<OK>>** to select the new layer and close the *Layer Selection* dialog box.

10. Expand the **Points Creation** parameters.

11. Set **Prompt For Elevations** to **None**.

This will automatically give the points a NULL elevation as they are created. This is important because if points with a NULL elevation are included in a surface they are ignored, while points with a zero elevation create a hole in the surface going down to elevation zero.

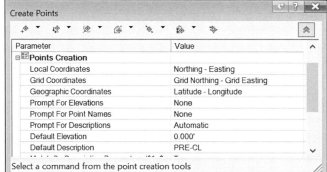

12. Set **Prompt For Point Names** to **None**.

13. Set **Prompt For Descriptions** to **Automatic**.

14. Enter a **Default Description** of **PRE-CL**.

This will automatically give the points a description of *PRE-CL* as they are created, rather than prompting you to enter the description of each point as it is created.

### 3.3.2    Setting Points on an Alignment

In this exercise, you will create points based on the alignment geometry.  These points are not linked to the alignment.  So if the alignment is changed you will need to delete and recreate the points.

1. Click the **down arrow** 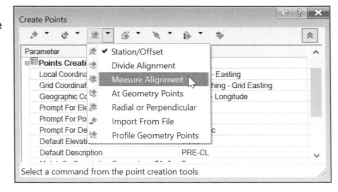 next to the third button from the left on the *Create Points* toolbar, to display the other alignment options.

2. From the drop-down list, select ⇒ **Measure Alignment**.

3. Select the **Pre L Street** alignment from the screen.

4. Accept the **default** starting and ending stations.

5. Accept the **default** offset of **0**.

This will place the points on the centerline.

6. Use a station interval of **50**.

7. **[Enter]** when asked to select another alignment to end the command.

8. In the *Points Creation* parameters, Set **Prompt For Descriptions** to **Automatic - Object**.

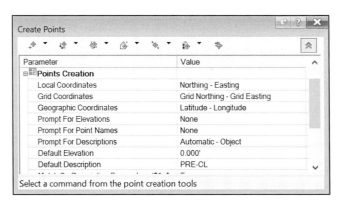

9.  Click the **down arrow** 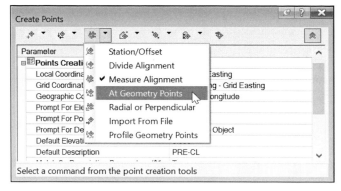 next to the third button from the left on the *Create Points* toolbar, to display the other alignment options.

10. Select ⇒ **At Geometry Points.**

11. Select the **Pre L Street** alignment from the screen.

12. Accept the **default** starting and ending stations.

13. **[Enter]** when asked to select another Alignment to end the command.

14. Close the **Create Points** toolbar.

15. On the *Prospector* tab of the *Toolspace*, pick **Points**.

This will display a list of all the points in the preview window at the bottom of the Prospector.

16. Right-click on **any point in the preview window** of the *Prospector* and select ⇒ **Zoom to**.

This will zoom in to the selected point in the drawing editor and is a great command to help you locate a specific point. You can use the *Zoom to* command on any *Civil 3D* object, it is not limited to points.

17. **Zoom Extents** to view the entire drawing.

18. Save the drawing.

### 3.3.3    Creating a Point Group

*Civil 3D* creates a default point group called *_All Points*.  As you might expect by the name this point group contains every point in the drawing.  You will want to create other, more specific, point groups so that you can easily select the desired points for different commands. Point groups can also control the display of the points by assigning a *Point Style* and a *Point Label Style* to the group.  *Point Styles* and a *Point Label Styles* will be covered in detail in *Chapter 4.*

In this exercise you will create a *Point Group* of the *Preliminary Centerline Points*.  This point group will be used to export these specific points to the surveyors.

1.   On the *Prospector* tab of the *Toolspace*, right-click on **Point Groups** and select ⇒ **New**.

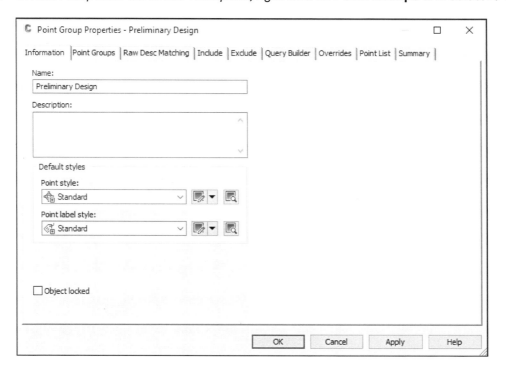

2.   Enter **Preliminary Design** for the **Name**.

Leave the *Point Style* and *Point Label Style* set to the default values.  You can control the display of the *Point Style* (symbol) and the *Point Label Style* (text) through the point groups. However, you will leave them as the defaults for now and explore them in detail in a later exercise.

If you pressed Enter after inputting the name of the Point Group it will close the dialog box. To reopen it just expand Point Groups in the Prospector, right-click on the Point Group named Preliminary Design and select Properties.

3. Select the **Include** tab in the *Point Group Properties* dialog box.

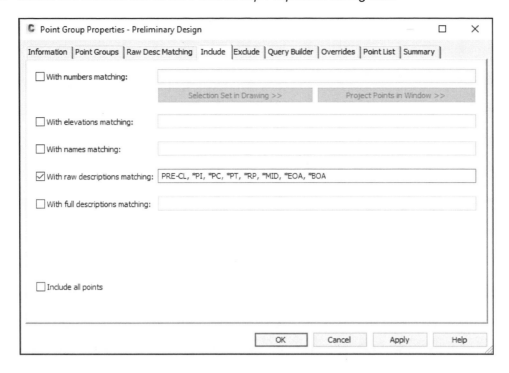

4. **Enable** the option **With raw descriptions matching**.

5. Enter **PRE-CL, *PI, *PC, *PT, *RP, *MID, *EOA, *BOA** in the adjacent field.

The asterisks (*) works as a wild card and in this example will select any points that have a description the ends with PI or any of the other descriptions using the wildcard.

6. Click **<<OK>>** to create the new *Point Group* for the preliminary design points.

### 3.3.4 Creating a Point Import/Export Format

In this exercise, you will create an *Import/Export* format.

1. On the *Settings* tab of the *Toolspace*, expand the **Point** node, and then expand the **Point File Formats** node under it.

Here you can see all the import/export point file formats that are currently in the drawing.
These originally came from the drawing template that you used to create the drawing.

2. Under the *Point* node, right-click on **Point File Formats** and select ⇒ **New**.

3. Select **User Point File** and click **<<OK>>**.

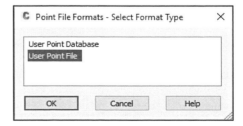

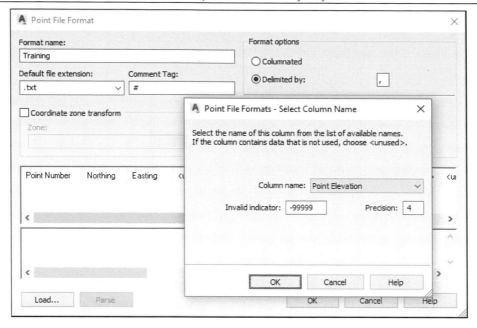

4.  Name the format **Training**.

5.  Set the **Format options** to **Delimited by:**

6.  Enter a **comma** in the **delimiter field.**

7.  Enter the **#** symbol as the **Comment Tag.**

*Civil 3D* will ignore any line that begins with the *Comment Tag* symbol during the import of the file.  So if you want to have information in the header of the point file, as in this example, you must use a *Comment Tag.*

When picking any of the column headers at the bottom of the dialog box you can select the type of data in that column, by default all display as unused.

8.  Create a format that contains columns for **Point Number, Northing, Easting, Point Elevation,** and **Raw Description,** in that order.

9.  When setting up the *Point Elevation* field, set the **Invalid Indicator** to **–99999**.

You can use the *Invalid indicator* option to set the value that your data collector uses for null entries.

10. To test your new format you can **<<Load>>** an example file that would use the new format.  This example has loaded the file:  **C:\A Practical Guide\Civil 3D 2020\Points\Site.txt**

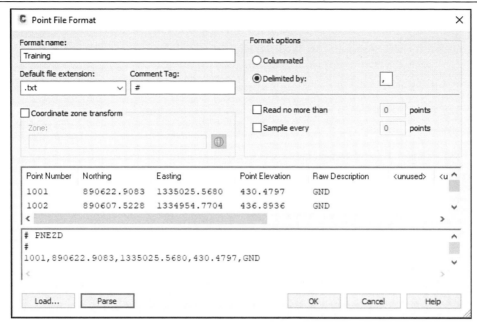

Once you load the example file it will be displayed in the text box at the bottom of the dialog box.

11. With an example file loaded you can click **<<Parse>>** to test the new format.

12. Click **<<OK>>** when you are finished setting up the format to save it and exit the dialog box.

### 3.3.5    Exporting Points to an ASCII File

In this exercise, you will export the points in the *Preliminary Design* point group to an ASCII file using the format you created in the previous exercise. This file could then be uploaded to your data collector.

1.  On the *Prospector* tab of the *Toolspace*, expand the **Point Groups** node.

2.  Right-click on **Preliminary Design** and select ⇒ **Export Points**.

3.  In the *Export Points* dialog box, set the **Format** to **Training**.

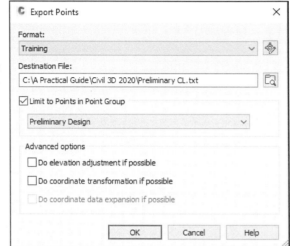

4.  Click **the Destination File browse** [icon] **button** to select the location you would like to save the exported point file. Browse to the path: **C:\A Practical Guide\Civil 3D 2020\**

5.  Enter a file name of **Preliminary CL.txt**.

6.  Confirm that the option is enabled to limit to points in the *Point Group* **Preliminary Design**.

7.  Disable all of the *Advanced Options*.

8.  Click **<<OK>>** to export the points.

The points in the *Point Group* are new exported to a text file. You can find the file that you just exported in *Windows Explorer* and open it in *Notepad* or any other text editor to review the results.

# Chapter 4

# 4 - Creating a Survey Plan

In this chapter you will work with *Description Keys* and *Point Groups* to organize the drawing as you import survey data. You will also work with *Styles* to control the display and labeling of points and parcels. There are several exercises devoted to controlling point display through the use of *Description Keys, Point Groups*, and *Layers*. Take your time and don't be afraid to experiment with them on your own. Managing points can be a very powerful, and complex, process and there are several ways to approach it. After you become familiar with how the commands work, you can make decisions about the method that makes the most sense for your projects. You will finish the chapter by working with parcels and parcel segment labeling.

This chapter focuses on importing and managing survey data. If you are transitioning from *Land Desktop*, you will see some concepts that look familiar, and some that look very different. As you work through the exercises take your time and keep an open mind. This will change the workflow that you may be used to. However, it will also allow you to do things that you could not do before, such as more point display options, controlling point display by point group and better parcel area tables and reports.

## Lesson: Importing Survey Points
In this lesson, you will learn to work with description keys and import points from an ASCII file.

## Lesson: Working with Point Groups
In this lesson, you will learn to manage points by using point groups.

## Lesson: Controlling Point Display
In this lesson, you will learn the concepts and process of creating and editing point styles and point label styles. You will also learn how point styles can be used with point groups.

## Lesson: Drawing Linework Using Transparent Commands
In this lesson, you will learn to use the transparent commands to draw lines by point number and by graphically selecting points.

## Lesson: Working with Parcels
In this lesson, you will learn to create parcels from existing AutoCAD objects. You will then learn about the different types of reports that can be created from parcels.

## Lesson: Labeling Linework
In this lesson, you will learn to label parcel segments and create line, curve, and area tables. You will also learn to label basic AutoCAD objects.

## 4.1    Lesson:  Importing Survey Points

### Introduction

In this lesson, you will learn to import survey points from an ASCII file.  You will also learn ways to manage and display these points using *Description Keys*.

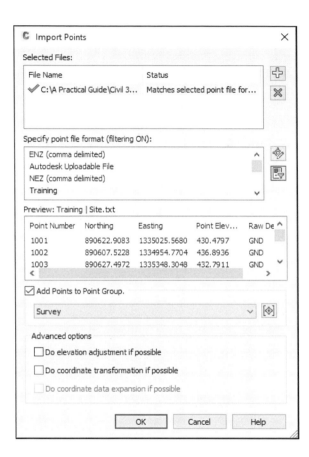

### Key Concepts

Concepts and key terms covered in this lesson are:

- Description Keys
- Point Settings
- Importing Points from an ASCII File

### Objectives

After completing this lesson, you will be able to:

- Describe Description Keys and their uses.
- Create a Description Key File.
- Control Point Settings.
- Import Points from an ASCII File.

## Description Keys

*Description Keys* control points as they are created or inserted into the drawing. They filter points based on their *Raw Description* and can control the layer points are inserted on, the full description displayed on the point, the point style, and the point label style as well as scale and rotation.

You are allowed to have more than one description key set in a drawing and the *Description Key Sets Search Order* controls the priority that different description key files are given if the same code is contained in more than one description key set. The *Description Key Sets Search Order* is found by right-clicking on the *Description Key Sets* node on the *Settings* tab of the *Toolspace*.

If you are familiar with using description keys in *Land Desktop,* you will notice a difference in *Civil 3D*. There is not an option for inserting a block or symbol with the point. This is now controlled by the *Point Style*, which means that you no longer have a separate *Point* and *Symbol*. Instead, the symbol is part of the point object. You do have new options in the description key to control the *Point Style* and *Point Label Style*. However, you also have the ability to control the *Point Style* and *Point Label Style* with *Point Groups*. Since Point Groups give you the ability to change the *Point Style* and *Point Label Style* of large sets of points quickly and easily this book will use *Point Groups* rather than *Description Keys* to control these styles.

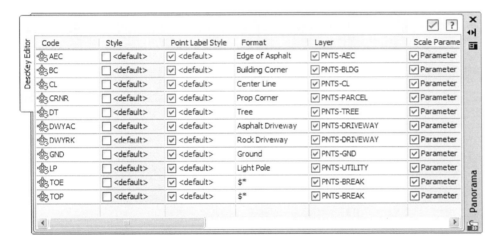

Definitions of the terminology used to create *Description Keys*:

**Code:** *Raw Description* or the description entered in the field by the surveyors.

**Format:** *Full Description* or the Description that will be shown on the *Point Object* in the drawing.

**Layer:** *Layer* in the drawing that the *Point Object* will be inserted on.

## Importing Points from an ASCII File

Points can be imported from an ASCII text file from a variety of standard point file formats. You can also easily create your own custom point file format is what you need is not available.

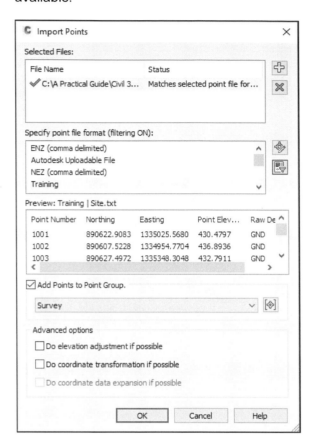

The *Import Points* command allows you to import multiple point files at the same time. The imported points can automatically be added to a point group for easy organization.

### Exercises: Import Survey Points

In these exercises, you will import survey points from an ASCII point file. First you will create a description set file to help organize and manage the points in your drawing. Then you will import the points and verify the description keys worked as expected.

You do the following:

- Create Description Keys.
- Import Points from an ASCII Point File.
- Confirm the Points were placed on the correct layers.

### 4.1.1 Creating a Description Key Set

1. Continue working in the drawing **Design.dwg**.

*Reminder:* You can also open the drawing with this exercise number in the
*Chapter Drawings* folder of the dataset if you prefer a fresh start at this point.

2. On the *Settings* tab of the *Toolspace*, expand the **Point** node.

3. Under the *Point* node, right-click on **Description Key Sets** and select ⇒ **New**.

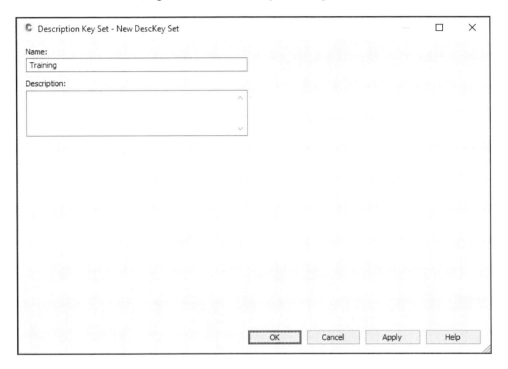

4. Enter the **Name** as **Training** and click **<<OK>>**.

5. On the *Settings* tab of the *Toolspace*, expand the **Description Key Sets** node under the *Point* node to display the new set.

6. Right-click on the **Training** *Description Key Set* and select ⇒ **Edit Keys** to open the DescKey Editor.

The first line contains the default *New DescKey* with default values which you will edit. You will need to expand some of the columns to read the complete headers.

In this exercise you are only using *Description Keys* to convert the Raw Description to a Full Description and set the Point Layer. The Styles of the Points will be controlled by *Point Groups*.

7. Change the **Code** to **GND**.

The *Code* is case sensitive.

8. Change the **Format** to **Ground**.

9. **Enable** the **Point Layer** checkbox to activate that field, then click in the field to open the *Layer Selection* dialog box.

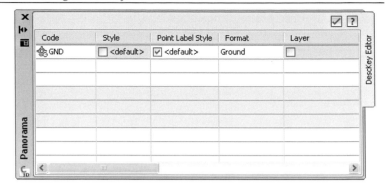

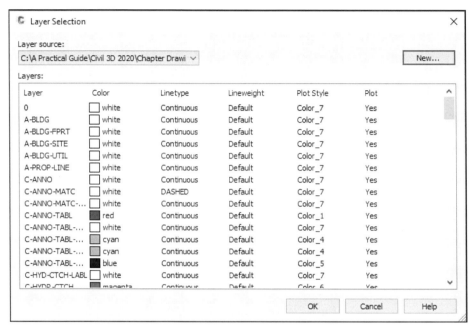

10. Click **<<New...>>** to open the *Create Layer* dialog box.

11. Change the **Layer name** to **PNTS-GND**.

12. Click **<<OK>>** to save and dismiss the *Create layer* dialog box.

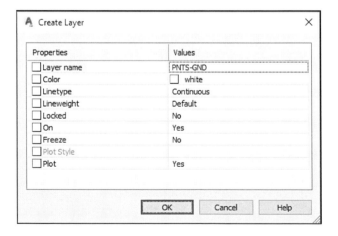

13. Click **<<OK>>** to dismiss the *Layer Selection* dialog box.

14. Right-click anywhere on the new description key *GND* and select ⇒ **New...** to create a new description key with default values below it.

15. Change the **Code** to **BC**.

16. Change the **Description Format** to **Building Corner**.

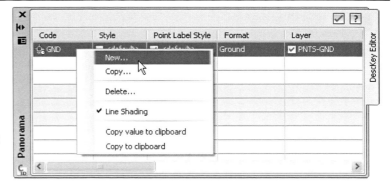

17. **Enable** the **Point Layer** checkbox to activate that field, then click in the field to open the *Layer Selection* dialog box, then click **<<New>>** to open the *Create Layer* dialog box.

18. Change the **Layer name** to **PNTS-BLDG**, then click **<<OK>>** to dismiss the *Create layer* dialog box and click **<<OK>>** again to dismiss the *Layer Selection* dialog box.

19. Repeat this process for the rest of the keys until the *DescKey* editor table looks like the table below.

Notice that there are two layers, *PNTS-DRIVEWAY* and *PNTS-BREAK*, which are used more than once. For these description keys you can use the copy option when creating the second, similar, description key to save time on data entry.

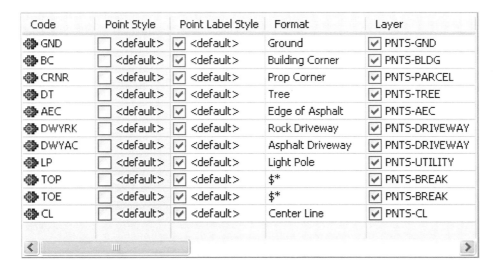

| Code | Point Style | Point Label Style | Format | Layer |
|------|-------------|-------------------|--------|-------|
| GND | ☐ <default> | ☑ <default> | Ground | ☑ PNTS-GND |
| BC | ☐ <default> | ☑ <default> | Building Corner | ☑ PNTS-BLDG |
| CRNR | ☐ <default> | ☑ <default> | Prop Corner | ☑ PNTS-PARCEL |
| DT | ☐ <default> | ☑ <default> | Tree | ☑ PNTS-TREE |
| AEC | ☐ <default> | ☑ <default> | Edge of Asphalt | ☑ PNTS-AEC |
| DWYRK | ☐ <default> | ☑ <default> | Rock Driveway | ☑ PNTS-DRIVEWAY |
| DWYAC | ☐ <default> | ☑ <default> | Asphalt Driveway | ☑ PNTS-DRIVEWAY |
| LP | ☐ <default> | ☑ <default> | Light Pole | ☑ PNTS-UTILITY |
| TOP | ☐ <default> | ☑ <default> | $* | ☑ PNTS-BREAK |
| TOE | ☐ <default> | ☑ <default> | $* | ☑ PNTS-BREAK |
| CL | ☐ <default> | ☑ <default> | Center Line | ☑ PNTS-CL |

The format $* will create a Full Description that is exactly the same as the Raw Description.

20. Close the *Description Key Editor* when finished.

21. Save the drawing.

### 4.1.2 Importing Points from an ASCII File

In this exercise, you will import survey points from an ASCII text file using the format that you created in *Chapter 3*. As these points are created in the drawing the description keys will sort them to specific layers and convert the *Raw Descriptions* provided by the surveyors in the ASCII file to a more explanatory *Full Description*.

1. Freeze the layers **C-ROAD-Pre L Street** and **PNTS-Preliminary Design**.

You should only see the surface displayed as contours on your screen. If you still see the alignment labels, use a Regen to clean up the display.

2. Select **Ribbon: Home ⇒ Create Ground Data ⇒ Points ⇒ Point Creation Tools**.

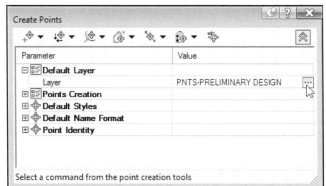

3. Select the **chevron** button on the right of the *Create Points* toolbar to expand it and show the point settings.

4. Expand the **Default Layer** parameters.

5. Select the **Layer value** field and click the more **<<...>>** button.

6. In the *Layer Selection* dialog box click **<<New>>**.

7. Enter **PNTS-MISC** for the new **Layer name**.

8. Confirm the option to **Freeze** the layer is set to **No**.

9. Click **<<OK>>** to create the new layer.

10. Click **<<OK>>** to select the new layer and close the *Layer Selection* dialog box.

By setting *PNTS-MISC* as the default layer for points, if any of your description keys do not work, the points will end up on this layer and be easy to find and fix.

11. Click the **Import Points** button on the *Create Points* toolbar.

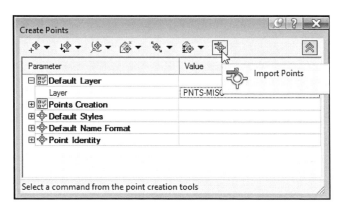

12. In the *Import Points* dialog box, click the **Add** button to select *the Source File* you want to import:

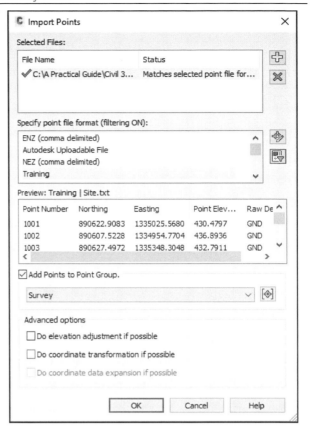

**C:\A Practical Guide\Civil 3D 2020\Points\Site.txt**

13. Select **Training** as the **point file format**.

14. **Enable** the **Add Points to Point Group** option.

15. Click the Add Point Group button to the right of the drop down list, to enter a new point group called **Survey**.

This will create a *Point Group* for all of the survey points and allow you to easily track which points are survey points collected in the field and which points are design points or other points generated in the office. You might also consider adding a date to the name of the *Point Group* if you have multiple sets of survey data coming in as the project progresses.

16. Confirm the *Advanced Options* are disabled.

17. Click **<<OK>>** to import the points.

18. Close the **Create Points** toolbar.

19. You may need to **Zoom to Extents** to see the imported points.

20. Zoom in to and examine several points. You should see the longer Full Descriptions that you entered in the *Description Keys*.

### 4.1.3 Confirming the Description Keys Worked Properly

1. Turn off all the layers that start with **PNTS-** except the layer **PNTS-MISC**.

If any points are still displayed they do not properly have a *Description Key* assigned to them. If so, you will need to examine the points to find the description of the points with description key problems. Then check the description keys to find the error. *Description Keys* are not dynamic; they do not update or change points after they are edited. So once you edit (or create new) description keys, you will need to apply the description keys to the points by right-clicking on the point group, on the *Prospector* tab of the *Toolspace*, and selecting ⇒ *Apply Description Key***s.**

You can also just move the points to the proper layer with the *AutoCAD Properties* command, but this will not update the *Description Keys*, so any points imported with the missing description in the future will be on the current layer.

2. Turn on all the layers that start with **PNTS-** except the layer **PNTS-PRELIMINARY DEIGN**.

If the points do not display correctly, *Regen* to update the display.

3. Save the drawing.

## 4.2    Lesson: Working with Point Groups

### Introduction

*Point Groups* are selection sets of points that are saved with the drawing. Once you define a *Point Group*, whether it is simple or complex, you can then select points by that group while using any point related command. *Point Groups* can also control the display of the points by assigning a *Point Style* and a *Point Label Style* to the group.

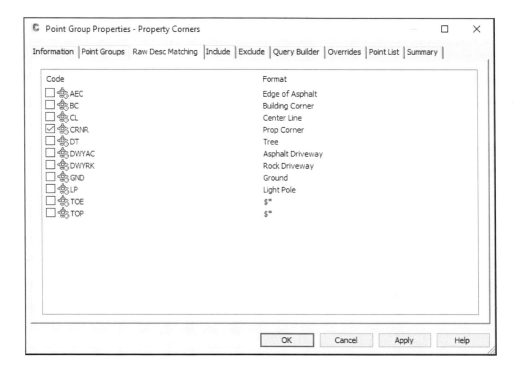

### Key Concepts

Concepts and key terms covered in this lesson are:

- Point Groups
- Locking Points
- Locking Point Groups

### Objectives

After completing this lesson, you will be able to:

- Describe Point Groups and their uses.
- Create a Point Group.
- Lock Points and Point Groups.

## Locking Points

- Points can be locked to prevent accidental changes
- There are no user privileges or passwords involved, they can be unlocked by anyone
- Right click on a point and select Lock to lock a point
- Right click on a point group and select Lock Points to lock all the points in that group

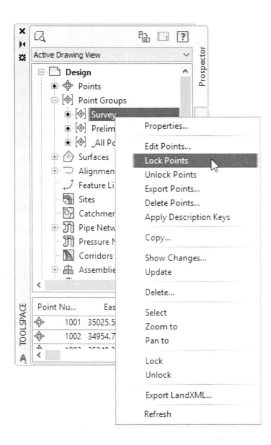

## Locking Point Groups

- Point groups can be locked to prevent changes to the group
- This does not lock the points within the group
- There are no user privileges or passwords involved, they can be unlocked by anyone
- Right click on a point group and select Lock to lock that group

## Advantages of using Point Groups

Point Groups can be used to organize and manage points in Civil 3D. Some uses of Point Groups include:

- Controlling Point Display
- Selecting Points to build a Surface
- Exporting specific Points
- Creating Point Tables
- Generating reports

## Creating Point Groups

Point Groups are selection sets of points. They can be created by setting up a query (or filter) that sorts through all the points in the drawing and selects the ones that match the criteria.

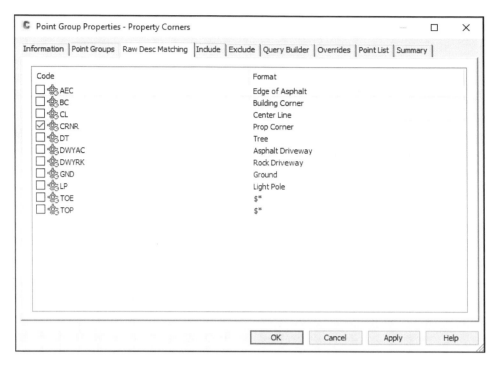

Components of the Query can include any combination of:

- Other Point Groups
- Raw Descriptions Matching
  - This uses the description keys to filter the points
  - It is a common method if description keys have been used as the filter is already set up
- Include
  - With numbers matching
  - With elevations matching
  - With names matching
  - With raw descriptions matching
  - With full descriptions matching
  - All Points
- Exclude
  - With numbers matching
  - With elevations matching
  - With names matching
  - With raw descriptions matching
  - With full descriptions matching

## Exercises: Create and Manage Point Groups

In these exercises, you will create several Point Groups. You will use these point groups to control the display of points as well as lock the points to protect them from inadvertent edits.

You do the following:

- Lock Points.
- Lock a Point Group.
- Create several Point Groups.
- Assign a Point Style to a Point Group.

### 4.2.1 Locking Points and Group Properties

1. Continue working in the drawing **Design.dwg**.

*Reminder:* You can also open the drawing with this exercise number in the *Chapter Drawings* folder of the dataset if you prefer a fresh start at this point.

2. On the *Prospector* tab of the *Toolspace*, right-click on the **Survey** point group and select ⇒ **Lock Points.**

This locks all the points that are in the selected group so that they cannot be edited. Notice that the lock symbol is added beside each individual point number in the preview window at the bottom of the *Prospector*.

3. On the *Prospector* tab of the *Toolspace*, right-click on the **Survey** point group and select ⇒ **Lock**.

This locks the *Properties* of the point group so that the definition of the point group cannot be changed. It does not lock or protect the points in the group. Once a point group's *Properties* are locked the icon changes to include a locked symbol.

### 4.2.2 Creating a Point Group for Property Corners

In this exercise, you will create a *Point Group* for the property corner points. This group will search for all the points in our drawing that use a certain description key. This is an example of a *Point Group* where you could save the group properties to a drawing template. This way when you start a new drawing the point group is automatically created. Then when points are imported to the drawing that fit into the properties of the point group they are automatically added to the group.

1. On the *Prospector* tab of the *Toolspace*, right-click on **Point Groups** and select ⇒ **New**.

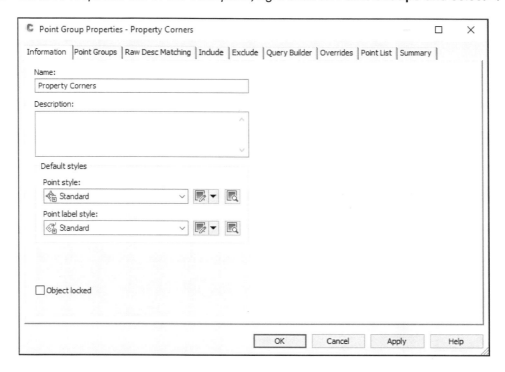

2. Enter **Property Corners** for the **Name**.

3. Confirm the **Point style** and the **Point label style** are both set to **Standard**.

*Point Groups* can control the display of the points contained in that group, by applying *Point Styles* and *Point Label Styles*. While you are not changing the styles in this exercise, you will assign different styles to *Point Groups* in future exercises.

4.  Select the **Raw Desc Matching** tab in the *Point Group Properties* **dialog box**.

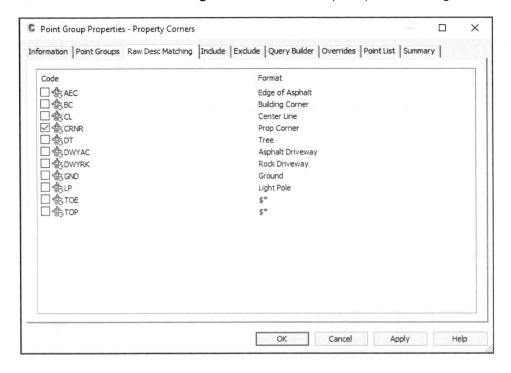

5.  Select the Raw Description **CRNR**.

These codes come from the description key set that you created in an earlier exercise.
Codes can be added and modified by editing the description key set.

6.  *Select the* **Point List** tab in the *Point Group Properties* **dialog box,** and you will see the point numbers that match your filter.

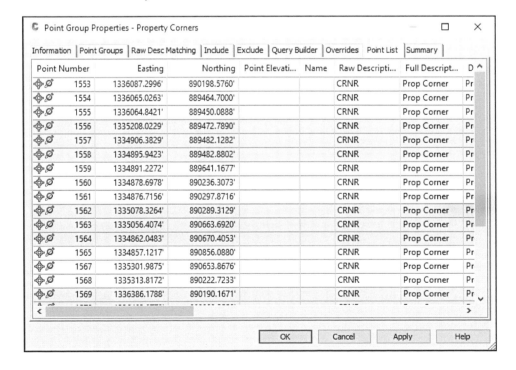

7.  Click **<<OK>>** to save the group.

### 4.2.3 Creating a Point Group for Center Line Points

Repeat the procedure from the previous exercise to create a *Point Group* for the points that use the *CL* description key.

1. On the *Prospector* tab of the *Toolspace*, right-click on **Point Groups** and select ⇒ **New**.

2. Enter **Center Line** for the **Name**.

3. Confirm the **Point Style** and **Point Label Style** are both set to **Standard**.

4. Select the **Raw Desc Matching** tab in the *Point Group Properties* **dialog box**.

5. Select the Raw Description **CL**.

6. Click **<<OK>>** to save the group.

### 4.2.4 Creating a Point Group for Breakline Points

Repeat the procedure from the previous exercise to create a *Point Group* for the points that use the *AEC, DWYAC, DWYRK, Top, and TOE* description keys.

1. On the *Prospector* tab of the *Toolspace*, right-click on **Point Groups** and select ⇒ **New**.

2. Enter **Breaklines** for the **Name**.

3. Confirm the **Point Style** and **Point Label Style** are both set to **Standard**.

4. Select the **Raw Desc Matching** tab in the *Point Group Properties* **dialog box**.

5. Select the Raw Descriptions **AEC, DWYAC, DWYRK, TOE,** and **TOP**.

6. Click **<<OK>>** to save the group.

### 4.2.5    Creating a Point Group for Tree Points

In this exercise, you will repeat the procedure from the previous exercise to create a *Point Group* for the points that use the *DT* description key.  You will also apply a *Point Style* to display a tree symbol as part of the point object.

1.   On the *Prospector* tab of the *Toolspace,* right-click on **Point Groups** and select ⇒ **New**.

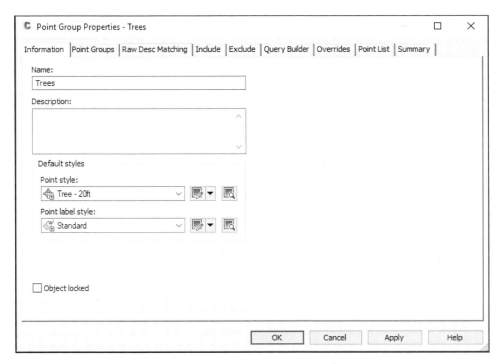

2.   Enter **Trees** for the **Name**.

3.   Set the **Point style** to **Tree - 20ft**.

4.   Select the **Raw Desc Matching** tab in the *Point Group Properties* **dialog box**.

5.   Select the *Raw Description* **DT**.

6.   Click **<<OK>>** to save the group and display the tree points with a green tree symbol, as defined by the *Point Style.*

7.   On the *Prospector* tab of the *Toolspace,* select the *Point Group* **Trees.**  This will display a list of all the tree points in the preview window at the bottom of the *Prospector*, if the *Prospector* is docked.  If the *Prospector* is not docked it will display on the side.

8.   Right-click on one of the points in the preview window and select **Zoom to**.

You will see the point in the center of your screen with the *new Point Style* applied displaying a tree symbol. You may need to zoom out to see the entire point symbol.  If trees do not display properly type Regen at the command line.

## 4.3 Lesson: Controlling Point Display

### Introduction

*Point Styles* control the display of the point marker while *Point Label Styles* control the display of the *Point Label* text. In this lesson, you will create a custom *Point Style* and *Point Label Style*. Then you will apply these new styles to a *Point Group* and explore controlling point display through *Point Groups*.

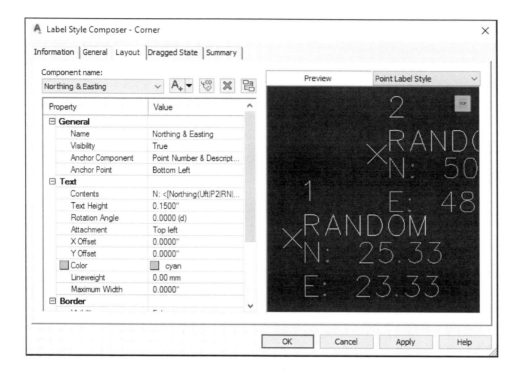

### Key Concepts

Concepts and key terms covered in this lesson are:

- Point Styles
- Point Label Styles
- Dragged State of Label Styles
- Point Group Display Order

### Objectives

After completing this lesson, you will be able to:

- Create Point Styles.
- Create Point Label Styles.
- Describe Point Group Display Order.
- Understand How Labels are sized.

## Point Styles

*Point Styles* control the display of the point marker. They can use an *AutoCAD Point*, a *Custom Marker* similar to *Land Desktop*, or an *AutoCAD Block* for the marker. *Point Styles* are saved in the drawing and can be created and edited on the *Settings* tab of the *Toolspace*. *Point Styles* can be applied to individual points, point groups, or point group overrides.

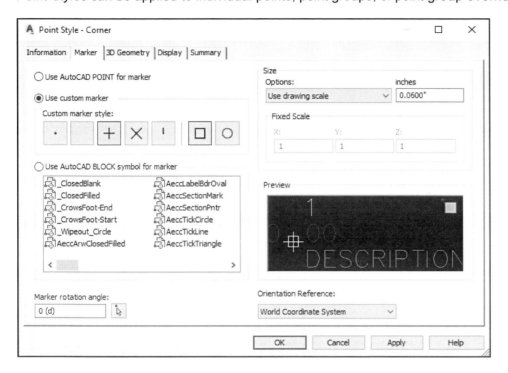

Marker symbols include:

- AutoCAD Points which are controlled by the PDMODE and PDSTYLE variables.
- Custom Markers
- AutoCAD Blocks

The marker size can be based on:

- The Drawing Scale (this will resize the marker based on the viewport scale)
- A Fixed Scale
- A Size in Absolute Units
- A Size Relative to the Screen

## Point Label Styles

Point Label Styles control the display of the point label text. Point Label Styles are saved in the drawing and can be created and edited on the Settings tab of the Toolspace. Point Label Styles can be applied to individual points, point groups, or point group overrides.

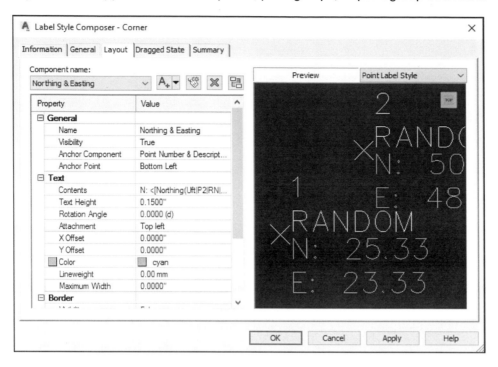

In the Label Style Composer you can configure text components to display any information related to the point. This includes a long list of point properties like point number, point elevation, description, northing, easting, and many others. These components can be attached and oriented to the point in almost any position. The text size, color and border can also be determined in this label style.

 The text size is a plotted height and the text will resize based on the viewport scale.

 The dialog box used to configure point label styles is the same dialog box used when you work with label styles for other objects in Civil 3D. This consistency means if you can master creating label styles for one object type, those skills will easily translate to label styles for other objects.

## Point Group Display Order

It will be very common for the same point to be contained in multiple groups. If each of these groups is using different point styles and different point label styles Civil 3D must determine which point group, and its corresponding styles, take precedence. This is determined by the point group display order.

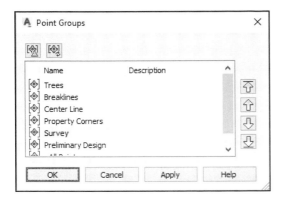

Point groups at the top of the display order list take precedence over the groups below them. In the example above, if points are contained in both the Property Corners group and the Survey group, the display of those points will be determined by the styles applied to the Property Corners group.

## Assigning Styles to Points

Styles can be assigned to points two different ways.

- By object
- By group

## By Object

Point styles and point label styles can be assigned to individual points. You can change point styles in the edit points command. This is also the way styles are assigned to points if you select styles in a Description Key Set.

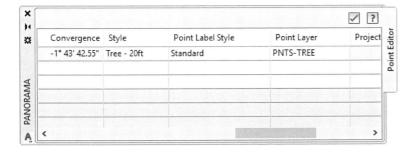

Any styles assigned to individual point objects will override styles assigned to a point group.

## By Group

Point styles and point label styles can be assigned to point groups. You can change point styles in the Point Group Properties.

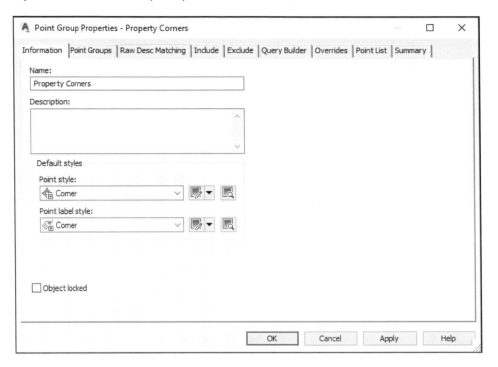

## Exercises: Create and Manage Point Styles and Point Label Styles

In these exercises, you will create a Point Style and a Point Label Style to represent the property corner points. You will then assign those new styles to the property corner point group. Finally, you will explore how the point group display order and other drawing settings effect the display of the points.

You do the following:

- Create a Point Style.
- Create a Point Label Style.
- Assign a Point Style and Point Label Style to a Point Group.
- Change the drawing scale.
- Change the Point Group Display Order.

### 4.3.1 Creating Point Styles

In this exercise, you will create a new *Point Style* that displays a blue plus with a box over it that will resize with the drawing scale.

1. Continue working in the drawing **Design.dwg**.

*Reminder:* You can also open the drawing with this exercise number in the *Chapter Drawings* folder of the dataset if you prefer a fresh start at this point.

2. On the *Settings* tab of the *Toolspace*, expand the **Point** node, and then expand the **Point Styles** node under it.

3. Under the *Point Styles* node, right-click on **Standard** and select ⇒ **Copy**.

You may need to scroll down to locate the *Point Style* called *Standard*.

4. Change the **Name** of the new *Point Style to* **Corner**.

5. Enter **Property Corner** for the **Description** of the new *Point Style*.

6. Select the **Marker** tab of the *Point Style* dialog box.

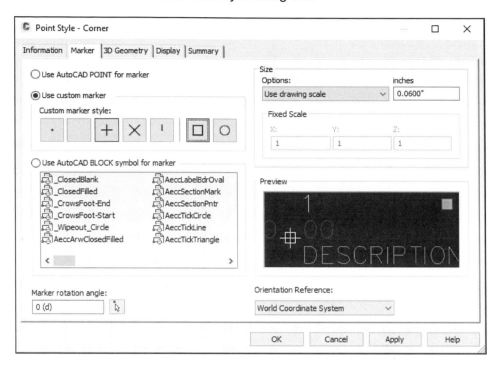

7. Choose the **Use custom marker** option.

8. Click the **plus** and **square** custom marker options.

The option to use an *AutoCAD BLOCK* displays a list of all the blocks currently defined in the drawing. You can also right-click on one of the blocks in the list to browse and insert any *AutoCAD Drawing* on your system as a block.

9. Select the **3D Geometery** tab of the *Point Style* dialog box.

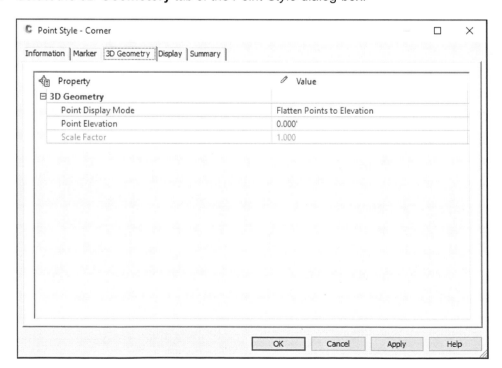

10. Set the **Point Display Mode** to **Flatten Points to Elevation**.

11. Confirm the **Point Elevation** is set to **0**.

This will set the *AutoCAD* elevation of the points that are displayed with this style to 0. It will not change the *Point Elevation* attribute. So, if you draw a line and use an object snap to snap to this point, the line will be at elevation 0. However, if you use this point to build a surface, or draw a line to this point using the *Civil 3D Point Number* transparent command, it will use the *Point Elevation* attribute.

12. Select the **Display** tab of the *Point Style* dialog box.

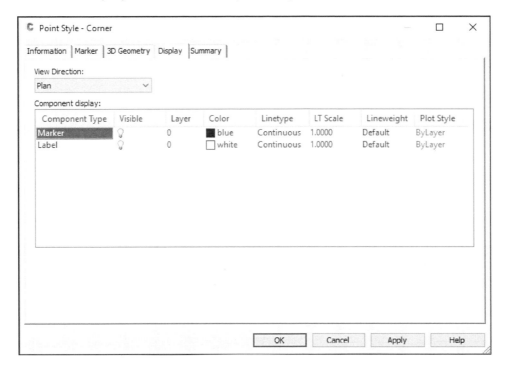

13. Set the **Marker** color to **Blue**.

This will set the color of the *Point Marker* to blue, rather than controlling it with the layer properties. This is a way that you can apply your organization's CAD standards through the use of *Civil 3D Styles*. All users will need to do is select the correct style for each object and they will be in compliance with the organizations standards, rather than memorizing or looking up layer, color, and linetype standards in a book.

14. Click **<<OK>>** to save the new *Point Style*.

This new style has been created and saved in the drawing. However, it has not yet been assigned to any points. So you will not see a change in the display of any of the points at this time. You will assign this new style to points in a future exercise.

### 4.3.2   Creating Point Label Styles

In this exercise, you will create *a Point Label Style* for the property corners that displays the *Point Number, Description, Northing,* and *Easting.*

1.  On the *Settings* tab of the *Toolspace,* expand **Label Styles** under the *Point* node.

2.  Under the *Label Styles* node, right-click on **Standard** and select ⇒ **Copy**.

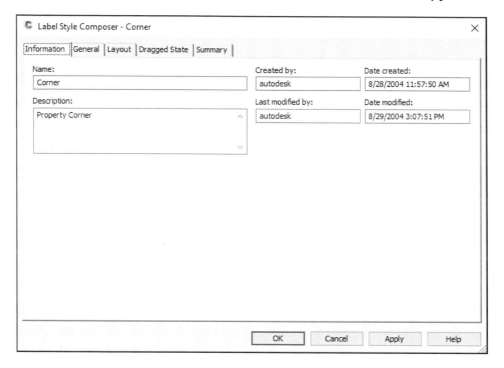

3.  Enter **Corner** for the **Name** of the new Point Label Style.

4.  Enter **Property Corner** for the Description.

5. Select the **General** tab of the *Label Style Composer*.

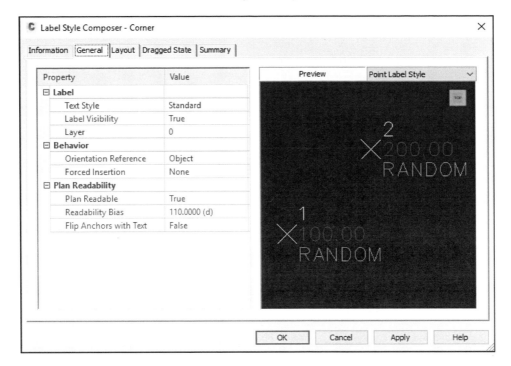

On the *General* tab you can set the Text Style for the label and the Layer that the label is created on. If you leave the layer set to 0 the label will be controlled by the Point Style. The *General* tab also allows you to set the Plan Readability for the label.

The *Label Style Composer* is very similar for all *Civil 3D* label styles. This consistency will make it easier to create label styles for any object type as you become familiar with the interface.

For this exercise you will not make any changes on the *General* tab.

6. Select the **Layout** tab of the *Label Style Composer*.

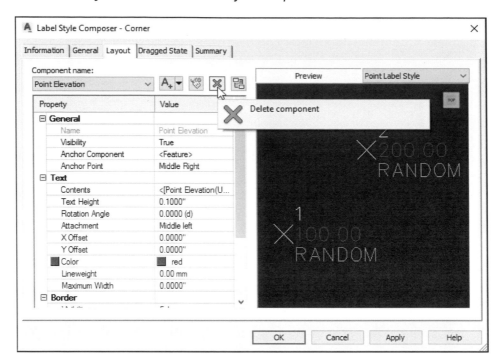

Before you add the *Northing* and *Easting* components you will first delete the *Elevation* and *Point Number* components. Then you will reposition the *Description* and add the *Point Number* to that component. Minimizing the number of components used in a label style uses less resources and improves performance in Civil 3D.

7. Select **Point Elevation** from the drop-down list to make it the active **Component name**.

8. Click the **Delete** button to remove the **Point Elevation** component from this *Label Style*.

You will receive a warning that this label component is used as an anchor. Deleting this component will affect the position of the other text and will need to be fixed before the *Label Style* is complete.

9. Click **<<Yes>>** to delete the component.

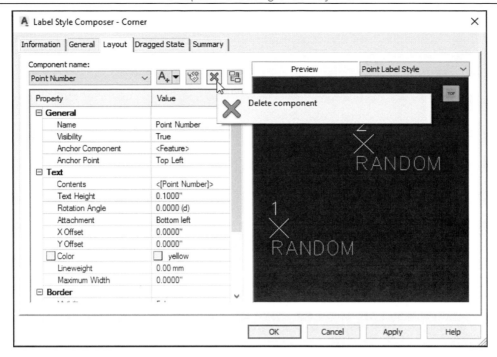

10. Select **Point Number** from the drop-down list to make it the active **Component name**.

11. Click the **Delete** [X] button to remove the **Point Number** component from this *Label Style*.

12. Select **Point Description** from the drop-down list to make it the active **Component name**.

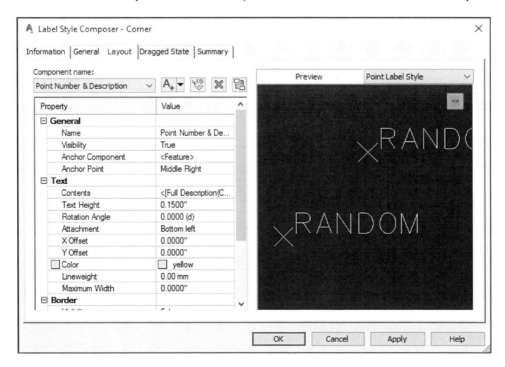

13. Change the component **Name** to **Point Number & Description**.

14. Confirm that the **Anchor Component** is set to **<Feature>**.

15. Click in the **Anchor Point** *Value* field to activate it, and then choose **Middle Right** from the drop-down list.

This attaches the *Point Number & Description* component to the middle right of the *Point Marker*.

16. Set the **Text Height** to **0.15**.

This value is the plotted height for the text. The *Civil 3D* styles will resize the text according to the scale of your viewports. So the text in this label will always plot 0.15 in height. This makes it easy to change the scale of a drawing or even have 2 viewports on the same sheet with different scaled viewports.

17. Set the **Attachment** to **Bottom left**.

This will attach the bottom left of the *Point Description* text to the middle right of the *Point Marker* that you set in a previous step.

18. Set the **Color** to **Yellow**.

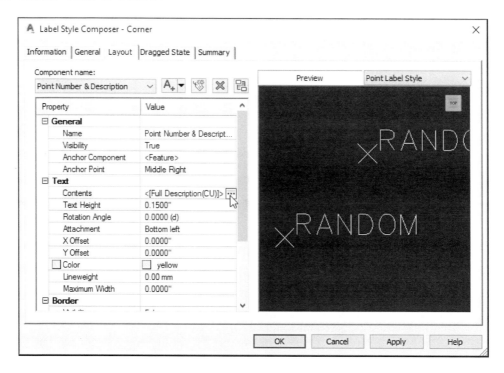

19. Click the **Text Contents** *Value* field to activate the **more <<...>>** button.

20. Click the **more <<...>>** button to open the *Text Component Editor*.

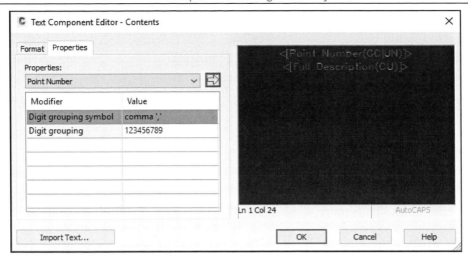

21. Place your cursor in front of the *Full Description* code and **[Enter]** to create a new line of text in the label component.

22. Place your cursor on the new blank line.

23. Select **Point Number** from the **Properties** drop down list.

Take a moment to explore all of the available properties that you can use to label points.

24. Click the **right arrow** button to insert the code which will display the point number.

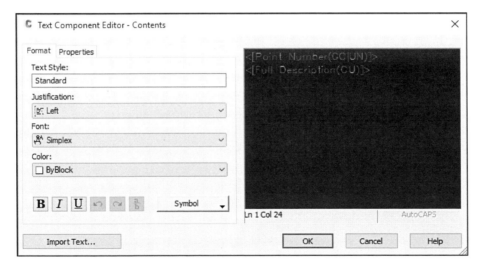

25. Select the **Format** tab.

26. Set the **Justification** to **Left**.

27. Click **<<OK>>** to save the contents of the new component.

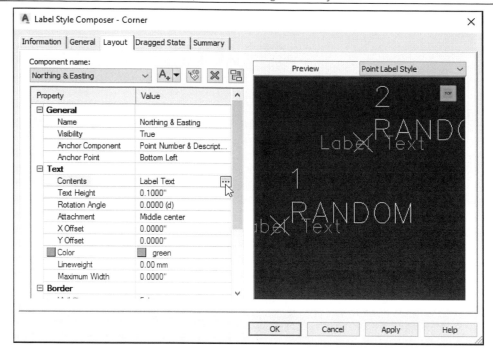

28. Back in the *Label Style Composer* dialog box, click the **Text** 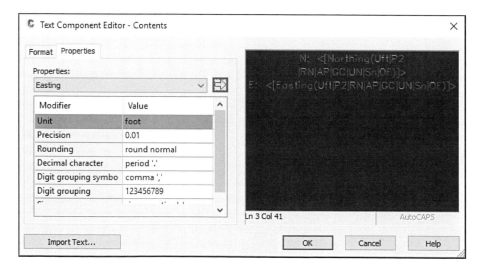 **button** to the right of the **Component name** drop down list.

This will create a new component for you to configure, called *Text.1*.

29. Enter **Northing & Easting** as the **Name** of the new component.

30. Set the **Anchor Component** to **Point Number & Description**.

31. Set the **Anchor Point** to **Bottom left.**

This will attach the *Northing* text to the bottom left of the *Point Description* text.

32. Click the **Text Contents** *Value* field to activate the **more <<...>>** button.

33. Click the **more <<...>>** button to open the *Text Component Editor*.

34. Delete the default **Label Text** displayed in the editor by dragging across it to highlight, then pressing **[Delete]**.

35. Select **Northing** from the **Properties** drop down list.

Take a moment to explore all of the available properties that you can use to label points.

36. Set the **Precision** to **0.01** (two decimal places), by selecting it from the drop-down list.

37. Click the **right arrow** 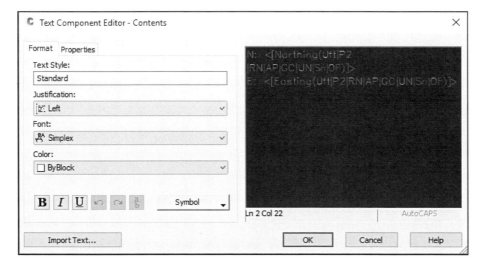 button to insert the code which will display the Northing of the point.

38. Enter **N:** in the editor before the code to better describe the label.

39. Place your cursor after the *Northing* code and **[Enter]** to create a new line of text in the label component.

40. Place your cursor on the new blank line.

41. Select **Easting** from the **Properties** drop down list.

42. Set the **Precision** to **0.01** (two decimal places), by selecting it from the drop-down list.

43. Click the **right arrow** button to insert the code which will display the Easting of the point.

44. Enter **E:** in the editor before the code to better describe the label.

45. Select the **Format** tab.

46. Set the **Justification** to **Left**.

47. Click **<<OK>>** to save the contents of the new component.

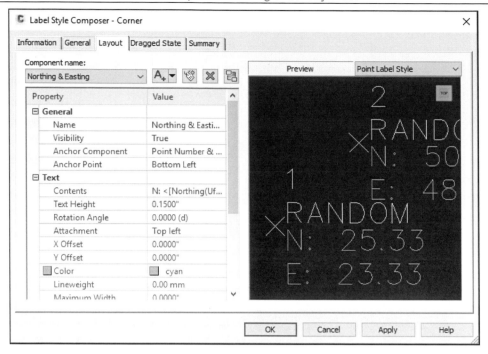

48. Back in the *Label Style Composer* set the **Text Height** to **0.15**.

49. Set the **Attachment** is set to **Top left**.

This will attach the top left of the Northing text to the bottom left of the Point Description text that you set in a previous step.

50. Set the **Color** to **Cyan**.

51. Click **<<OK>>** to save the new **Point Label Style**.

52. Save the drawing.

You have created and saved a new *Point Style* and *Point Label Style* in your drawing. However, neither style has been applied to any *Points*. They are only available and ready to be used. In the next exercise you will apply these new styles to a *Point Group*.

### 4.3.3 Controlling Point Display with Point Groups

*Point Styles* and *Point Label Styles* can be assigned to point groups. If a point is contained in more than one group, which is common, the display is controlled by the order of the *Point Groups* as set in the *Point Group Properties*.

1. On the *Prospector* tab of the *Toolspace*, right-click on the *Point Group* **Property Corners** and select ⇒ **Properties**.

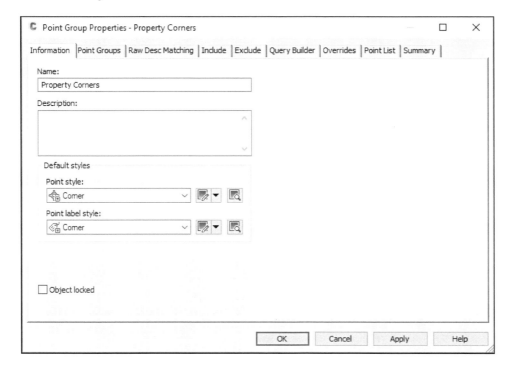

2. Set the **Point style** to **Corner** on the *Information* tab of the *Point Group Properties* dialog box.

3. Set the **Point label style** to **Corner.**

4. Click **<<OK>>** to close the **Point Group Properties** dialog box and apply the new *Point Style and Point Label Style* to the point group.

5. On the *Prospector* tab of the *Toolspace*, select the *Point Group* **Property Corners.**

This will display a list of all the property corner points in the preview window at the bottom of the *Prospector*, if the *Prospector* is docked. If the *Prospector* is not docked it will display on the side.

6. Find point number **1556** in the preview window.

7. Right-click on point **1556** and select **Zoom to**.

Notice point 1556 in the center of your screen with the new *Point Style* and *Point Label Style* applied. You may need to zoom out to see the entire Point object.

8. Select the label text for point **1556** to enable one diamond shaped and one square grip.

9. Select the **square** grip on the *Point Label* and drag the label to a new location where the text does not overlap other points.

Notice the point label text changes to green, resizes, and draws a leader back to the point marker. This behavior is controlled by the *Dragged State* which is a component of the *Point Label Style*.

### 4.3.4 Controlling the Dragged State

*The Dragged State* is a component of the *Point Label Style* that controls the display of a label when it is moved, or dragged, away from its original location. In this exercise you will modify the *Point Label* Style named *Corner* to set the *Dragged State* to display blue text with rounded border and a red spline leader.

1. On the *Settings* tab of the *Toolspace*, expand **Label Styles** under the *Point* node.

2. Under the *Label Styles* node, right-click on **Corner** and select ⇒ **Edit**.

The *Point Style Corner* is displayed with an orange triangle beside the name on the *Settings* tab of the *Toolspace*. This indicates that the style is in use by an object(s) in the drawing.

3. Select the **Dragged State** tab of the *Label Style Composer*.

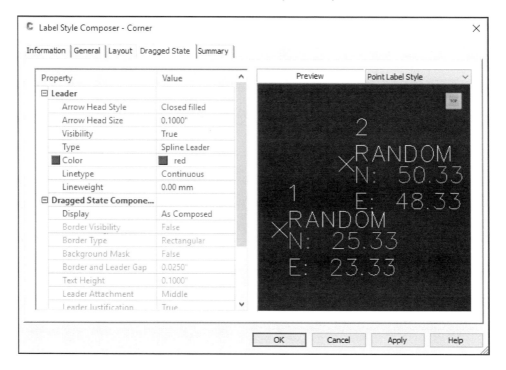

4. Set the **Leader Type** to **Spline Leader**.

5. Set the **Leader Color** to **Red**.

6. Set the **Display** to **As Composed**.

This option will keep the label text formatted exactly as it is when it is in the normal position on the point. If you want the text to be stacked you can use the *Stacked Text* option. This will align and stack the text while changing it all to the color and formatting defined below.

7. Click **<<OK>>** to save the changes to the *Point Label Style*.

Notice *Point 1556* updates to show the point label that is in the dragged state with a red spline leader and the original text formatting as defined in the *Point Label Style*.

### 4.3.5   Controlling Point Label Size in Model Space

In the previous exercises you created *Label Styles* that included settings to define the plotted text height. This text height uses the viewport scale to determine the size of the text so it plots correctly. In Model Space there is no viewport scale to control the text height. To control these sizes in Model Space *Civil 3D* uses a *Drawing Scale* setting. In this exercise you will change the *Drawing Scale* to resize the *Point Labels*. This drawing scale controls the size of all *Civil 3D Label Styles* the same way, it is not limited to points.

1.   On the *Settings* tab of the *Toolspace*, right-click on the drawing **Design** at the top of the *Toolspace* and select ⇒ **Edit Drawing Settings**.

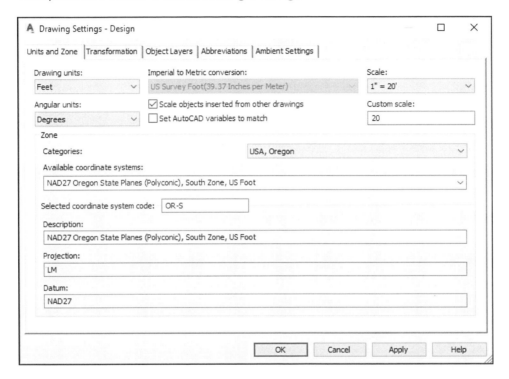

2.   Set the **Scale** to **1=20'**.

You can also set the drawing units and coordinate system in this dialog box along with setting the default object layers, abbreviations, and many other settings for the drawing.

3.   Click **<<OK>>** to apply the new scale to the drawing.

It may take a moment to redisplay, but you will see all the labels resize to the new drawing scale.

You can also change the drawing scale by selecting the desired annotation scale from the status bar.

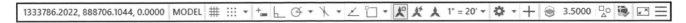

### 4.3.6 Controlling Point Group Display Order

It is common for points to reside in more than one *Point Group*. However, only one *Point Group* can control the display of a point at one time. To give you control over which *Point Group* is used to display each point *Civil 3D* allows you to set the *Point Group Display Order*.

1. On the *Prospector* tab of the *Toolspace*, right-click on **Point Groups** and select ⇒ **Properties**.

2. Select the *Point Group* **Survey** and move it to the **top** of the list using the **up arrow** ⬆ button.

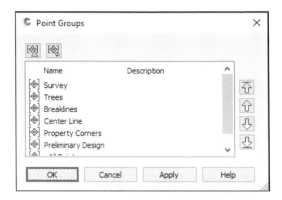

By moving the *Point Group Survey* to the top of the display order it will control the display of all the points in that group. Since the points in the groups *Trees, Breaklines, Center Line,* and *Property Corners* are also included in the *Survey* group their display, and layers, will change to the definitions found in the *Survey* group.

3. Click **<<OK>>** to redisplay the points.

4. Notice that all the points are now displayed with the *Style* standard, according to the *Point Group Survey*.

5. On the *Prospector* tab of the *Toolspace*, right-click on **Point Groups** and select ⇒ **Properties**.

6. Select the *Point Group* **Survey** and move it below the group *Property Corners* using the **down arrow** ⬇ button.

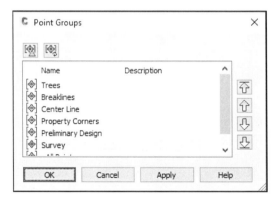

7. Click **<<OK>>** to redisplay the points.

The point display will return to its previous state with the *Trees* and *Property Corners* groups controlling the display of their points.

## 4.4    Lesson:  Drawing Linework Using Transparent Commands

### Introduction

The transparent commands in *Civil 3D* allow you to use *Point Numbers* and *Point* objects as locations during any *AutoCAD* command that asks you to specify one.  There are many other transparent commands that do not involve points such as specifying a location by *Bearing* and *Distance*.

### Key Concepts

Concepts and key terms covered in this lesson are:

- Using Transparent Commands
- Drawing Lines by Point Number
- Drawing Lines by Point Object

### Objectives

After completing this lesson, you will be able to:

- Describe Transparent Commands and their Uses.
- Draw Lines by Point Number.
- Draw Lines by Point Object.

## Transparent Commands in Civil 3D

The transparent commands in Civil 3D allow you to specify locations using methods of coordinate entry that are more common to civil engineers and surveyors, like bearing and distance, or angle and distance. The transparent commands must be run once you have started another command, and after it has prompted you for a location.

Transparent commands can be accessed a number of different ways:

- From a Toolbar
- Entering them at the command line
- From the Ribbon

## The Transparent Command Toolbar

The toolbar below contains the Civil 3D transparent commands.

## Line Commands on the Ribbon

On the Home tab, Draw panel of the ribbon you will find the Line commands. These are special versions of the transparent commands as they are scripted together with the AutoCAD Line command. In this case you only need to run one command and it will start the Line command with a particular transparent command active, rather than starting the Line command and then selecting a transparent command.

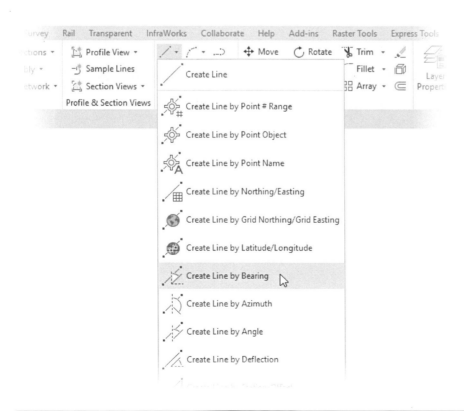

## Transparent Commands at the Command Line

A quick and flexible way to use transparent commands is to enter them at the command line any time you are prompted for a location and you would prefer to enter it in a different format. The table below lists the transparent commands and the required command line entry.

Notice that all of the transparent commands start with an apostrophe. This is critical and easy to miss.

| Transparent Command | Command Line Entry |
|---|---|
| angle and distance | 'AD |
| bearing and distance | 'BD |
| azimuth and distance | 'ZD |
| deflection angle and distance | 'DD |
| northing and easting | 'NE |
| grid northing and grid easting | 'GN |
| latitude and longitude | 'LL |
| point number | 'PN |
| point name (alias) | 'PA |
| point object, a point in a drawing | 'PO |
| side shot from a point | 'SS |
| station and offset | 'SO |
| station along the parent alignment of a profile view | 'STAE |
| station along the parent alignment of a profile view, elevation from surface | 'SSE |
| station along the parent alignment of a profile view, elevation from a COGO point | 'SPE |
| station and elevation in a profile view | 'PSE |
| grade and length in a profile view | 'PGL |
| grade and station in a profile view | 'PGS |

## Exercises: Draw Linework with the Transparent Commands

In these exercises, you will draw lines by point number and by selecting point objects graphically to represent parcels.

You do the following:

- Draw lines by Point Number.
- Draw lines by Point Number Range.
- Draw lines by selecting Point Objects graphically.

### 4.4.1 Drawing Lines by Point Number

1. Continue working in the drawing **Design.dwg**.

*Reminder:* You can also open the drawing with this exercise number in the *Chapter Drawings* folder of the dataset if you prefer a fresh start at this point.

2. Create a new layer named **EX-PROP-LINE**, set it **Current** and color **Yellow**.

3. **Freeze** the layer **C-TOPO-Pre-EG** and all the layers that begin with **PNTS-** except **PNTS-PARCEL**.

You should only see the *Property Corner Points* displayed on your screen. If all the other points are not turned off, type Regen at the command line.

4. Select **Ribbon: Home ⇒ Draw ⇒ Line ⇒ Create Line by Point # Range**.

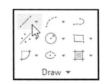

This starts the *AutoCAD Line* command and uses the *Point Number* transparent command to change the prompt to Enter point number:

You could also accomplish this by starting the *AutoCAD Line* command and picking the *Point Number* transparent command from the toolbar, or entering *'PN* at the command line. Either way you are just drawing *AutoCAD* line segments, these are not *Civil 3D* objects.

5. Enter points **1565, 1573, 1567, 1568, 1560, 1561, 1564, 1565**.

The point numbers can either be entered separated by commas without spaces, or with an **[Enter]** after each number.

6. Press **[Esc]** to end the Point Number prompt.

7. **[Enter]** to end the line.

### 4.4.2    Drawing Lines by a Range of Point Numbers

1.  Select **Ribbon: Home ⇒ Draw ⇒ Line ⇒ Create Line by Point # Range**.

2.  At the command line enter:  **1553-1560**.

3.  **[Enter]** to draw the line.

4.  **[Esc]** to end the *Point Number* prompt.

5.  **[Enter]** to end the line.

6.  Select **Ribbon: Home ⇒ Draw ⇒ Line ⇒ Create Line by Point # Range**.

7.  Now enter:  **1561-1564**.

8.  **[Enter]** to draw the line.

9.  **[Esc]** to end the **Point Number** prompt.

10. **[Enter]** to end the line.

11. Select **Ribbon: Home ⇒ Draw ⇒ Line ⇒ Create Line by Point # Range**.

12. Now enter:  **1568 [Enter] 1553 [Enter] 1569-1573**.

Be sure to **[Enter]** after each non-sequential point number as shown above.

13. **[Enter]** to draw the line.

14. **[Esc]** to end the **Point Number** prompt.

15. **[Enter]** to end the line.

When finished the parcels should look like the graphic below.

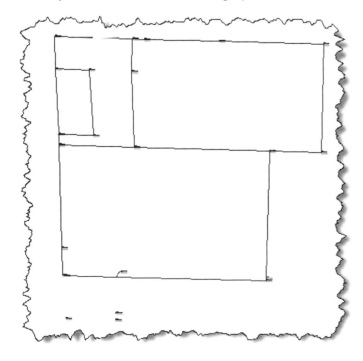

### 4.4.3 Drawing Lines by Point Object

1. On the *Prospector* tab of the *Toolspace*, select the *Point Group* **Property Corners**. This will display a list of all the property corner points in the preview window at the bottom of the *Prospector*, if the *Prospector* is docked. If the *Prospector* is not docked it will display on the side.

2. Find point numbers **1563** and **1567** and select them both using the **[Ctrl]** key in the preview window.

3. Right-click on point **1563** and select **Zoom to**.

4. Select **Ribbon: Home ⇒ Draw ⇒ Line ⇒ Create Line by Point Object**.

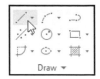

This starts the *AutoCAD Line* command and uses the *Point Object* transparent command to change the prompt to Select point object:

You could also accomplish this by starting the *AutoCAD Line* command and picking the *Point Object* transparent command from the toolbar, or entering *'PO* at the command line. Either way you are just drawing *AutoCAD* line segments, these are not *Civil 3D* objects.

5. Select Points **1563 and 1567** on the screen to draw a line between them.

You can select the *Point Label* or the *Point Marker*, whichever is easier.

This command does not show the rubber band line from the last point selected like you may be expecting to see. However, the command prompt will change from asking for the *First Point* to asking for the *Next Point*. If you select a point more than once you will create zero length lines at that location.

6. **[Enter]** to end the **Point Object** prompt.

You can also use the [Esc] key.

7. **[Enter]** a second time to end the line.

8. **Zoom to** points **1556, 1574, 1575, 1576, and 1558** at the southwestern corner of the site.

9. Select **Ribbon: Home ⇒ Draw ⇒ Line ⇒ Create Line by Point Object**.

10. Select Points **1556, 1574, 1575, 1576** and **1558**.

11. **[Enter]** to end the **Point Object** prompt.

You can also use the [Esc] key.

12. **[Enter]** a second time to end the line.

13. Save the drawing.

When finished the parcels should look like the graphic below.

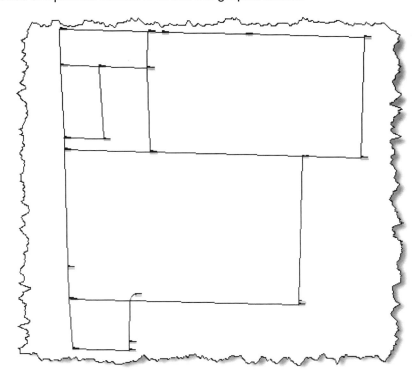

## 4.5    Lesson:  Working with Parcels

### Introduction

Parcels are closed polygons defined in *Civil 3D* and saved in the drawing as part of a *Site*. Parcels within a *Site* interact with each other and cannot overlap.  If parcels within the same *Site* overlap a third parcel will be created.  If parcels share a common boundary line, editing that boundary line will cause one parcel to get larger and the other smaller.

### Key Concepts

Concepts and key terms covered in this lesson are:

- Parcels
- Sites
- Parcel Labels
- Parcel Reports

### Objectives

After completing this lesson, you will be able to:

- Describe the concept of a Site and its uses.
- Create Parcels from existing objects.
- Label Parcel Areas.
- Create reports based on Parcel geometry.

## Understanding Sites

A *Site* is a collection of objects that relate to and interact with each other. *Alignments, Parcels*, and *Grading Groups* can all be contained in a *Site*. By using multiple *Sites* in your drawing you can control which of these objects interact with each other.

Parcels created within the same site use a topology model and interact with each other. For example, when two parcels share a boundary line there is only one line used, not overlapping duplicate lines. When that boundary line is moved or stretched both parcels change size. If new parcel segments and parcels are created in the same location as existing parcels their area will be subtracted from the existing parcels where they overlap as long as all of the parcel segments are in the same Site. This is one way that you can subdivide parcels.

You may want to use different sites for different phases of a project or for different design alternatives.

## Parcels

Parcels can be created by using the Parcel Layout Tools or by selecting existing AutoCAD lines, arcs or polylines. When parcels are created the geometry must be closed. You can create parcel segments that are not closed. However, only parcel segments that together form a closed boundary in the same site will create a parcel.

If the parcel segments are edited and are no longer closed the parcel will be deleted. However, the parcel segments will remain and could be closed again to create a new parcel.

## Parcel Area Labels

When a parcel is created an area label is displayed. The parcel can be selected graphically by picking the area label. The display of the area label is controlled by the Parcel Area Label Style.

## Parcel Reports

Parcel reports can be generated from the Reports Manager found in the Toolbox tab of the Toolspace. Parcel reports include:

- Area Report
- General Legal Description for Parcels
- Inverse Report
- Meets and Bounds
- Parcel Area in CSV
- Parcel Map Check Report
- Parcel Volume Report
- Surveyors Certificate

## Exercises: Define and Manage Parcels

In these exercises, you will define Parcels from existing lines in the drawing. You will then explore the parcel reports that are available in Civil 3D and create Area and Legal Description reports.

You do the following:

- Define Parcels from existing lines.
- Generate a Parcel Area report.
- Generate a Parcel Legal Description report.

### 4.5.1 Defining a Parcel from Existing Geometry

Parcels can be created from existing lines, curves, and polylines; or by using the *Parcel Layout Tools*. In this exercise you will define several parcels based on the lines that you created in the previous exercises.

1. Continue working in the drawing **Design.dwg**.

*Reminder:* You can also open the drawing with this exercise number in the *Chapter Drawings* folder of the dataset if you prefer a fresh start at this point.

2. **Freeze** the layer **PNTS-PARCEL**.

You should only see the property lines on your screen. If all the points are not turned off type Regen at the command line.

3. Select **Ribbon: Home ⇒ Create Design ⇒ Parcel ⇒ Create Parcel from Objects**.

4. Select the 6 parcel lines that make up the parcel in the southwest corner of the site.

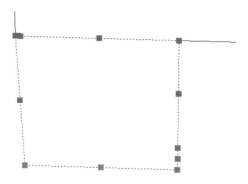

In *Civil 3D* a *Site* is a collection of objects that relate to and interact with each other. *Alignments, Parcels*, and *Grading Groups* can all be contained in a *Site*. By using multiple *Sites* in your drawing you can control which of these objects interact with each other. You may want to uses different sites for different phases of a project or for different design alternatives.

5. Click the **Create New Site** button to open the *Site Properties* dialog box.

6. **Name** the new Site **Proposed**.

7. Click **<<OK>>** to create the new site and return to the *Create Parcels - From Objects* dialog box.

8. Confirm the **Parcel style** is set to **Property**.

9. Set the **Area label style** to **Name Area & Perimeter**.

10. Confirm **Erase existing entities** is enabled.

11. Click **<<OK>>**.

When the parcel is created the yellow lines are converted to cyan parcel segments. The color and linetype of the parcel segments are controlled by the *Parcel Style*. The parcel is also labeled according to the parcel label style. In this example you will see a green parcel label showing the Name, Area, and Perimeter of the parcel.

If the parcel segments or the parcel label is not displayed confirm that the layers *C-PROP* and *C-PROP-LINE* are on and thawed. The Parcel will also be displayed in the Prospector. If the parcel segments do not close the parcel will not be created or labeled.

12. On the *Prospector* tab of the *Toolspace*, expand **Sites**.

13. Expand the *Site* **Proposed**.

14. Expand the **Parcels** node under the *Site* **Proposed** to display the parcel **PROPERTY: 1**.

If there are no parcels displayed under the site then the parcel has not been defined. You may have converted the lines to parcel segments. However, if they are not closed they will not be defined as a parcel.

You can define additional objects as parcel segments or edit the existing parcel segments to close the area and the parcel will automatically be created. If you edit any of the parcel segments the parcel will update to display the new area and perimeter in the label. However, if you edit the parcel segments and the parcel is no longer closed, the parcel will be deleted and you will be left with only parcel segments. As you edit parcel segments you can use the Undo command to undo any changes.

15. Select **Ribbon: Home** ⇒ **Create Design** ⇒ **Parcel** ⇒ **Create Parcel from Objects**.

16. Select all the remaining parcel lines with a window and [Enter].

17. Confirm the **Site** is set to **Proposed**.

18. Confirm the **Parcel style** is set to **Property**.

19. Set the **Area label style** to **Name Area & Perimeter**.

20. Click **<<OK>>**.

The remaining parcels will all be defined and labeled. Parcels created within the same site use a topology model and interact with each other. For example, when two parcels share a boundary line there is only one line used, not overlapping duplicate lines. When that boundary line is moved or stretched both parcels change size. If new parcel segments and parcels are created in the same location as existing parcels their area will be subtracted from the existing parcels where they overlap as long as all of the parcel segments are in the same Site. This is one way that you can subdivide parcels.

### 4.5.2 Creating a Parcel Area Report

1. If the *Toolbox* tab is not already displayed on the *Toolspace*, select **Ribbon: Home ⇒ Palettes ⇒ Toolbox**.

This will open a new Tab called the *Toolbox* in the *Toolspace*.

2. On the *Toolbox* tab of the *Toolspace*, expand **Reports Manager,** and then expand **Parcel**.

3. Under the *Parcel* node, right-click on **Area_Report** and select ⇒ **Execute**.

4. Confirm that all the Parcels are selected under the *Site* **Proposed** and click **<<OK>>**.

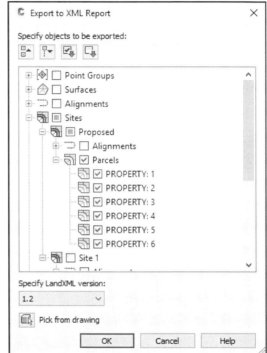

You have the option here to be selective about the parcels you want to include in the report. You can also improve performance by disabling options for other objects that will not be used in the report like surfaces and alignments.

5. When asked for location you would like to save the report. Browse to the path:
**C:\A Practical Guide\Civil 3D 2020\**

6. Enter a file name of **Parcel Area.html**

You also have the option to change the file type and save the report as a Word document, Excel spreadsheet, text file, or a PDF.

The *Parcel Area* report is now generated and displayed in your web browser.

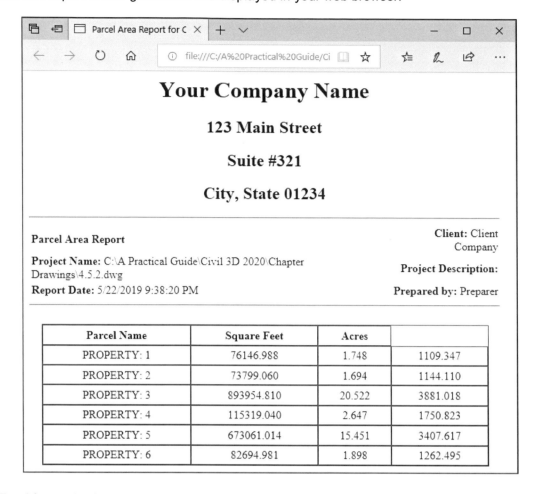

7.  After reviewing the report, **close** your web browser and return to *Civil 3D*.

This created a static report that was exported out of Civil 3D. You also have the option of creating dynamic tables, including parcel area tables, that are saved in the Civil 3D drawing. You will explore this type of dynamic table later in the chapter.

### 4.5.3  Creating a Parcel Legal Description Report

1.  If the *Toolbox* tab is not visible in the *Toolspace* Select **Ribbon: Home ⇒ Palettes ⇒ Toolbox**.

This will open a new Tab called the *Toolbox* in the *Toolspace*.

2.  On the *Toolbox* tab of the *Toolspace*, expand **Reports Manager**, and then expand **Parcel**.

3.  Review the different reports that are available.

4.  Under the *Parcel* node of the Report Manager in the Toolbox, right-click on **General_Legal_Description_for_Parcels** and select ⇒ **Execute**.

5. Confirm that all the Parcels are selected under the *Site* **Proposed** and click **<<OK>>**.

You have the option here to be selective about the parcels you want to include in the report. You can also improve performance by disabling options for other objects that will not be used in the report like surfaces and alignments.

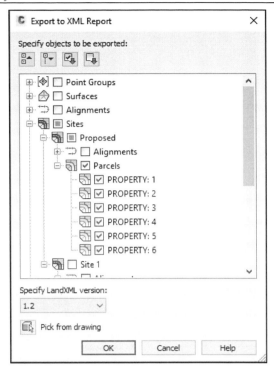

Internet Explorer is now opened with options for you to select an individual or all parcels to include in the Legal Description report.

6. If you receive a warning about **ActiveX controls** or **blocked content** select the option to **allow** it. (This depends on your Internet Explorer security settings and is usually displayed as a yellow bar at the bottom or top of the page.)

7. **Enable** the **Select all Parcels** option.

8. Click **<<Append to Report>>** near the bottom of the sidebar.

The *Legal Descriptions* of the parcels are now displayed. You can print, save, or copy from the report and paste into other programs like *Word* for further editing and formatting.

9. After reviewing the *Legal Descriptions*, **close Internet Explorer** and return to *Civil 3D*.

10. Save the drawing.

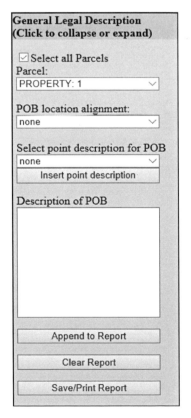

## 4.6    Lesson: Labeling Linework

### Introduction

The *Add Labels* command in *Civil 3D* can be used to label lines and curves if they are either part of a parcel segment or if they are standard *AutoCAD* lines, arcs, or polylines. In this lesson, you will first learn to label parcel segments, then you will learn to label lines, curves and polylines. It is important to remember that the commands to label and edit parcel segments and *AutoCAD* objects are very similar. The major difference is that you will select a different feature in the *Add Labels* command.

### Key Concepts

Concepts and key terms covered in this lesson are:

- Parcel Segment Labels
- Parcel Labels
- Parcel Tables

### Objectives

After completing this lesson, you will be able to:

- Label Parcel Segments.
- Label Parcel Areas.
- Create tables for line and curve data.
- Label AutoCAD lines and curves.

## Labeling Parcel Segments

Parcel Segment labels are defined by Parcel Line and Parcel Curve Label Styles. These styles are saved in the drawing and can be created and edited on the Settings tab of the Toolspace or on the fly in the Add Labels dialog box.

Parcel Segment Labels can be grip edited and erased with standard AutoCAD commands. Other commands specifically for labels can be found by right-clicking on the labels or on a context sensitive ribbon, once they are selected.

## Tags

To create Line and Curve Tables you must first tag the Parcel Segments with a Tag Label. This can be done by labeling the line or curve with a label style that has been configured in the Tag Display Mode or if the Parcel Segments are already labeled those labels can be converted to tags when the table is created.

## Tables

Once objects have been tagged or labeled they can be used to create line, curve, or segment tables. The display of these tables is controlled by the Table Style and the table can be dynamically linked to the objects so if there is a change in geometry the table will automatically update.

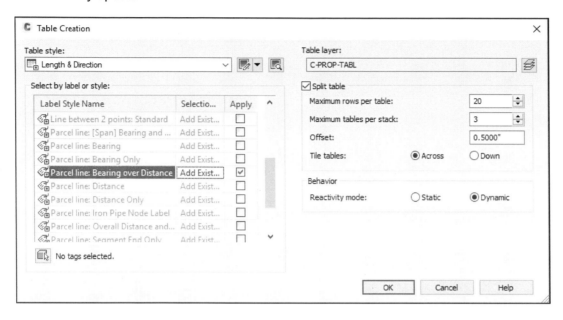

## Labeling AutoCAD Objects

Labeling AutoCAD objects is very similar to labeling parcel segments. The only difference is you will set the Feature to Line and Curve instead of Parcel.

Editing the labels and modifying label styles is also accomplished in the same way as it is with parcel segments.

## Exercises: Define and Manage Parcels

In these exercises, you will label parcel segments and learn to manipulate those labels. You will also tag parcel lines and create a line table. Next you will create a table style and use it to generate a table showing parcel areas. Finally, you will label a basic AutoCAD polyline using the Civil 3D label commands.

You do the following:

- Label parcel lines.
- Edit parcel segment labels.
- Tag parcel lines and create a line table.
- Create a parcel area table style.
- Create a parcel area table.
- Label an AutoCAD polyline.

### 4.6.1    Labeling Parcel Lines

1. Continue working in the drawing **Design.dwg**.

*Reminder:* You can also open the drawing with this exercise number in the *Chapter Drawings* folder of the dataset if you prefer a fresh start at this point.

2. Select **Ribbon: Annotate ⇒ Labels & Tables ⇒ Add Labels.**

This will display the *Add Labels* dialog box where you can select the feature, type of label, and label styles that you would like to use.

3. Set the **Feature** to **Parcel**.

4. Set the **Label Type** to **Multiple Segment**.

5. Confirm the **Line Label Style** is set to **Bearing over Distance**.

6. Confirm the **Curve Label Style** is set to **Distance over Radius & Delta**.

7. Click **<<Add>>**.

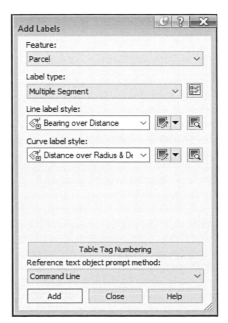

When creating *Multiple Segment Labels,* you must pick the *Parcel Label* at the center of the parcel rather than the lines that you want to label. This will select all of the *Parcel Segments* that make up the parcel and label them at their midpoints simultaneously.

8.  Pick the **Parcel Area Label** at the center of one of the parcels.

The particular parcel you label is not important since this is just an example of labeling and will not be important to future exercises.

9.  **[Enter]** to accept the default direction of **Clockwise**.

Labels will be created at the midpoints of all the *Parcel Segments* around the selected parcel according to the *Label Style* selected in the *Add Labels* dialog box. These *Label Styles* can be modified similar to the way that you created and edited the *Point Label Styles* in previous exercises.

10. **[Enter]** to end the command.

11. Set the **Label Type** to **Single Segment**.

12. Confirm the **Line Label Style** is set to **Bearing over Distance**.

13. Confirm the **Curve Label Style** is set to **Distance over Radius & Delta**.

14. Click **<<Add>>**.

When creating *Single Segment Labels* you must pick the *Parcel Segment* at the location that you want to create the label.

15. Select a **Parcel Segment** at the location that you want to create the line label.

A label will be created at the location you picked the *Parcel Segment* according to the *Label Style* selected in the *Add Labels* dialog box. These *Label Styles* can be modified similar to the way that you created and edited the *Point Label Styles* in previous exercises.

16. Click **<<Close>>** in the *Add Labels* dialog box when you are finished.

## 4.6.2 Working with Parcel Segment Labels

In this exercise, you will make several changes to the labels you just created, to demonstrate how the editing commands work.

1. Select one of the **Parcel Segment Labels**.

2. Select the diamond shaped grip on the label and drag it to a new location.

If you move the label to a location along the *Parcel Segment,* using the diamond shaped grip, it will not change appearance. If you select the square grip and move the label off the line, the label display will change to the *Dragged State* values defined in the *Label Style* and draw a leader back to the original location. You can use the *Undo* command to return the label to its previous location.

3. With the label still selected notice the context sensitive ribbon.

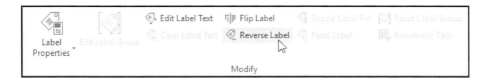

4. Select **Ribbon: Labels - Parcel Segment Label ⇒ Modify ⇒ Reverse Label**.

This will reverse the direction of the label, for example, changing southeast to northwest.

5. With the label still selected notice the context sensitive ribbon.

6. Select **Ribbon: Labels - Parcel Segment Label ⇒ Modify ⇒ Flip Label**.

This will flip the label text from one side of the line to the other.

7. **[Esc]** to clear the selection and dismiss the context sensitive ribbon.

## 4.6.3 Creating a Line Table

If you want to display the geometry information in a table rather than on the objects you can create a table. When you add objects that have been labeled to a table the standard labels are converted to tags.

1. Select **Ribbon: Annotate ⇒ Labels & Tables ⇒ Add Tables ⇒ Parcel ⇒ Add Line**.

This opens the *Table Creation* dialog box where you can select the table style, layer, and select the objects that you would like to include in the table.

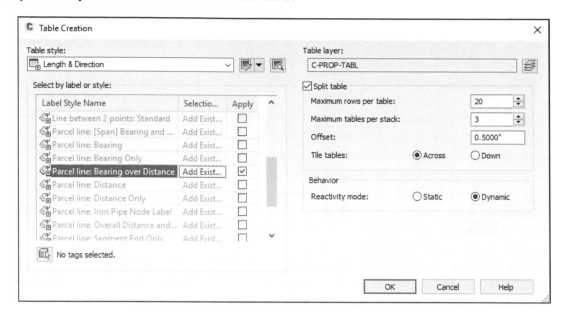

2.  Confirm the **Table style** is set to **Length & Direction**.

The display of the table, including the columns of data displayed is controlled by the *Table Style*.

3.  **Enable** the **Label Style** name **Parcel line: Bearing over Distance**.

4.  Set the **Selection Rule** to **Add Existing and New**.

This selection option will add all of the lines that are currently labeled with that style as well as any new lines that are labeled with that style to the table.

You can also set the layer the table will be created on as well as if the table is *Dynamic* or *Static*.

5.  Click **<<OK>>**.

6.  Select a location for the *Line Table*.

The table is a single object and can be moved or erased with standard *AutoCAD* commands. The display of the table is controlled by the *Table Style*. This includes the color of the lines and text as well as the data contained in each column.

Depending on the number of tags and the order that you created them, the line tag numbers may not be in sequential order in the table. The *Table Style* also determines sorting of the table. You can sort any column in the table in ascending or descending order.

7.  Select the table, right-click and select ⇒ **Edit Table Style**.

Select the **Data Properties** tab of the *Table Style* dialog box.

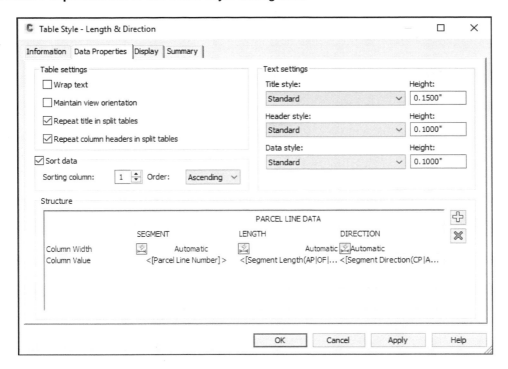

8. **Enable** the **Sort Data** option.

9. Confirm that the **Sorting Column** is set to **1**.

10. Confirm that the **Order** is set to **Ascending**.

11. Click **<<OK>>** to save the changes to the *Table Style* and sort the table.

The table will now be updated with the first column sorted in ascending order.

### 4.6.4 Creating a Parcel Area Table

In this exercise, you will create a parcel table that displays the parcel areas in both acres and square feet, along with the parcel perimeter. This table is dynamic so if you edit the parcels the table values will be automatically updated.

1. Select **Ribbon: Annotate** ⇒ **Labels & Tables** ⇒ **Add Tables** ⇒ **Parcel** ⇒ **Add Area.**

This opens the *Table Creation* dialog box where you can select the table style, layer, and select the objects that you would like to include in the table.

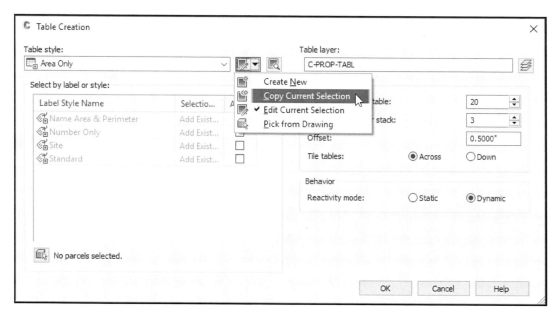

2. Confirm **Area Only** is set as the current **Table style**.

3. Click the **down arrow** button to the right of the *Table style.*

4. Select ⇒ **Copy Current Selection.**

Since this drawing does not contain a *Table Style* that is formatted with all the information you want to display, you will need to start by creating a table style that displays the area in both acres and square feet, along with the parcel perimeter all with the desired decimal precision and formatting. Like all other styles, if you save this *Table Style* in your template it will be available in all future drawings created from that template and you will not need to create it again.

5. Name the new style **Parcel Area & Perimeter.**

6. Select the **Data Properties** tab of the *Table Style* dialog box.

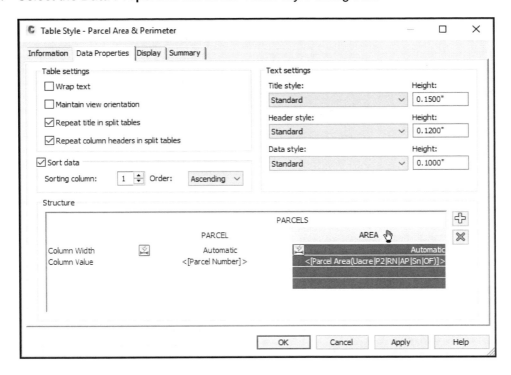

7. Enter **0.12** for the **Header Text Height.**

8. Double click on the header of the column currently named **AREA**, to open the *Text Component Editor*.

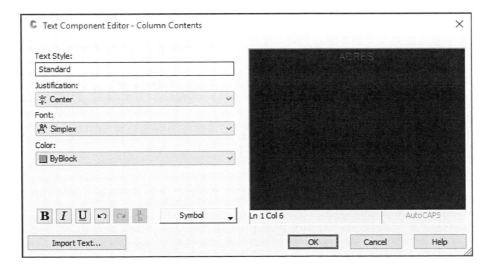

9. In the *Text Component Editor*, delete the default text **AREA** displayed in the editor by dragging across it to highlight, then pressing **[Delete]**.

10. Enter **ACRES** in the editor.

11. Click **<<OK>>** to change the name of the column.

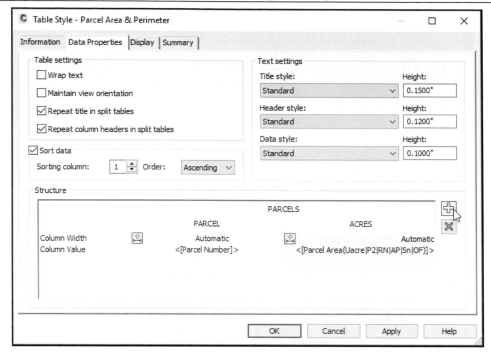

12. Back in the *Table Style* dialog box click the **Add Column** button.

This will create a new, blank, column in the table; you may need to scroll to the right to see it.

13. Double click on the **header** of the new column to open the *Text Component Editor.*

14. Enter **SQUARE FEET** as the name of the column in the *Text Component Editor.*

15. Click **<<OK>>** to add the name to the column and close the Text Component Editor.

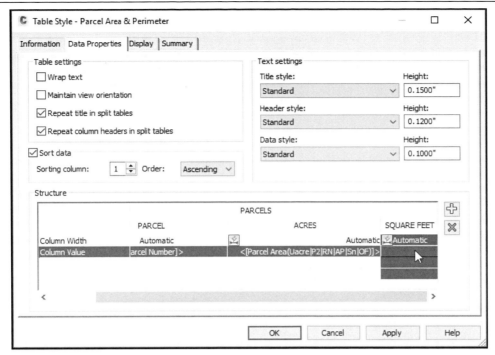

16. Back in the *Table Style* dialog box double-click on the **Column Value** field of the **SQUARE FEET** column.

This is where you will assign the data to the new column. For this exercise, you will populate the column with the parcel area in square feet, rounded to the nearest foot.

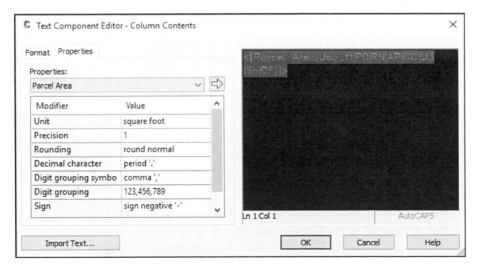

17. Select **Parcel Area** from the **Properties** drop down list.

18. Confirm that the **Unit** value is set to **square foot**.

19. Set the **Precision** to **1** (rounded to the nearest square foot), by selecting it from the drop-down list.

20. Set the **Digit grouping** to **123,456,789**.

21. Click the **right arrow** button to insert the code which will display the Area of the parcel in square feet.

22. Select the **Format** tab in the *Text Component Editor*.

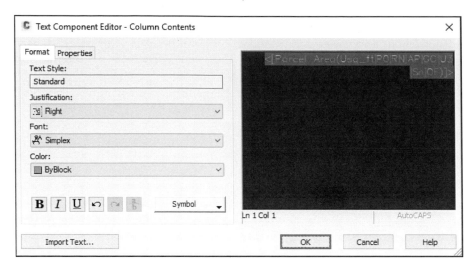

23. Set the **Justification** to **Right**.

By default the column is left justified. Changing the data in this column to be right justified is more typical for numeric data and will match the other columns in the table.

24. Click **<<OK>>** to save the contents of the new column.

25. Back in the *Table Style* dialog box click the **Add Column** button.

This will create a new, blank, column in the table you may need to scroll to the right to see it.

26. Double click on the **header** of the new column to open the **Text Component Editor**.

27. Enter **PERIMETER** as the name of the column in the *Text Component Editor*.

28. Click **<<OK>>** to add the name to the column and close the *Text Component Editor*.

29. Back in the *Table Style* dialog box double-click on the **Column Value** field of the **PERIMETER** column.

This is where you will assign the data to the new column. For this exercise you will populate the column with the parcel perimeter in feet, rounded to the nearest tenth of a foot.

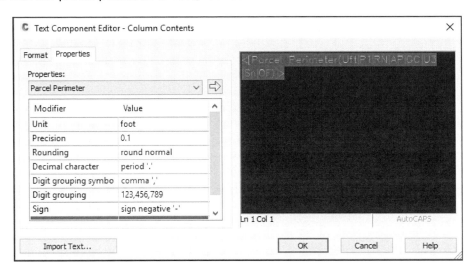

30. Select **Parcel Perimeter** from the **Properties** drop down list.

31. Confirm that the **Unit** value is set to **foot**.

32. Set the **Precision** to **0.1**, by selecting it from the drop-down list.

33. Set the **Digit grouping** to **123,456,789**.

34. Click the **right arrow** 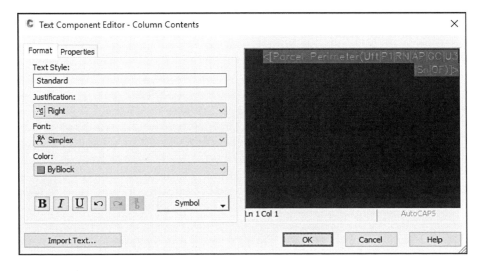 **button** to insert the code which will display the Area of the parcel in square feet.

35. Select the **Format** tab in the Text Component Editor.

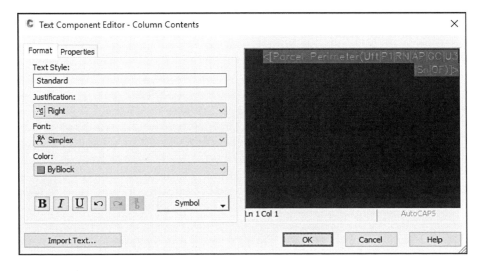

36. Set the **Justification** to **Right**.

37. Click **<<OK>>** to save the contents of the new column.

38. Back in the *Table Style* dialog box click **<<OK>>** to save the new table style and return to the *Table Creation* dialog box.

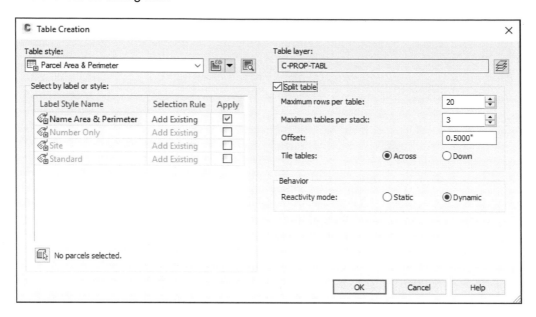

39. **Enable** the **Label Style** name **Name Area & Perimeter**.

This will automatically select all the parcels that are labeled with the selected style, and add them to the table. This is much easier than picking individual parcels graphically to add them to the table, which is also an option.

40. Set the **Selection Rule** to **Add Existing**.

This selection option will add all of the parcels that are currently labeled with this style to the table.

You can also set the layer the table will be created on as well as if the table is *Dynamic* or *Static*.

41. Click **<<OK>>**.

42. Select a location for the *Parcel Area Table*.

The table is a single object and can be moved or erased with standard *AutoCAD* commands. The display of the table is controlled by the *Table Style*. This includes the color of the lines and text as well as the data contained in each column.

## 4.6.5    Labeling AutoCAD Objects

In this exercise, you will import a point file collected during a wetland delineation.  You will then create the wetland boundary by connecting the points using the polyline command with the *Civil 3D* transparent point selection commands.  Finally, you will label the bearing and distance of the polyline segments representing the wetland boundary.

This exercise brings together many of the procedures and concepts that you have covered earlier in this chapter as you import points and create the boundary of the wetland.  For more detail you can refer back to those previous exercises.  Once the wetland boundary is created you will learn to use the *Civil 3D* labeling commands to label standard *AutoCAD* objects.  This process is very similar to labeling parcel segments.

1. On the *Settings* tab of the *Toolspace*, expand the **Description Key Sets** node under the *Point* node to display the **Training** *Description Key Set*.

2. Right-click on the **Training** *Description Key Set* and select ⇒ **Edit Keys** to open the DescKey Editor.

Adding *Description Keys* is not something that you should need to do in every project.  It is only needed when you have points that with new descriptions that are not part of your current *Description Key Set*.  As long as you use consistent descriptions for your points from project to project, you will be able to use the *Description Key Set* that is saved in your template.

3. Right-click anywhere on one of the existing description keys and select ⇒ **New** to create a new description key with default values at the bottom of the list.

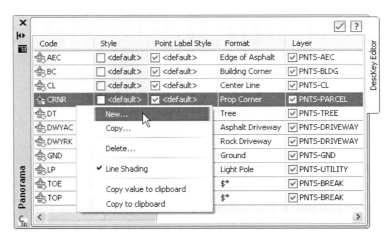

4. Change the **Code** to **WTLND**.

5. Change the **Description Format** to **Wetland**.

6. **Enable** the **Point Layer** checkbox to activate that field, then click in the field to open the *Layer Selection* dialog box, then click **<<New>>** to open the *Create Layer* dialog box.

7. Change the **Layer name** to **PNTS-WTLND**, then click **<<OK>>** to dismiss the *Create layer* dialog box.

8. Click **<<OK>>** to dismiss the *Layer Selection* dialog box.

9. Close the *Description Key Editor*.

10. Select **Ribbon: Home** ⇒ **Create Ground Data** ⇒ **Points** ⇒ **Point Creation Tools**.

This opens the *Create Points* toolbar.

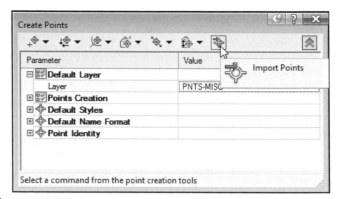

11. Select the **chevron** button on the right of the *Create Points* toolbar to expand it and show the point settings.

12. Expand the **Default Layer** parameters.

13. Confirm the **Default Point Layer** is set to **PNTS-MISC**.

This is important; if there is a problem with your description keys, the points will be inserted onto this layer. This will allow you to easily find the points and switch them to the proper layer, using the *AutoCAD* properties command.

14. Click the **Import Points** button on the *Create Points* toolbar.

15. In the *Import Points* dialog box, click the **Add** button to select *the Source File* you want to import:

**C:\A Practical Guide\Civil 3D 2020\Points\Wetland.txt**

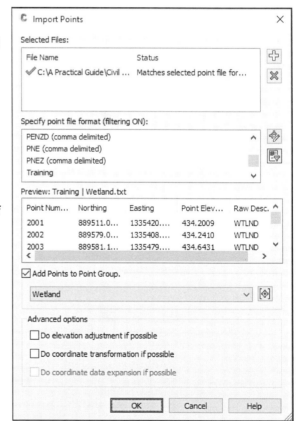

16. Select **Training** as the **point file format**.

17. **Enable** the **Add Points to Point Group** option.

18. Click the **Add Points** button to the right of the drop down list, to enter a new point group called **Wetland**.

19. Click **<<OK>>** to import the points.

20. Close the **Create Points** toolbar.

21. Zoom in to the wetland points along the southern border of the largest parcel.

22. Create a new layer named **EX-WETLAND-LINE**, set it **Current** and color **Green**.

23. Start the AutoCAD **Polyline** command.

24. Enter **'PN** to change the prompt to Point Number.

25. At the command line enter: **2001-2007,2001**.

26. **[Enter]** to draw the polyline.

27. **[Esc]** to end the Point Number prompt.

28. **[Enter]** to end the polyline.

29. Select **Ribbon: Annotate ⇒ Labels & Tables ⇒ Add Labels**

This will display the *Add Labels* dialog box where you can select the feature, type of label, and label styles that you would like to use.

30. Set the **Feature** to **Line and Curve**.

31. Set the **Label type** to **Multiple Segment**.

32. Confirm that the **Line label style** is set to **Bearing over Distance**.

33. Click **<<Add>>**.

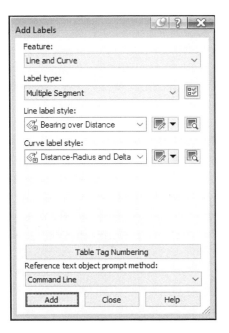

34. Select the wetland boundary polyline.

35. Click **<<Close>>** in the *Add Labels* dialog box when you are finished.

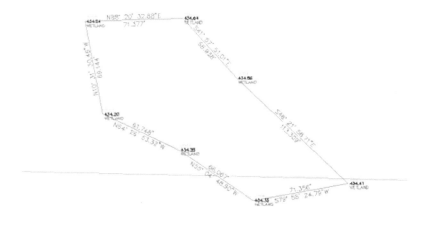

Labeling *AutoCAD* objects with the *Civil 3D* labeling commands is very similar to labeling parcel segments. Editing the labels and modifying label styles is also accomplished in the same way as it is with parcel segments.

# 5 - Building a Survey Quality Surface

In this chapter, you will use points and breaklines from the survey data to create a survey quality existing ground surface. You will learn ways to leverage the use of *Point Groups* to efficiently build and edit a *Surface* by editing the source data and also editing the *Surface* itself. You will also explore various ways of editing and analyzing surfaces including the use of the preliminary surface to add extra data beyond the limits of the survey. Finally, you will learn to display and label contours working with *Surface Styles* and *Contour Label Styles*.

Creating an accurate Surface is one of the most important parts of any *Civil 3D* project. The *Profiles, Sections, Corridor Models*, and *Grading* as well as *Volume Calculations* that you create later in the project are all based on this *Surface*. This chapter will explore ways to create an existing ground surface from survey data as well as ways to check, display, analyze, and edit the surface.

## Lesson: Building Surfaces from Survey Data
In this lesson, you will learn to build a surface from different types of surface data.

## Lesson: Editing Surfaces
In this lesson, you will learn the concepts and process of editing surfaces by editing the source surface data and by editing the TIN itself.

## Lesson: Surface Analysis
In this lesson, you will learn different ways to preform surface analysis that include elevation banding, slope analysis, and direction arrows.

## Lesson: Working with Contours
In this lesson, you will learn to display and label contours by working with surface styles and surface label styles.

## 5.1    Lesson: Building Surfaces from Survey Data

### Introduction

Any time you build a surface the most important step is to understand what data you have available to work with.  In this chapter, you will work with points that will be managed with a *Point Group* and breaklines that you will create based on some of those same survey points.

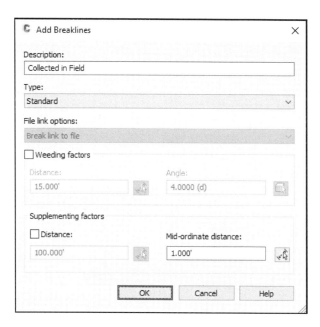

### Key Concepts

Concepts and key terms covered in this lesson are:

- Surface
- Points
- Point Group
- Breaklines
- Surface Styles

### Objectives

After completing this lesson, you will be able to:

- Create a Point Group for use building a Surface
- List the types of data that can be used to build a Surface.
- Describe what a breakline is.
- Draw and define breaklines.

## Types of Surface Data

Surfaces can be built from a combination of many different types of data:

- Boundaries
- Breaklines
- Contours
- DEM files (Digital Elevation Models)
- Drawing Objects
- Point Files
- Point Groups
- Point Survey Queries
- Figure Survey Queries

## Boundaries

A boundary is a closed polygon that limits the triangulation of a surface.

## Boundary Types:

- Outer
  - o Defines the outer boundary of a surface
  - o Triangles outside of this boundary are removed
- Show
  - o Displays the triangles inside the boundary
  - o Can be used inside of a Hide boundary
- Hide
  - o Removes triangles inside of the boundary
  - o Creates a hole in the surface
  - o Can be used for building footprints to keep contours from crossing through them
- Data Clip
  - o Keeps data outside this boundary from being added to the surface
  - o Must be added before other surface data or moved up in priority in the surface definition
  - o Useful for limiting the size of large datasets

---

## Non-destructive breakline boundaries

Outer, Show and Hide boundaries have the option to be created as non-destructive breaklines. When this option is enabled it trims the TIN lines at the boundary. When it is not used it erases all the TIN lines that touch the boundary.

This can be a good option if you have good surface data on each side of the boundary as it will cut a clean and straight boundary through the surface. However, if this option is used on an outer boundary where all of the surface data is inside the boundary and the only triangle touching it are long and inaccurate, then you may be left with short triangles along the edge that are still at the wrong slope.

## Breaklines

Breaklines define grade breaks in a surface. They are lines in a TIN that represents a distinct interruption in the slope of a surface; like road centerlines, curbs, gutters, streams, tops and toes of slopes, or any other grade break. No triangle in a TIN may cross a breakline (in other words, breaklines are enforced as triangle edges).

## Types of breaklines:

- Standard
  - o Defined by selecting 3D polylines, 3D lines, feature lines, or splines
- Proximity
  - o Defined by selecting a 2D polyline, feature line or spline
  - o The vertices of the breakline are snapped to the nearest point in the TIN, or closest proximity
  - o Accuracy is dependent on how close the vertices of the proximity breakline are to the points in the TIN
  - o Can be very accurate and efficient if you have drawn the selected object from point to point
- Wall
  - o Defined by selecting 3D polylines, 3D lines, feature lines, splines or by selecting points.
  - o You enter the elevation on each side of the wall at each vertex
- From file
  - o Can be imported from an ASCII FLT file
- Non-destructive
  - o Break the triangles in the TIN without changing the slope of the lines

## Contours

Contour data in the form of 2D polylines can be added to your surface.

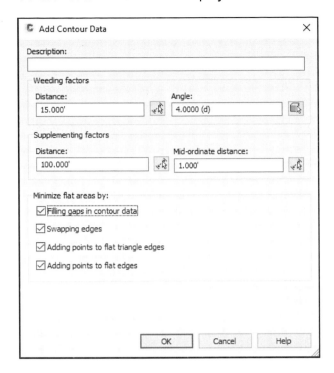

Weeding factors can help you skip over extra, unnecessary vertices when the data is added to the surface. While supplementing factors will allow you to sample extra points off long contours with minimal vertices.

Since by its nature, contour data tends to create flat triangles that do not accurately reflect the surface, there are several options to minimize those flat triangles. In most cases it is a best practice to enable all four options to minimize flat areas when adding contour data to a surface.

## DEM Files

DEM files (Digital Elevation Models) are grid based surfaces. This is a format that is used by many different Civil, Survey, and GIS programs.

DEM files are a format that is commonly used by the USGS and there is a tremendous amount of data that is available online for free in this format.

## Drawing Objects

AutoCAD object that have elevations can be used to build a surface. These objects include:

- Points
- Lines
- Blocks
- Text
- 3D Faces
- Polyface

## Point Files

ASCII point files can be imported directly into the surface. This is a good option for large datasets or points that you do not need in the drawing for anything other than building a surface.

## Point Groups

Point groups can be used to add a specific selection set of points to a surface. It may be common that some of the points in your drawing are not related to a surface. For example, you would not want to include a point representing the invert of a manhole in the surface. A point group consisting of only surface related points is an efficient way to add only the appropriate points to the surface.

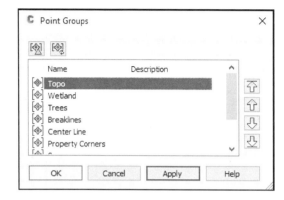

## Point Survey Queries

Point Survey Queries are a dynamic reference to a selection of survey points that are included in a survey database. If the points in the survey database are updated, the surface will be marked as out of date and will use the updated values when it is rebuilt.

## Figure Survey Queries

Figure Survey Queries are a dynamic reference to a selection of survey figures that are included in a survey database. If the figures in the survey database are updated, the surface will be marked as out of date and will use the updated values when it is rebuilt.

## Exercises: Build a Surface from Survey Data

In these exercises, you create a new surface from point group data. You will draw breaklines from survey points and add them to the surface. Then you will view the surface in the Object Viewer to examine it in 3D from different angles.

You do the following:

- Create a Point Group of surface related points.
- Create a Surface.
- Draw Breaklines.
- Add Breaklines to the Surface.
- View the Surface in 3D using the Object Viewer.

### 5.1.1 Creating a Point Group to Be Used As Surface Data

Before you create the surface you need to create a *Point Group* that will be used to select only the points that you want to use for the surface data. Points that should not be included in the surface should not be included in the point group. Points for utility potholes or points that are part of the project for horizontal control and do not have accurate surface elevations are examples of points that should not be included in this group.

1.  Continue working in the drawing **Design.dwg**.

This drawing contains the *Points, Alignment, Parcels*, and *Surface* from the previous chapters. Currently only the parcel lines and labels are displayed.

*Reminder:* You can also open the drawing with this exercise number in the *Chapter Drawings* folder of the dataset if you prefer a fresh start at this point.

2.  On the *Prospector* tab of the *Toolspace*, right-click on **Point Groups** and select ⇒ **New**.

3.  Enter **Topo** for the **Name**.

4.  Select the **Raw Desc Matching** tab in the *Point Group Properties* **dialog box**.

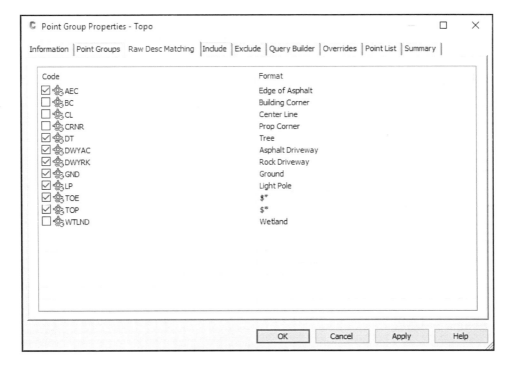

5.  Select the description keys **AEC, DT, DWYRK, DWYAC, GND, LP, TOE,** and **TOP**.

6.  Click **<<OK>>** to create the *Point Group*.

### 5.1.2   Creating the Survey Surface

1.  On the *Prospector* tab of the *Toolspace,* right-click on **Surfaces** and select ⇒ **Create Surface**.

2.  Confirm that **TIN surface** is selected as **Type**.

3.  Enter **Survey** for the **Name**.

4.  Set the **Style** to **Border & Contours**.

5.  Confirm the *Surface layer* is set to **C-TOPO-Survey**.

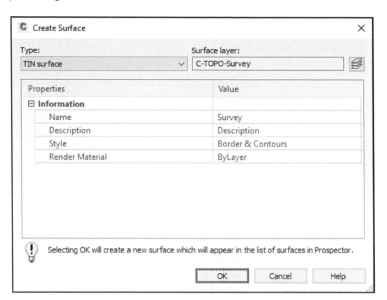

This layer name that includes the surface name as a suffix was setup in an earlier exercise through the Drawing Settings command.

6.  Click **<<OK>>** to close the *Create Surface* dialog box and create the surface.

At this time the surface has not been given any data so it is not displayed.  However, it has been created and you will see it in the *Prospector*.  This is where you will access the surface definition commands and add data to the surface.

### 5.1.3   Adding Point Group Data to a Surface

Point information contained in a *Point Group* can be added to a *Surface* through the *Prospector*.  Once the *Point Group* is added the *Surface* is automatically rebuilt to incorporate and display the new data.

1.  On the *Prospector* tab of the *Toolspace,* expand **Surfaces**.

2.  Expand the *Surface* **Survey**.

3.  Expand the **Definition** node under *Survey*.

4.  Right-click on **Point Groups** under *Definition* and select ⇒ **Add**.

5.  Select the *Point Group* **Topo**.

6.  Click **<<OK>>** to add the point group data to the surface.

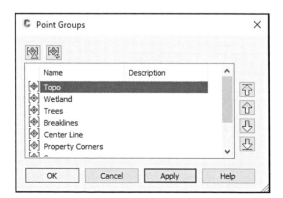

The surface is built with the point group data and displays 5 foot contours colored brown and green with a yellow border. This display is controlled by the surface style you selected when you created the surface. If the surface is not visible turn on and thaw the layer *C-TOPO-Survey*.

### 5.1.4    Creating Breaklines by Point Number

*Civil 3D* does not use special commands for drawing and defining breaklines the way that *Land Desktop* and many other programs do. Instead, you draw the breaklines with standard *AutoCAD* commands, like the *3D Polyline* command, and then define these objects as breaklines after they have been drawn.

1.   Create a new *Layer* named **Breaklines-Survey** and set it **Current**.

2.   Thaw the layers **PNTS-AEC, PNTS-BREAK,** and **PNTS-DRIVEWAY**.

3.   Freeze the layers **C-ANNO, C-PROP, C-PROP-LINE, C-PROP-TABL, EX-WETLAND-LINE,** and **PNTS-WTLND**.

The drawing will now display the surface as contours and points that you will use for breaklines. You may need to *Regen* to clean up the display.

4.   Enter **3P** at the command line to start the **3D Polyline** command.

5.   Enter **'PN** to change the prompt to **Point Number**.

Alternatively, you can also select the *Point Number* button ⚘ from the *Transparent Commands* toolbar.

6.   At the command line enter:  **1408-1447** and **[Enter]** to draw the line.

7.   **[Esc]** to end the Point Number prompt.

8.   **[Enter]** to end the line.

9.   Enter **3P** at the command line to start the **3D Polyline** command.

10. Use the points in the following list of points to draw the breaklines the same way that you drew the previous line. Be sure to use the **Point Number** transparent command to change the prompt to Point Number and to end the command completely after drawing each line. Also be sure to **[Enter]** after each non-sequential point number as shown below in the list.

**Point Numbers**
1448-1486
1008-1021
1191-1209
1226-1257
1258-1278
1281-1324
1295 [Enter] 1661-1710
1622-1660 [Enter] 1294
1286 [Enter] 1348-1398 [Enter] 1287
1022-1074
1075-1105
1155-1158
1159-1160
1153-1154
1143-1151
1130-1142
1121-1129

The new *3D Polylines* will look like the graphic below. However, they have not yet been added to the surface as breaklines.

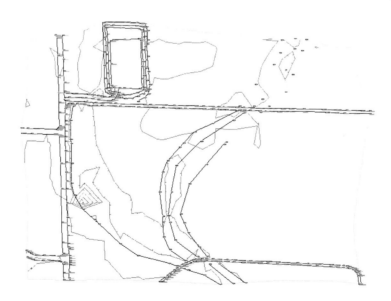

### 5.1.5 Creating Breaklines by Point Selection

1. On the *Prospector* tab of the *Toolspace*, select the *Point Group* **Breaklines.**

This will display a list of all the points used in the surface in the preview window at the bottom of the *Prospector*, if the *Prospector* is docked. If the *Prospector* is not docked it will display on the side.

2. Find point number **1110** in the preview window.

3.  Right-click on point **1110** and select **Zoom to**.  You may want to zoom out some to see the surrounding points.

4.  Enter **3P** at the command line to start the **3D Polyline** command.

5.  Enter **'PO** to change the prompt to **Point Object**.

Alternatively, you can also select the *Point Object* button 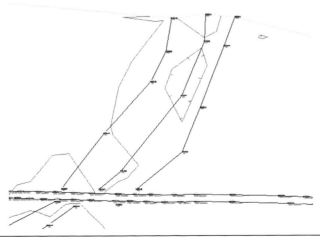 from the *Transparent Commands* toolbar.

6.  Pick point **1110** from the screen.

7.  Then pick points **1109, 1108, 1107, and 1106** to draw a breakline between the TOP points toward the northeast corner of the site.

When using the *Point Object* transparent command to draw lines between point objects you will not see the rubber band line that you normally see with the line command.

8.  **[Enter]** to end **the Point Object** prompt.

9.  **[Enter]** again to end the line.

10. Starting at point **1116,** define a second breakline along the bottom of the ditch using the **3D Polyline** command with the **'PO** transparent command and points **1116, 1117, 1118, 1119**, and **1120**.

11. **[Enter]** to end the Point Object prompt.

12. **[Enter]** again to end the line.

13. Starting at point **1111,** define a third breakline along the bank of the ditch using the **3D Polyline** command with the **'PO** transparent command and points **1111, 1112, 1113, 1114**, and **1115**.

14. **[Enter]** to end the Point Object prompt.

15. **[Enter]** again to end the line.

16. Save the drawing.

The three new *3D Polylines* will look like the graphic below.  However, they have not yet been added to the surface as breaklines.

### 5.1.6    Adding Breaklines to the Surface

1.  Select **Ribbon: Home** ⇒ **Layers** ⇒ **Isolate**.

2.  Pick one of the breaklines and one of the contours from the surface to isolate the **Breaklines-Survey** and **C-TOPO-Survey** layers.

3.  Confirm that the **Definition** under the *Surface* **Survey** is expanded on the *Prospector* tab of the *Toolspace*.

4.  Right-click on **Breaklines** under the **Definition** and select ⇒ **Add**.

5.  Enter a **Description** for the breakline set of **Collected in Field**.

6.  Confirm that the **Type** is set to **Standard**.

You will not use any *Weeding* or *Supplementing factors* in this exercise.   These options allow you to remove or add vertices to breaklines respectively.  These are useful options if you have breaklines that have been over digitized and may have thousands of extra vertices very close together or if you need to add vertices to a breakline that has long distances between vertices.

7.  Click **<<OK>>**.

8.  Select the **Breaklines** with a crossing window.

9.  **[Enter]** to add the breaklines to the surface.

The surface is now updated to include the new breakline data.

10. Select **Ribbon: Home** ⇒ **Layers** ⇒ **Unisolate** to restore the previous layer state.

11. Save the drawing.

### 5.1.7 Viewing the Surface

The Object Viewer is a separate window that will allow you to view a selected object or objects in 3D and rotate them in real-time.

1. Pick one of the **contours** to highlight the entire surface.

2. **Right-click** and select ⇒ **Object Viewer**.

3. In the **Object Viewer**, click and drag while holding down the left mouse button to rotate the surface in 3D.

Once you rotate to a 3D view the contours will change to 3D faces. This is controlled by the surface object style.

4. If the surface is not shaded right-click and select **Visual Styles ⇒ Shades of Gray**.

5. Continue to rotate the surface to examine it from different angles. You will notice a large hole, or spike, in the surface.

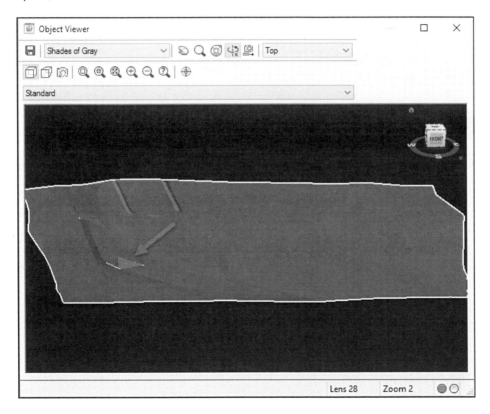

6. When you are finished viewing the surface close the object viewer window to return to the drawing editor. You should also be able to identify this hole by looking at the contours in plan view.

In the next lesson, you will learn to edit the surface to fix this and other errors.

## 5.2    Lesson:  Editing Surfaces

### Introduction

*Civil 3D* surfaces can be edited by either modifying the data used to build the surface or by using the surface editing commands found in the *Prospector* to directly edit the triangulation. In this lesson, you will learn to use both methods and gain exposure to several different ways to edit a surface.

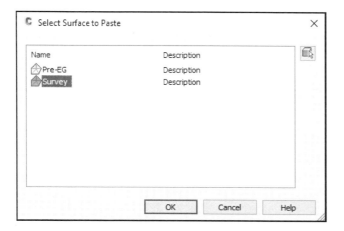

### Key Concepts

Concepts and key terms covered in this lesson are:

- Editing Surfaces
- Editing Points
- Pasting Surfaces

### Objectives

After completing this lesson, you will be able to:

- Describe different methods of editing a Surface.
- Delete Surface TIN Lines.
- Edit Points.
- Edit Breaklines,
- Paste Surfaces together.

## Editing Surfaces

There are two different methods for editing surfaces in Civil 3D.

- Editing the source surface data
- Editing the surface directly

## Editing the source surface data

When points, breaklines, boundaries, or other data that was used to build a surface is modified, the surface will become out of date. When you finish editing and rebuild the surface, it will be updated to reflect the current geometry of the source data. This allows you to edit a surface without actually editing the surface itself.

## Editing the surface directly

There are several surface editing commands in Civil 3D that will allow you to edit the surface directly. These can be found under Edits in the surface definition in the Prospector. They can also be found on a context sensitive ribbon when you select the surface.

Surface editing commands include:

- Add Line
- Delete Line
- Swap Edge
- Add Point
- Delete Point
- Modify Point
- Move Point
- Minimize Flat Areas
- Raise/Lower Surface
- Smooth Surface
- Paste Surface
- Simplify Surface

 To use any of the surface editing commands that require you to select a TIN line or point, you must first assign a surface style that displays the triangles and/or points.

## Pasting Surfaces

Pasting one surface into another allows you to merge or combine surfaces and create a composite of the two. When you paste a surface into another surface, the data within the extents of the source surfaces is overwritten in the destination surface.

For example, you can paste the top surface from a completed corridor design of a road into a copy of your existing ground surface to create a surface representing the final site conditions of the area. In this example, the data from the road surface overwrites and replaces the surface data in the copy of the existing ground surface within the extents of the road.

The paste is saved in the edit history. If the surface is changed the surface it is pasted into will become out of date and will paste the updated version of the surface in again when it is rebuilt.

Best practices to remember when pasting surfaces:

- Paste the smaller surface into the larger one
- Paste the surface representing newer conditions (typically the finished surface) into the older one (typically the existing ground)
- Don't paste into an Existing Ground surface. Make a copy of it first.

 To copy a surface you can make a new surface and paste the surface you want to copy into it. This will create a dynamic copy that is updated if the original surface changes.

## Exercises: Edit a Surface

In these exercises, you edit a surface first by editing the source data; the points and breaklines used to build the surface. Then you will edit the surface object itself by deleting TIN lines that are outside of the extents of the survey data. Finally, you will paste the Pre-EG surface and the Survey surface into a new surface to create a new surface called EG that uses the survey data where it is available and the aerial survey information as a buffer outside of that.

You do the following:

- Edit Points to update the Surface.
- Edit Breaklines to update the Surface.
- Delete TIN lines from the Surface.
- Paste Surfaces together.

### 5.2.1 Editing Point Data

1. Continue working in the drawing **Design.dwg**.

*Reminder:* You can also open the drawing with this exercise number in the *Chapter Drawings* folder of the dataset if you prefer a fresh start at this point.

The surface is displayed showing contours and you will see the large hole that you identified earlier in the object viewer in the southwest quarter of the surface.

If a point is creating a hole in your surface there are a number of ways to correct it and the best way depends on the data in your project. If the point causing the hole is completely incorrect and has no value to the project you can erase the point from the drawing and rebuild the surface. Another alternative is that this point may not have a good surface elevation but it still might be valuable to your project. This can be common with control points or the invert of a manhole. In this situation you should edit the point to remove it from the group and rebuild the surface. Finally, you might have survey notes giving you information to edit the point and correct the elevation error. In this case you will edit the point and rebuild the surface. This final example is what you will do in this exercise. You will locate and edit the point that is creating the hole in the surface to give it the correct elevation.

2. Thaw the layer **PNTS-GND**.

You may need to Regen if the points do not display.

3. Zoom to point **1221**. This is the point with an incorrect elevation that is creating the hole.

4. Select point **1221** and right-click to select ⇒ **Edit Points**.

5. In the *Point Editor* right-click on point **1221** and select ⇒ **Unlock**.

6. Change the elevation of point **1221** to **434.5**.

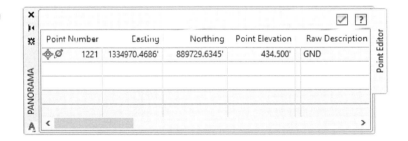

7. Right-click on point **1221** and select ⇒ **Lock**.

8. Close the *Point Editor* by clicking the **green check button**.

9. On the *Prospector* tab of the *Toolspace*, notice the *Surface* **Survey** is displayed with the *Out of Date* marker, right-click on the *Surface* **Survey** and select ⇒ **Rebuild**.

Once the surface is rebuilt the contours will update to reflect the change. You can also review the surface in the Object Viewer to confirm that the hole created by the incorrect elevation for point 1221 is now gone.

### 5.2.2 Editing Breaklines

The breaklines that you have defined in your surface are standard *AutoCAD 3D polylines*. This means that they can be grip edited or edited with the Polyedit command. Once you edit a breakline the surface and the breakline definition will display as out of date in the *Prospector*. You will then rebuild the surface to update it to display the changes made to the breakline.

If you set the surface option to *Rebuild Automatic*, the surface will automatically be rebuilt after each edit. This is a nice feature but may be inconvenient with larger surfaces because you will have to wait for them to rebuild and redisplay after each edit. If this option is disabled you can make several changes and rebuild when you are ready to review them.

1. Zoom to point **1151**.

2. Select the polyline that represents the breakline.

3. Place your cursor in the grip at the end of the polyline but do not click there. This will display the commands for the multifunction grips.

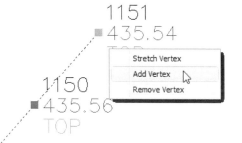

4. Select **Add Vertex**.

5. Insert a vertex at point **1152** to extend the breakline. You can use the **'PN** transparent command to enter the point number.

6. **[Esc]** to deselect the polyine.

In the *Prospector*, the breaklines and the surface will now show an icon that indicates they are out of date.

7. Right-click on the surface **Survey** and select ⇒ **Rebuild** to incorporate the edits to the breakline.

The contours around the additional segment that you added to the breakline will update reflecting the change to the breakline. If you make a mistake you can use the Undo command to backup and edit the breakline again.

### 5.2.3 Deleting Lines

TIN lines can only be deleted from a surface if you display the surface using a style that makes the lines visible. When deleting lines from a surface it is important to use the ⇒ *Delete Line* command found in the *Edits* node under the definition of the surface in the Prospector. This command will allow you to select and delete individual TIN lines from a surface. If you use the *AutoCAD* Erase command it will erase the entire surface.

The ⇒ *Delete Line* command is best suited to cleaning up the edges of a surface. If you use it to delete a line on the interior of a surface it will create a hole, or a void area, in the surface where the line was removed. If you need to delete triangles on the interior of a surface use the *Delete Point* command instead. This will remove the selected point and retriangulate over the area.

1. On the *Prospector* tab of the *Toolspace*, right-click on the *Surface* **Survey** and select ⇒ **Surface Properties**.

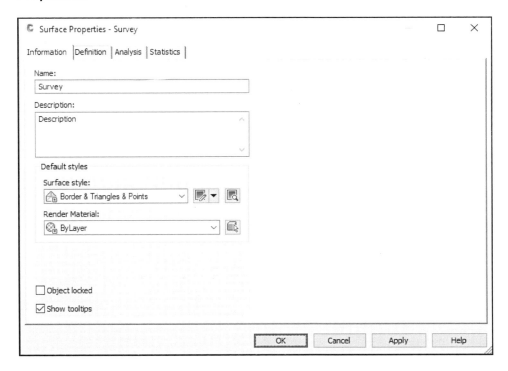

2. Set the **Surface Style** to **Border & Triangles & Points**.

3. Click **<<OK>>** to display the surface triangles.

4. On the *Prospector* tab of the *Toolspace*, confirm that the **Definition** node of the *Surface* **Survey** is expanded.

5. Right-click on **Edits** under the **Definition,** and select ⇒ **Delete Line**.

6. Pick the long lines along the edge of our surface that have triangulated outside of our survey data as shown in the example below along the northern edge of the surface.

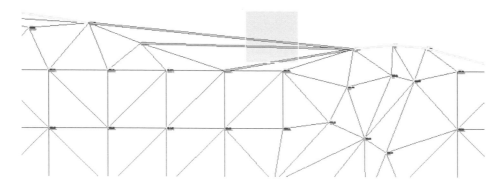

You can use standard *AutoCAD* selection options like *Fence [F]*, *Crossing Window [CW]*, or *Crossing Polygon [CP]* by entering the options at the command line.

7. Continue to Pan and Zoom along the edge of the surface to delete all undesired TIN lines.

Long skinny triangles are typically incorrect and need to be deleted. As you look at the TIN lines that connect each point ask yourself, Should these points be associated with each other in the surface? A line between two points will create a straight slope three dimensionally between them.

8. **Save** the drawing when you are finished deleting lines.

When finished, the surface should look similar to the graphic below.

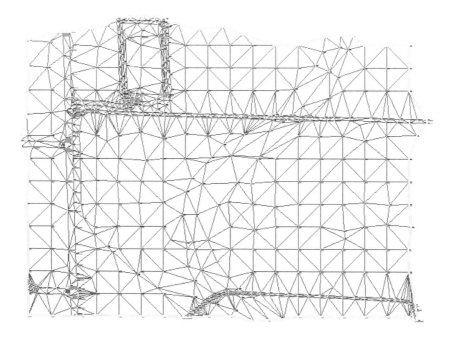

## 5.2.4 Pasting Surfaces

The final step is to combine the survey surface with the preliminary existing ground surface. You will use the preliminary existing ground surface as buffer data around the site-specific survey. You will do this with the *Paste Surface* command.

1.  Set layer **0** current.

2.  Freeze the layers **Breaklines-Survey, C-TOPO-Survey** and all the layers that start with **PNTS-.**

The drawing editor will now be blank. In the following steps you will create a new surface and paste the *Pre-EG* and *Survey* surfaces into it.

3.  On the *Prospector* tab of the *Toolspace,* right-click on **Surfaces** and select ⇒ **Create Surface**.

4.  Confirm that **TIN surface** is selected as **Type**.

5.  Enter **EG** for the **Name**.

6.  Set the **Style** to **Border & Triangles & Points**.

7.  Confirm the *Surface layer* is set to **C-TOPO-EG**.

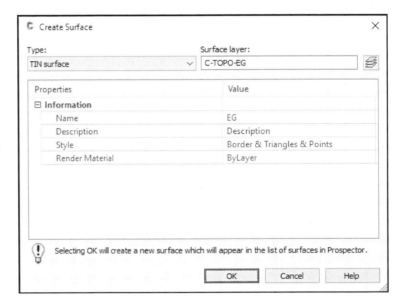

This layer name that includes the surface name as a suffix was setup in an earlier exercise through the Drawing Settings command.

8.  Click **<<OK>>** to close the *Create Surface* dialog box and create the surface.

At this time the surface has not been given any data so it is not displayed. However, it has been created and you will see it in the *Prospector*. This is where you will access the surface definition commands and add data to the surface.

9.  Expand the *Surface* **EG** on the *Prospector* tab of the *Toolspace*.

10. Expand the **Definition** node under *Surface* **EG**.

Be sure that you are under the surface *EG* in the *Prospector*. As you continue to add surfaces to your drawing it can become easy to have the wrong surface expanded and edit the wrong surface.

11. Right-click on **Edits** under the *Definition,* and select ⇒ **Paste Surface**.

12. Select *Surface* **Pre-EG**.

13. Click **<<OK>>** to paste the surface *Pre-EG* into the surface *EG*.

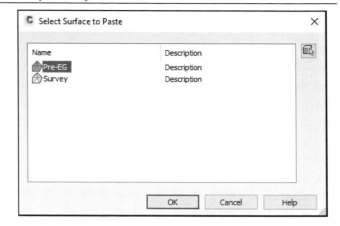

The surface *EG* will now be displayed as triangles, according to the style you selected earlier. By pasting the surface *Pre-EG* into the surface *EG* there is a dynamic link created. If the surface *Pre-EG* is updated at any point, the surface *EG* will become out of date. When you rebuild the surface *EG* it will be built using the current version of the surface *Pre-EG*.

Next you will paste the surface Survey into the surface *EG*. This will overwrite all the surface data that is covered by the surface *Survey* in the surface *EG*.

14. Right-click on **Edits** under the *Definition* of the surface *EG*, and select ⇒ **Paste Surface**.

15. Select *Surface* **Survey**.

16. Click **<<OK>>** to paste the surface *Survey* into the surface *EG*.

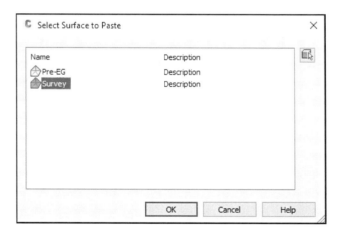

The surface *Survey* has now been pasted into the surface *EG*. You will see the triangles have updated in the area where the new surface was pasted.

17. **Save** the drawing.

## 5.3    Lesson: Surface Analysis

### Introduction

A surface can be analyzed and displayed in many different ways.  The display of the surface is controlled by the *Surface Style*.  Depending on the information that you want to display you may need to create a new surface style for your analysis.  In this lesson, you will display slope arrows and elevation bands.  However, the process is similar for other types of surface analysis like slope analysis and watersheds.

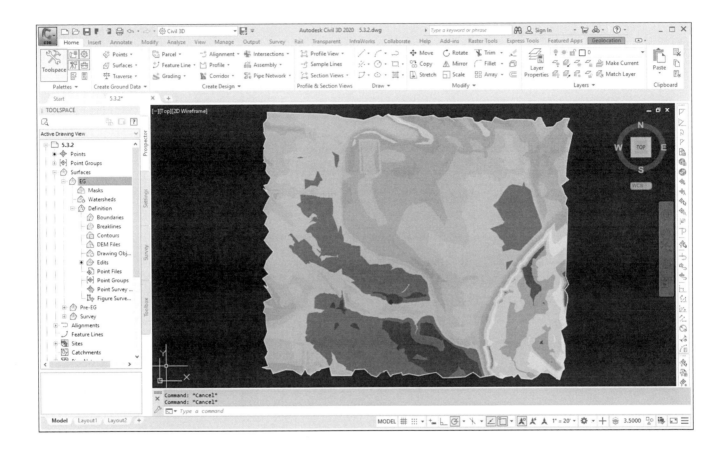

### Key Concepts

Concepts and key terms covered in this lesson are:

- Surfaces Styles
- Surface Analysis

### Objectives

After completing this lesson, you will be able to:

- Describe different methods of analyzing a Surface.
- Create a new Surface Style.
- Display elevation bands for a Surface.
- Perform a slope analysis.

## Surface Analysis

Surface analysis is a two-step process that is accomplished by assigning a surface style that has been set up to display the analysis and then running the analysis.

Types of surface analysis include:

- Contours
- Directions
- Elevation Banding
- Slopes
- Slope Arrows
- User-defined contours
- Watersheds

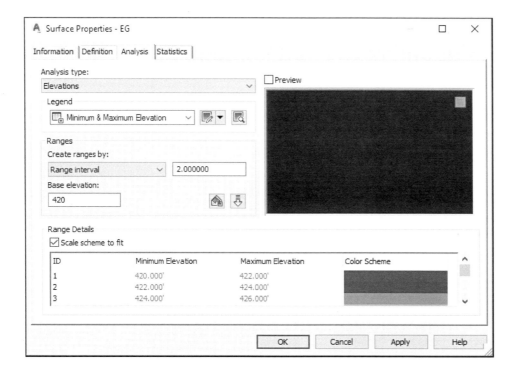

## Exercises: Analyze a Surface

In these exercises, you analyze a surface first by using a style to display contours with slope arrows showing the direction each triangle in the surface slopes. Then you create styles for both elevation banding and slope analysis and use them to perform the corresponding analysis on the surface.

You do the following:

- Display a Surface with slope arrows.
- Create a Style for Elevation Banding.
- Display Elevation Bands for the Surface.
- Create a Style for Slope Analysis.
- Display a Slope Analysis of the Surface.

### 5.3.1 Displaying Slope Arrows

Slope arrows can be displayed by editing the surface properties to display the surface using one of the styles predefined in the template you used to start the drawing.

1. Continue working in the drawing **Design.dwg**.

*Reminder:* You can also open the drawing with this exercise number in the *Chapter Drawings* folder of the dataset if you prefer a fresh start at this point.

2. On the *Prospector* tab of the *Toolspace*, right-click on **Surface EG** and select ⇒ **Surface Properties**.

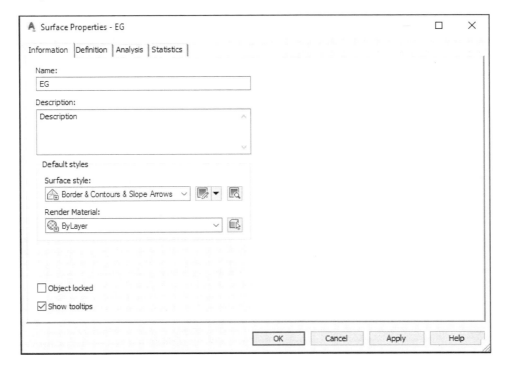

3. Select **Border & Contours & Slope Arrows** from the **Surface style** list on the *Information* tab of the *Surface Properties* dialog box.

4. Click **<<OK>>** to redisplay the surface with contours and an arrow showing the direction of slope on each triangle in the surface.

## 5.3.2 Elevation Banding

1. On the *Prospector* tab of the *Toolspace*, right-click on **Surface EG** and select ⇒ **Surface Properties**.

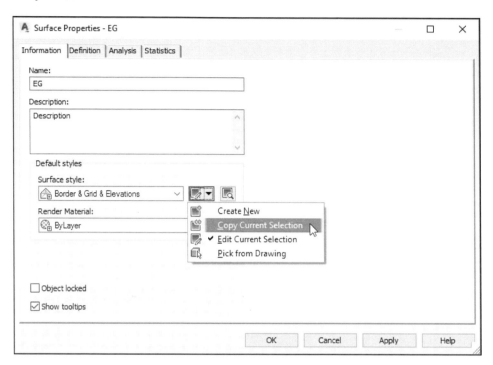

2. Select **Border & Grid & Elevations** from the **Surface style** list on the *Information* tab of the *Surface Properties* dialog box.

3. Click the **down arrow** button next to the **Surface style** to display the other style editing commands.

4. Select ⇒ **Copy Current Selection**.

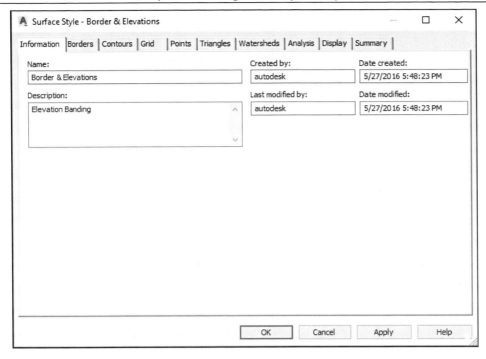

5. On the *Information* tab of the *Surface Style* dialog box, enter **Border & Elevations** for the **Name** of the new *Surface Style*.

6. Enter **Elevation Banding** for the **Description** of the new *Surface Style*.

7. Select the **Analysis** tab of the *Surface Style* dialog box.

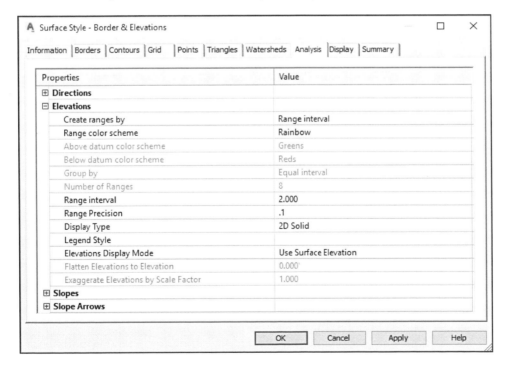

8. Expand the **Elevations** node.

9. Set **Create ranges by** to **Range interval**.

10. Set the **Range color scheme** to **Rainbow**.

11. Set the **Range interval** to **2**.

12. Set the **Range Precision** to **.1**.

This will set the default values that are used when you run the elevation analysis on the surface. The range interval, the color and beginning and end values of the range can each be changed, when you run the surface analysis.

13. Select the **Display** tab of the *Surface Style* dialog box.

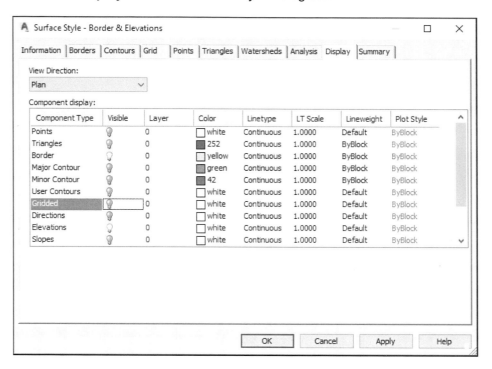

14. Confirm that the **View Direction** is set to **Plan**.

On the display tab you will see the list of components that are available to display for a surface. By turning the visibility of the components on and off you can control how the style displays the surface. There are also view directions available; Plan, Model and Section. Changing the visibility of components between the Plan and Model view directions is how the style can change the display of the surface from contours in plan view to triangles in a rotated 3D view.

15. Turn **Off** the **Gridded** *component*.

16. Confirm that the **Elevations** component is turned **On**.

It is important to turn the Elevations component on, otherwise you will be running the calculations for the surface analysis, but it will not be displayed.

17. Click **<<OK>>** to save the new **Surface Style** and return to the *Surface Properties* dialog box.

18. Select the **Analysis** tab of the *Surface Properties* dialog box.

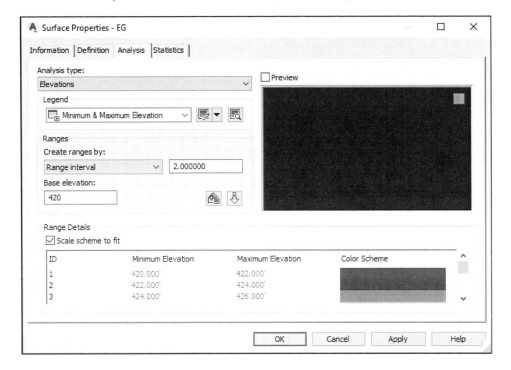

19. Confirm that the **Analysis type** is set to **Elevations**.

Even though you set all the defaults for the surface analysis when you created the *Surface Style*, you still need to run the analysis on this surface. Both the *Surface Style* and the *Surface Properties* dialog have analysis tabs. The *Surface Style* analysis tab allows you to set default values, while in the *Surface Properties* dialog box, the analysis tab is where you run the analysis on the selected surface.

20. Click the **Reset range properties from surface style** button.

This will set the *Create range by* option and *range interval*.

21. Set the **Base elevation** to **420**.

22. Click the **Run Analysis** button to analyze the surface.

The minimum and maximum elevations as well as the colors can all be changed by double clicking on the fields in the table.

23. Click **<<OK>>** to close the *Surface Properties* dialog box and apply the new *Surface Style*.

The surface should now be displayed with 2D solids representing the 2' elevation bands.

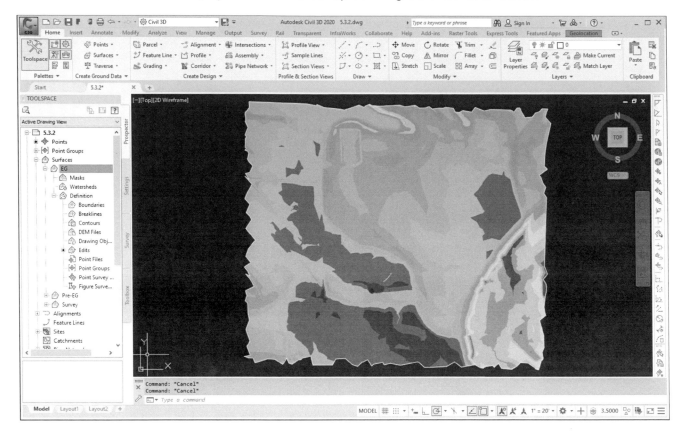

24. **Save** the drawing.

### 5.3.3 Slope Analysis

In this exercise, you will create a style and perform a slope analysis of the surface.

1. On the *Prospector* tab of the *Toolspace*, right-click on **Surface EG** and select ⇒ **Surface Properties**.

2. Select the **Information** tab of the *Surface Properties* dialog box.

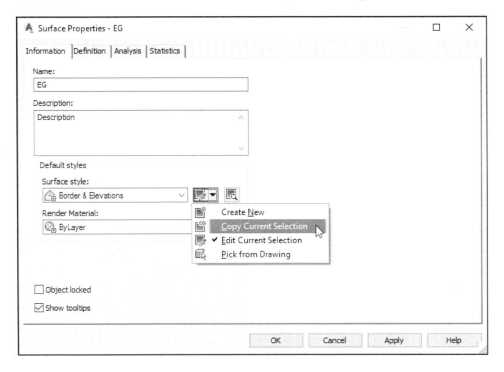

3. Confirm that **Border & Elevations** is the current **Surface style**.

4. Click the **down arrow** button next to the **Surface style** on the *Information* tab of the *Surface Properties* dialog box to display the other style editing commands.

5. Select ⇒ **Copy Current Selection**.

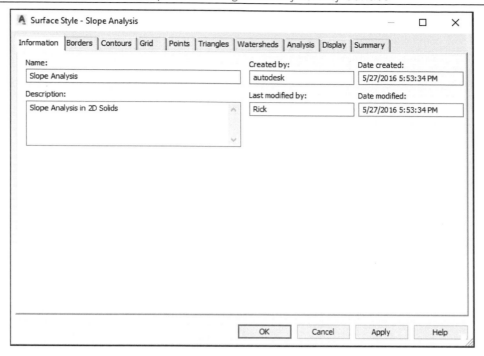

6.  On the *Information* tab enter **Slope Analysis** for the **Name** of the new *Surface Style*.

7.  Enter **Slope Analysis in 2D Solids** for the **Description** of the new *Surface Style*.

8.  Select the **Analysis** tab of the *Surface Style* dialog box.

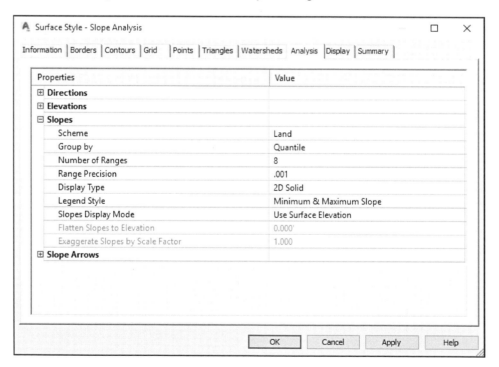

9.  Expand the **Slopes** node.

10. Set the **Scheme** to **Land**.

11. Set the **Group by** value to **Quantile**.

12. Set the **Range Precision** to **.001**.

13. Select the **Display** tab of the *Surface Style* dialog box.

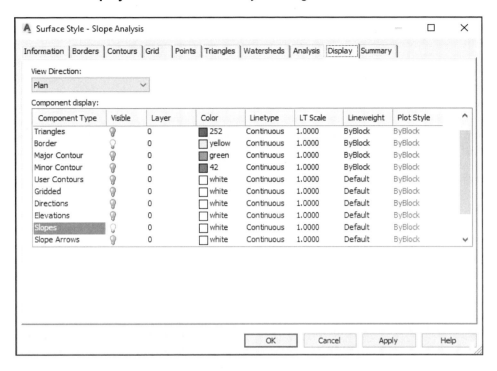

14. Confirm that the **View Direction** is set to **Plan**.

15. Turn **Off** the **Elevations** *component*.

16. Turn **On** the **Slopes** *component*.

17. Click **<<OK>>** to save the new **Surface Style** and return to the *Surface Properties* dialog box.

18. Select the **Analysis** tab of the *Surface Properties* dialog box.

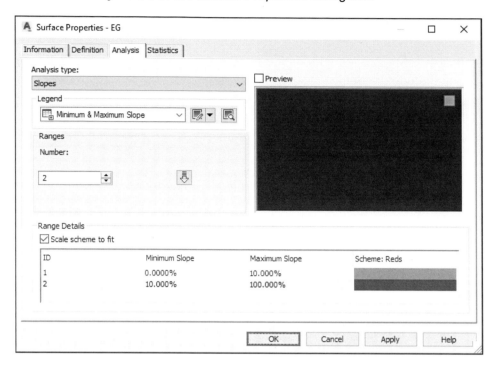

19. Set the **Analysis type** to **Slopes**.

20. Set the **Number** of *Ranges* to **2**.

21. Click the **Run Analysis** button to analyze the surface.

22. In the Range Details table enter slope ranges as shown below.

| Minimum Slope | Maximum Slope | Color |
|---|---|---|
| 0% | 10% | Green |
| 10% | 100% | Red |

23. Click **<<OK>>** to close the *Surface Properties* dialog box and apply the new *Surface Style*.

The surface should now be displayed with 2D solids representing the different slope ranges with slopes less than 10% green and greater than 10% red.

24. **Save** the drawing.

## 5.4    Lesson:  Working with Contours

### Introduction

Displaying a surface as contours is one of the most common types of surface display.  In this lesson, you will create a new surface style to learn how styles control all the aspects of contours.  You will also label the contours and work with contour label styles.

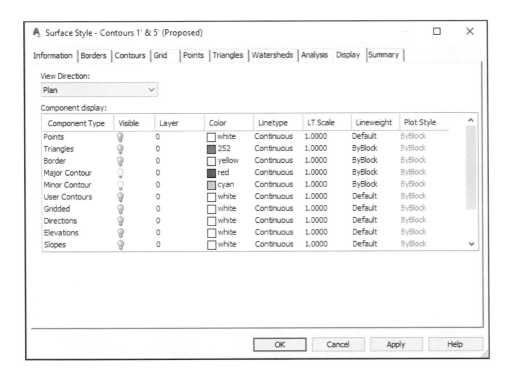

### Key Concepts

Concepts and key terms covered in this lesson are:

- Contours
- Surface Styles
- Contour Labels
- Label Styles

### Objectives

After completing this lesson, you will be able to:

- Describe the contour properties in a Surface Style.
- Create a new Surface Style to display contours.
- Label Contours.
- Edit and Delete contour labels.
- Create and assign a new Surface Label Style to existing contour labels.

## Surface Styles to Display Contours

There is no command to create contours in Civil 3D. Instead, you display contours by assigning a style to the surface that is configured to display the surfaces as contours. The contour interval, smoothing, color, and linetype can all be set in this surface style.

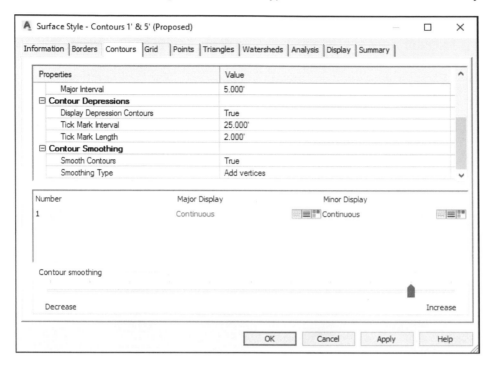

The contours displayed are actually the surface. So if you erase, move, or explode the contours you will be deleting or moving the actual surface itself.

## Labeling Contours

Contours are labeled by drawing or selecting a line across the contours that determines the contour label position. This will only label contours and will not impact any other lines that may currently be displayed on the screen.

The position of the labels is determined by these contour label lines. Contour labels can be deleted by erasing the contour label line. If you copy or stretch the contour label line so it crosses multiple contours labels will be displayed at each crossing point.

## Exercises: Display and Label Contours

In these exercises, you display the Surface as contours. Then, you create a new surface style to display contours at a one foot and five foot interval. Next, you label the contours. Finally, you create a new surface label style for the major contours and apply that style to the existing labels.

You do the following:

- Display a Surface with contours.
- Create a Style for 1' & 5' contours.
- Label contours.
- Create a new Surface Label Style and assign it to the major contour labels.

### 5.4.1    Displaying a Surface as Contours

There is no *Create Contour* command in Civil 3D. Contours are a display of a *Surface* that is controlled by the surface style. To display contours you simply change the surface style.

1.    Continue working in the drawing **Design.dwg**.

*Reminder:* You can also open the drawing with this exercise number in the *Chapter Drawings* folder of the dataset if you prefer a fresh start at this point.

2.    On the *Prospector* tab of the *Toolspace*, right-click on **Surface EG** and select ⇒ **Surface Properties**.

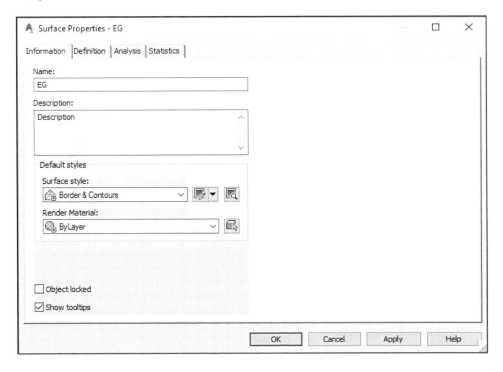

3.    Select **Border & Contours** from the **Surface style** list on the *Information* tab of the *Surface Properties* dialog box.

4.    Click **<<OK>>**.

The surface is now displayed showing 5 foot contours.

### 5.4.2    Creating a Surface Style to Display Contours

The current surface style displays the surface with contours at an interval of 5 and 25 feet. Since the site is relatively flat you may want to decrease the contour interval to show more detail.   You might also want to smooth the contours to improve their appearance and change the color of the contour lines to match your organizations standards.  All of these properties are controlled by the surface style.  The style is saved in the drawing and should be saved to a drawing template if it is your standard and will be used in future projects.

1.  On the *Prospector* tab of the *Toolspace*, right-click on **Surface EG** and select ⇒ **Surface Properties**.

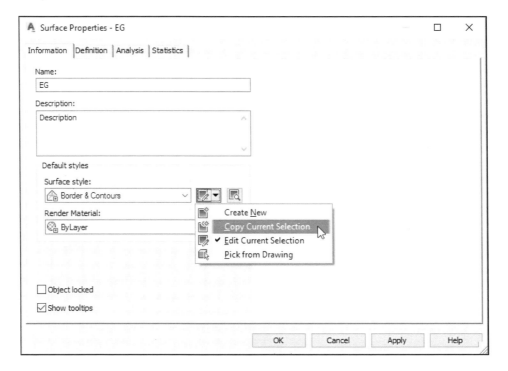

2.  On the *Information* tab, confirm that **Border & Contours** is the current **Surface style.**

3.  Click the **down arrow** button next to the **Surface style** on the *Information* tab of the *Surface Properties* dialog box to display the other style editing commands.

4.  Select ⇒ **Copy Current Selection**.

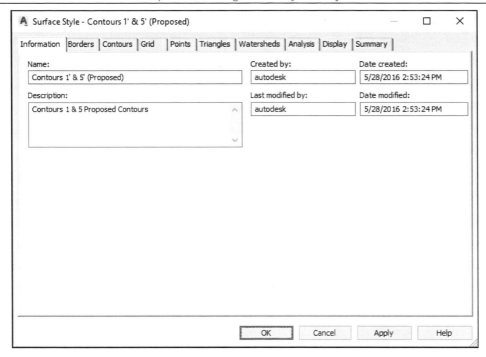

5.  On the *Information* tab, enter **Contours 1' & 5' (Proposed)** for the **Name** of the new *Surface Style*.

You will need a surface style that displayed contours for both existing and proposed contours if you want to display them differently.  You will start by creating a style for the proposed contours.

6.  Enter **1 and 5 Foot Proposed Contours** for the **Description** of the new *Surface Style*.

7.  Select the **Contours** tab of the *Surface Style* dialog box.

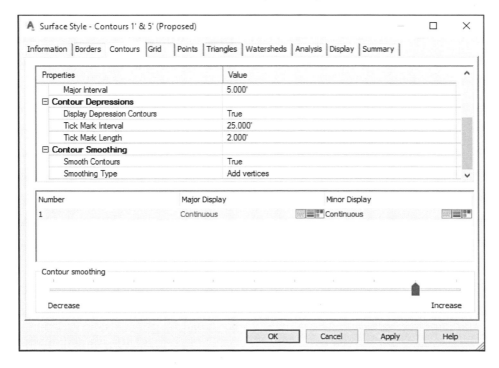

8.  Expand the **Contour Intervals** node.

9. Set the **Minor Interval** to **1**.

10. Click in the value field of the **Major Interval** and it should automatically change to **5**.

11. Expand the **Contour Depressions** node.

12. Set the **Tick Mark Interval** to **25**.

13. Set the **Tick Mark Length** to **2**.

This will add a tick 2' long at a 25' interval along all depression contours.

14. Expand the **Contour Smoothing** node.

15. Set the **Smooth Contours** value to **True**.

16. Confirm that the **Smoothing Type** is set to **Add vertices**.

17. Set the **Contour smoothing** slider to the second tick mark from the right.

18. Select the **Display** tab of the *Surface Style* dialog box.

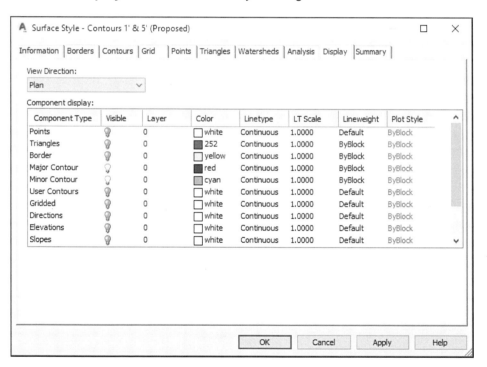

19. Confirm that the **View Direction** is set to **Plan**.

20. Turn **off** the **Border** *component*.

21. Set the *Color* of the **Major Contour** component to **Red**.

22. Set the *Color* of the **Minor Contour** component to **Cyan**.

23. Click **<<OK>>** to save the new *Surface Style* and return to the *Surface Properties* dialog box.

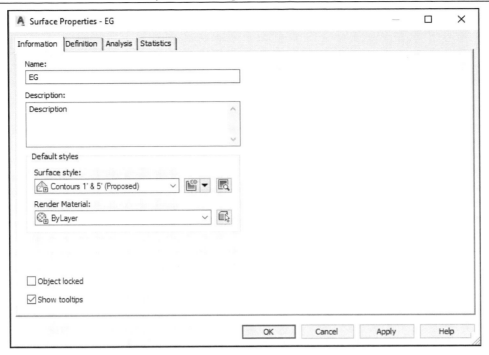

24. Click **<<OK>>** to close the *Surface Properties* dialog box and apply the new *Surface Style*.

The surface should now be displayed with red and cyan, one foot, smoothed contours. You may need to Regen if the display of the surface does not update.

### 5.4.3    Controlling Contour Display

There is already a surface style in the drawing that displays 1 and 5 foot existing counters. This style was in the template that you used to start the drawing originally. So rather than taking the time to create another style all you need to do is set it current in the object properties to display the surface as existing contours.

1.   On the *Prospector* tab of the *Toolspace*, right-click on **Surface EG** and select ⇒ **Surface Properties**.

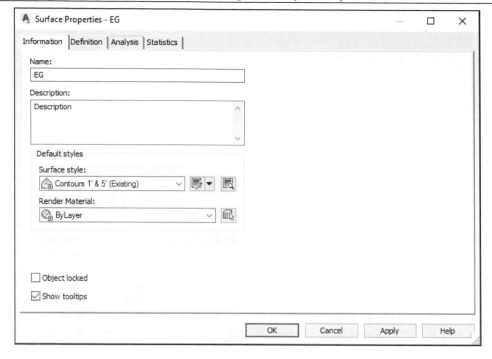

2. Select **Contours 1' and 5' (Existing)** from the **Surface style** list on the *Information* tab of the *Surface Properties* dialog box.

3. Click **<<OK>>**.

The surface is now displayed showing 1 foot contours screened back according to our organizational standards for existing contours.

### 5.4.4    Labeling Contours

1. Pick the *Surface* **EG** by selecting one of the contours in the drawing editor to display the context sensitive ribbon.

2. Select **Ribbon: Tin Surface: EG ⇒ Labels & Tables ⇒ Add Labels ⇒ Contour - Multiple at Interval.**

3. At the command prompt you are asked to **Pick the first point**. Draw a line across the surface at the location you would like the contours labeled.

4. At the command prompt Interval along contour, enter **300**.

This will add multiple labels at a 300' interval along each contour.

5. **[Esc]** to clear the selection and dismiss the context sensitive ribbon.

6. Zoom in and examine the new contour labels.

## 5.4.5　Moving Contour Labels

The position of the contour labels can be changed by moving, or grip editing, the contour label line.

> 1. Select one of the contour labels.

This activates the grips on the contour label line, which controls the position of the contour label.

> 2. Grip edit, or use the *AutoCAD move* command, to move the contour label line to a new position along the contour.

This will move the label to that new position.  If you move the contour label line off the contour, the label will disappear.

## 5.4.6　Deleting Contour Labels

Contour labels can be erased by using the *AutoCAD* erase command.  Just be sure that you do not select the surface or else you will delete the surface as well.

> 1. Use the *AutoCAD* erase command to delete one of the contour labels by picking the label, not the surface.
>
> 2. Select one of the contour labels.

You can use the Quick Select or the Select Similar command to create a selection set of all the contour labels in the drawing so that you can easily and safely delete all the contour labels.

> 3. Right-click and pick ⇒ **Select Similar**.

This will select all of the contour labels in the drawing.

> 4. Use the *AutoCAD* erase command to delete all the selected contour labels.

### 5.4.7 Labeling Only the Major Contours

In this exercise, you will create contour labels for the major contours only and not the minor contours.

1. Select **Ribbon: Annotate ⇒ Labels & Tables ⇒ Add Labels**

This will display the *Add Labels* dialog box where you can select the feature, type of label, and label styles that you would like to use.

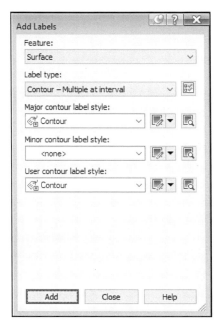

2. Set the **Feature** to **Surface**.

3. Set the **Label Type** to **Contour - Multiple at interval**.

4. Confirm the **Major contour label style** is set to **Contour**.

5. Set the **Minor contour label style** to **<none>**.

6. Click **<<Add>>**.

7. Select the *Surface* **EG**.

8. Draw a line across the surface at the location you would like the contours labeled.

9. At the command prompt Interval along contour enter **300**.

This will add multiple labels at a 300' interval along each contour.

10. Zoom in and examine the new contour labels.

You will now only see contour labels created along the major contours.

11. Close the *Add Labels* dialog box.

## 5.4.8    Editing Contour Labels

To change the appearance of the contour labels like the font or color of the text you must change the contour label style.

1.   Pick one of the contour labels in the drawing editor.

2.   Right-click and select ⇒ **Contour Label Line Properties**.

This opens the *AutoCAD Properties* palette.

3.   In the *Labels* section of the *Properties* palette go to the **Surface Contour Label Style Major** value and select **Create/Edit**.

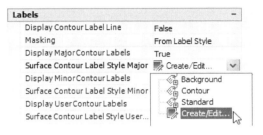

4.   Click the **down arrow** button next to the style name to display the other style editing commands.

5.   Select ⇒ **Copy Current Selection**.

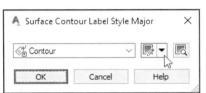

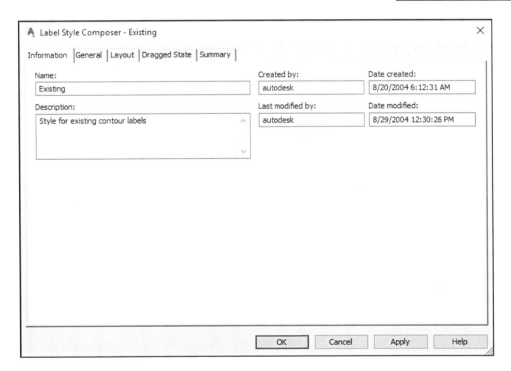

6.   Enter **Existing** for the **Name** of the new *Surface Style*.

7.   Enter **Style for existing contour labels** for the **Description** of the new *Contour Label Style*.

8. Select the **Layout** tab of the *Label Style Composer* dialog box.

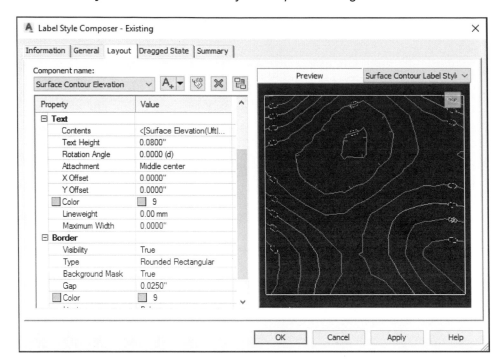

9. Confirm that **Surface Contour Elevation** is set as the active **Component name**.

10. Set the **Text Height** to **0.08**.

11. Set the **Color** to **9**.

12. Under the *Border* node, set the **Visibility** to **true**.

13. Confirm that the **Type** is set to **Rounded Rectangular**.

14. Set the **Color** to **9**.

15. Click **<<OK>>** to save the new **Contour Label Style** and return to the *Surface Contour Label Style Major* dialog box.

16. Click **<<OK>>** to close the *Surface Contour Label Style Major* dialog box and apply the new Contour Style to the selected label.

17. Close the *AutoCAD Properties* palette.

18. **[Esc]** to deselect the labels.

19. Zoom in and observe the changes to the contour label.

Notice that only the selected contour label was updated. This is because you created a new contour label style and that new style was only applied to the selected contour label. To update all of the contour labels you need to select all of the contour labels and change their properties to use the new contour label style.

20. Select one of the contour labels.

You can use the Quick Select or the Select Similar command to create a selection set of all the contour labels in the drawing.

21. Right-click and pick ⇒ **Select Similar**.

This will select all of the contour labels in the drawing.

22. Right-click and pick ⇒ **Properties**.

This opens the *AutoCAD Properties* palette.

Notice that the **Surface Contour Label Style Major** value is currently displayed as <VARIES>. This is because all of the selected contour labels are not set to the same style. Changing this value will set all of the selected labels to the same style.

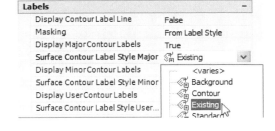

23. In the *Labels* section of the *Properties* palette go to the **Surface Contour Label Style Major** value and select **Existing**.

24. Close the *AutoCAD Properties* palette.

25. **[Esc]** to deselect the labels.

All of the contour labels should now display as grey text with a rounded border according to the new label style. If the contour line is visible through the label, *Regen* to clean up the display.

### 5.4.9 Controlling Surface Display for Performance

When any object is displayed in *Civil 3D* the program must display all of the individual *AutoCAD* entities that make up the components that the object style is configured to display. For example, there are many more lines displayed on the screen when you use a style displaying 1 foot contours as opposed to 5 foot contours.

You may have even noticed a change in the performance of the program as we changed to the *Surface Style* displaying 1 foot contours in the previous exercises. This depends on the size and geometry of your surface as well as your computer hardware. To speed up your drawing you can simply change the *Surface Style* to one that displays a smaller number of objects, and you can always switch the style back if you need to see more detail or if you are ready to plot.

1. On the *Prospector* tab of the *Toolspace,* right-click on **Surface EG** and select ⇒ **Surface Properties**.

2. Select **Border & Contours** from the **Surface style** list on the *Information* tab of the *Surface Properties* dialog box.

3. Click **<<OK>>**.

The surface is now displayed showing 5 foot contours. Notice the major contours are still labeled using the style and locations that you specified.

# Chapter 6

# 6 - Working with Alignments and Parcels

In this chapter, you will focus on laying out and editing *Alignments* and *Parcels*. You will also explore how *Alignments* and *Parcels* interact with each other in a *Site*. You will learn to use the *Parcel Layout Tools* to automatically subdivide and size parcels based on area and frontage criteria. The *Alignments* you create in this chapter will be used in later in the project to create the *Profile*, *Corridor Model*, and *Sections*.

## Lesson: Creating Alignments
In this lesson, you will learn the concepts and process of laying out horizontal alignments.

## Lesson: Editing Alignments
In this lesson, you will learn to edit alignments both graphically and in a tabular format.

## Lesson: Working with Alignment Labels
In this lesson, you will learn to create station labels along alignments as well as to work with other types of alignments labels like station and offset labels.

## Lesson: Laying Out Parcels
In this lesson, you will learn to create and edit parcels with specific areas and geometry.

## Lesson: Working With Parcel Styles and Labels
In this lesson, you will learn to create and modify parcel styles and labels for single parcels as well as large groups of parcels.

## 6.1 Lesson: Creating Alignments

### Introduction

The dynamic nature of the alignment object in *Civil 3D* allows you to easily make changes to the geometry of the alignment. This can change the way that you think about the design process. Rather than sketching things out on paper and then entering them into the program you can now lay out a draft of the alignment in *Civil 3D* and easily modify it to try several alternatives on the fly. The point is that you don't have to get it perfect the first time.

### Key Concepts

Concepts and key terms covered in this lesson are:

- Alignments
- Sites
- Alignment creation commands

### Objectives

After completing this lesson, you will be able to:

- Describe the way Alignments and Parcels interact within a Site.
- Create a new Alignment.
- List different commands used to lay out alignments.

## Creating Alignments

Alignments are Civil 3D objects that represent road centerlines, pipes, ditches, streams, and any other lineal feature. There are two methods of creating an alignment using the Alignment Layout Tools.

- The PI method
- The Entity based method

## The PI method

Using the PI method you pick locations for the points of intersection on the alignment. These PIs are connected by tangents or tangents with curves at each PI. Default curve parameters can be set in the Curve and Spiral Settings dialog box.

## The Entity based method

You can create an alignment by creating constraint based lines, curves or spirals. These entities can be either fixed, floating, or free and will be based on parameters like length and radius.

## Alignment Layout and Editing Tools

The Alignment Layout Tools toolbar contains many tools for creating and editing alignments.

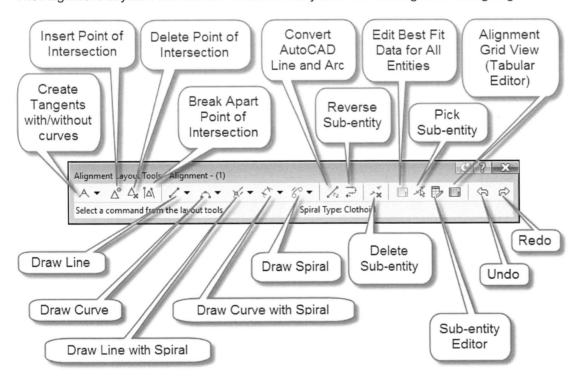

The dynamic nature of the alignment object in Civil 3D allows you to easily make changes to the geometry of the alignment. This allows you to approach the design process differently than you may have in the past with other programs. Now you can set a default curve radius for the alignment and lay out a rough draft in Civil 3D, them modify and revise it in real time.

## Exercises: Create an Alignment

In these exercises, you set the default curve settings and create an alignment using the PI method of creating tangents and curves.

You do the following:

- Create an Alignment
- Set the default curve settings.
- Lay out the Alignment using the PI method of creating tangents and curves.

### 6.1.1   Default Curve Settings

In this exercise, you will set the default curve settings for the alignment layout commands. Once the alignment is laid out you can edit individual curves as needed.

1. Continue working in the drawing **Design.dwg**.

*Reminder:* You can also open the drawing with this exercise number in the *Chapter Drawings* folder of the dataset if you prefer a fresh start at this point.

2. Thaw the layers **C-PROP** and **C-PROP-Line.**

3. Freeze the layers **C-TOPO-EG** and **C-TOPO-LABL**.

The drawing should currently display the cyan parcel lines with labels.

4. Zoom to the large parcel at the center of the site.

5. Select **Ribbon: Home ⇒ Create Design ⇒ Alignment ⇒ Alignment Creation Tools.**

This opens the *Create Alignment - Layout* dialog box where you can name and setup your alignment.

6. Enter **L Street** for the *Name* of the **Alignment**.

7. Confirm the Alignment *Type* is set to **Centerline**.

Alignment types automatically categorize alignments in the *Prospector* according to their properties and use, and enable you to create alignments with specialized behavior, like offsets, curb returns and rail. Offset alignments and curb return alignments can be dynamically linked to other alignments. In this exercise, you will be using a *Centerline Alignment*.

8. Set the **Site** to **Proposed**.

Alignments and parcels that are in the same *Site* interact with each other. When an alignment divides a parcel a new parcel is created. By placing the new alignment in the *Site* with the parcels you created in *Chapter 4* you will get to see this interaction. If you do not want an alignment to impact a set of parcels just set the *Site* to <None> or create a new *Site* for the alignment.

9. Confirm the *Alignment layer* is set to **C-Road-L Street**.

This layer name that includes the alignment name as a suffix was setup in an earlier exercise through the Drawing Settings command.

10. Confirm that the Alignment label set is set to **Major Minor & Geometry Point**.

The alignment label set controls the group of styles used to label the alignment. This includes displaying stationing, ticks, geometry information, and much more.

The *Design Criteria Tab* allows you to select design criteria based on minimum design standards. AASHTO standards in both imperial and metric units are included with *Civil 3D*. You also have the option to modify and create your own design standards. Using design criteria is optional and you will not be using it in this exercise.

11. Click **<<OK>>** to create the alignment and open the *Alignment Layout toolbar*.

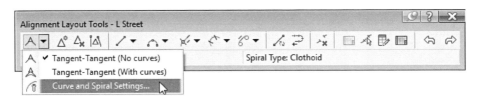

12. Click the **down arrow** next to the *Tangent-Tangent (No curves)* button on the *Alignment Layout* toolbar, to display the other creation commands.

13. **Select ⇒ Curve and Spiral Settings**.

14. Confirm that the default **Radius** is set to **150'**.

You can also enable the use of spirals and set their defaults if you are laying out an alignment for a highway that requires them.

15. Click **<<OK>>**.

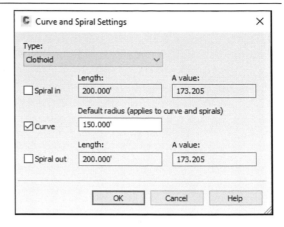

## 6.1.2   Creating Tangents with Curves

In this exercise, you will layout tangents with curves based on locations of points that you have imported for the *Points of Intersection*.

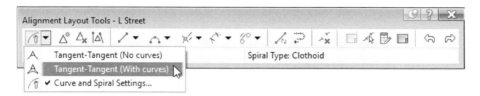

1. Click the **down arrow** next to the *Curve and Spiral Settings* button on the *Alignment Layout* toolbar to display the other creation commands.

2. Select ⇒ **Tangent-Tangent (With curves)**.

3. At the command line enter **'PN**.

Alternatively, you can also select the *Point Number* button ⊕ from the *Transparent Commands* toolbar.

4. Enter the Point Number Range: **1337-1340**.

The new alignment is drawn using the default curve settings that you configured in the previous exercise.  The parcel that the alignment passes through is also divided and a new parcel is created.  This is because the alignment and the parcel are in the same *Site*.

5. **[Esc]** to end the Point Number prompt.

6. **[Enter]** to end the alignment.

7. **Close** the *Alignment Layout* toolbar.

8. Save the drawing.

When finished, the alignment should look like the one in the graphic below. Notice, since the alignment was added to the same Site as the parcels, the original parcel where the alignment was drawn has now been divided into two parcels.

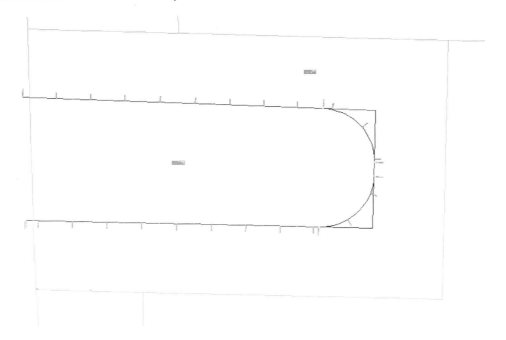

## 6.2    Lesson:  Editing Alignments

### Introduction

Alignments can be edited graphically with standard *AutoCAD* commands or with the
*Alignment Layout* tools which include a tabular option.  This allows you to graphically get the
alignment close to the desired geometry and then fine tune it in a table.

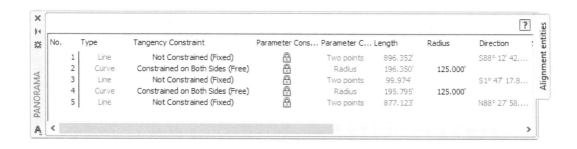

### Key Concepts

Concepts and key terms covered in this lesson are:

- Editing Alignments
- Grip Editing
- Alignment Grid View

### Objectives

After completing this lesson, you will be able to:

- Describe the ways Alignments can be edited.
- Edit an Alignment graphically.
- Edit an Alignment through a table.

## Editing Alignments

There are two different methods of editing an alignment. However, they are not exclusive of one another and can be used together to achieve the most efficient workflow for your project.

- Graphical Editing
- Tabular Editing

## Graphical Editing

- Grip Editing
  - Stretch and move PIs
  - Modify curve geometry
  - Move lines
- Commands from the Alignment Layout toolbar
  - Insert PIs
  - Delete PIs
  - Delete Sub-entities
  - Add lines, curves, or spirals

## Tabular Editing

The alignment can be edited in a table by using the Alignment Grid View.

 Try editing the alignment graphically first, then once the geometry is close to your desired design use the tabular method to clean up and refine the final geometry.

## Exercises: Edit an Alignment

In these exercises, you edit an alignment both graphically by grip editing and in a tabular format using the alignment grid view.

You do the following:

- Edit an Alignment graphically.
- Edit an Alignment using the Alignment Grid View.

### 6.2.1 Editing Alignments Graphically

*Civil 3D* alignments can be grip edited just like basic *AutoCAD* objects.

1. Continue working in the drawing **Design.dwg**.

*Reminder:* You can also open the drawing with this exercise number in the *Chapter Drawings* folder of the dataset if you prefer a fresh start at this point.

2. Pick the alignment *L Street* in the drawing editor to display the grips.

3. Select the grip at **PI** number **2,** at the northeast corner of the alignment.

4. At the command line, enter **@0,10** to stretch the PI 10 feet north.

5. **[Esc]** to clear the selection.

You can also stretch any of the grips on the curves to change the curve radius and you can stretch the grip at the middle of a tangent to move that tangent while holding the bearing and length. This also updates the sizes of the two parcels divided by the alignment. The *AutoCAD Undo* command can be used to undo these changes.

### 6.2.2 Editing Alignments in Grid View

1. Pick the alignment **L Street** in the drawing editor to display the context sensitive ribbon.

2. Select **Ribbon: Alignment: L Street ⇒ Modify ⇒ Geometry Editor**.

This opens the *Alignment Layout Tools* toolbar.

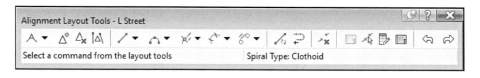

3. Click the **Grid View** [image] button.

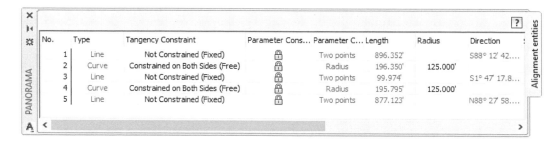

4. Scroll through the alignment information to find the curve radius column.

5. Change the **Radius** of the first curve to **125**.

6. Change the **Radius** of the second curve to **125**.

The alignment will update graphically after each change.  Also, you are not allowed to set a radius that does not fit the geometry of the alignment.  So you cannot create overlapping curves.

7.  Close the **Grid View**.

8.  Close the **Alignment Layout** toolbar.

9.  Save the drawing.

## 6.3    Lesson:  Working with Alignment Labels

### Introduction

Once an Alignment is created stationing is displayed according to the alignment label set you selected when the Alignment was first created.  Station and offset labels can also be created as well as labels annotating the geometry of the lines, curves and spirals that make up the Alignment.

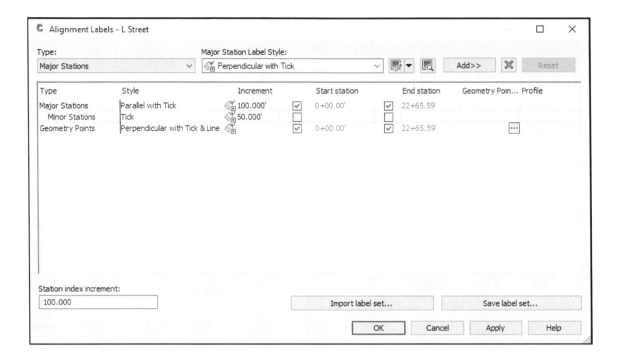

### Key Concepts

Concepts and key terms covered in this lesson are:

- Alignment Labels
- Alignment Label Sets
- Label Styles
- Offset Alignments

### Objectives

After completing this lesson, you will be able to:

- Describe an Alignment Label Set.
- Modify the stationing of an Alignment.
- Create station and offset labels.
- Create Offset Alignments.

## Alignment Label Sets

The alignment label set is a collection of alignment label styles that can be assigned to an alignment. The label set is initially selected when the alignment is created.

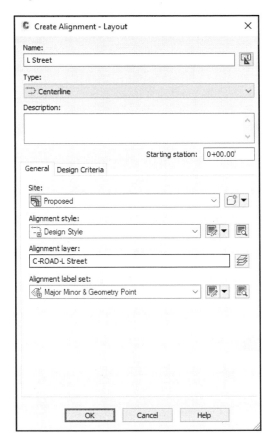

The label set or the individual label styles can be changed at any point by using the **Add/Edit Station Labels** command.

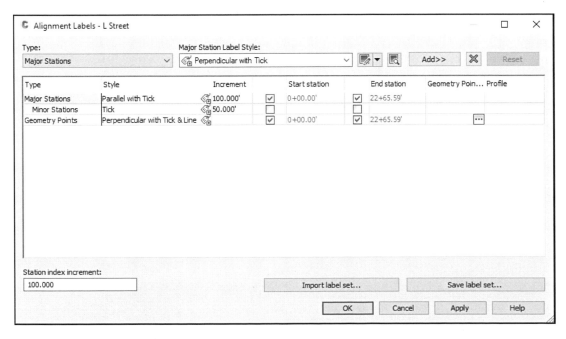

Alignment Labels are most commonly used to display stationing. However, they can also display *Northings, Eastings, Directions*, and *Design Speeds*.

## Changing the Stationing of an Alignment

The stationing of an alignment can be changed by editing the alignment properties.
Changing the stationing of an alignment will automatically update all associated labels as well
as sampled profiles.

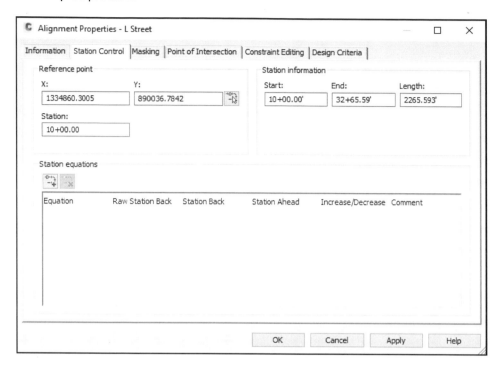

## Station and Offset Labels

Station and offset labels can be created that are dynamically lined to the alignment.  There
are two types of station and offset labels:

- Station/Offset - Fixed Point
    - This labels a fixed point
    - If the alignment is edited the station and offset values of the label are updated
- Station/Offset
    - This places the label at a specific station and offset from the alignment
    - If the alignment is edited the label moves to maintain the same station and offset values

## Offset Alignments

Offset Alignments are dynamically created at an offset from another Alignment. The geometry of this type of alignment cannot be edited directly; instead it is automatically updated based on changes to the parent alignment. Offset Alignments can be used to represent the edge of pavement or other road features. They can also be used to create right of way lines that dynamically update when the centerline is modified.

## Exercises: Label an Alignment and Create Offsets

In these exercises, you modify the stationing of an alignment. You also create station and offset labels. Finally, you offset an alignment to create static polylines and then create offset alignments that are dynamically linked to the centerline.

You do the following:

- Assign Alignment Label Styles to change the appearance of the stationing.
- Label Station and Offsets.
- Offset the Alignment to create polylines.
- Create dynamic Offset Alignments.

### 6.3.1 Working with Alignment Station Labels

1. Continue working in the drawing **Design.dwg**.

*Reminder:* You can also open the drawing with this exercise number in the *Chapter Drawings* folder of the dataset if you prefer a fresh start at this point.

2. Zoom in and examine the alignment station labels.

3. Pick the alignment **L Street** in the drawing editor to display the context sensitive ribbon.

4. Select **Ribbon: Alignment: L Street ⇒ Labels and Tables ⇒ Add Labels ⇒ Add/Edit Station Labels**.

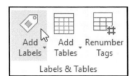

This opens the *Alignment Labels* dialog box where you can modify your station labels.

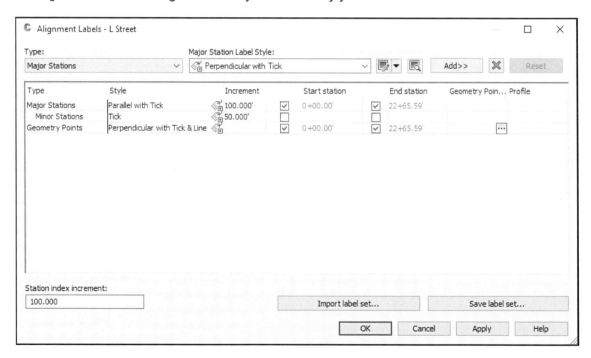

5. Change the **Major Station Style** to **Parallel with Tick** by clicking on the symbol in the *Style* field of the table.

You can also save and import *Label Sets* which are just saved collections of label styles so that you don't have to set each one individually.

6. Click **<<OK>>**.

7. **[Esc]** to clear the selection and dismiss the context sensitive ribbon.

8. Zoom in to review the changes to the stationing from the new alignment label style.

The alignment will be redisplayed with parallel stationing at the major stations. You can edit alignment label styles in an editor that is very similar to the one you used to create point label styles and contour label styles in the previous chapters.

### 6.3.2 Changing the Stationing of an Alignment

1. Pick the alignment **L Street** in the drawing editor to display the context sensitive ribbon.

2. Select **Ribbon: Alignment: L Street ⇒ Modify ⇒ Alignment Properties**.

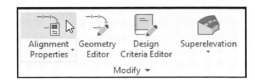

3. Select the **Station Control** tab.

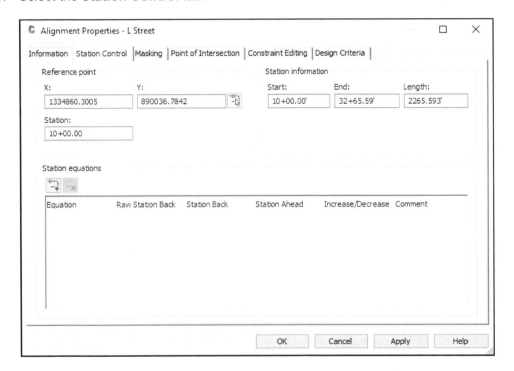

4. Change the **Station** of the *Reference Point* (by default the beginning of the alignment) to **1000**.

5. Click **<<OK>>**.

This warning notifies you that changing the stationing may affect objects and data already created from the alignment. You can reset any of these values to match the current stationing later.

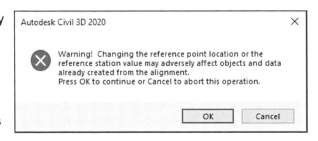

Changing the stationing of an alignment will also impact any *Finished Grade Profiles* that you have defined for this alignment. These are also defined by station values so they would need to be updated. *Existing Ground Profiles* are based directly on the alignment so a change in stationing will not cause any problem for them, the *Existing Ground Profiles* will automatically be updated.

In this exercise you have not created any of these station based features at this point. So you will not need to worry about this warning.

6. Click **<<OK>>** to clear the warning.

7. Click **<<OK>>** to close the *Alignment Properties* dialog box and apply the new stationing.

8. **[Esc]** to clear the selection and dismiss the context sensitive ribbon.

9. Zoom in to review the updated station values.

### 6.3.3    Labeling Station and Offset Values

1. Thaw the layer **PNTS-UTILITY**.

2. Pick the alignment **L Street** in the drawing editor to display the context sensitive ribbon.

3. Select **Ribbon: Alignment: L Street ⇒ Labels and Tables ⇒ Add Labels ⇒ Station/Offset - Fixed Point**.

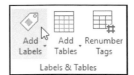

4. When asked to Select point: Enter **'PN** at the command line.

Alternatively, you can also select the *Point Number* button from the *Transparent Commands* toolbar.

5. Enter Point Number **1566**.

You could also snap to the point or just pick a location graphically instead of using the Point Number transparent command.

6. **[Enter]** to end the *Station/Offset labeling* command.

7. Zoom in and examine the new station and offset label at point number 1566. Notice the station and offset values.

The contents of the label along with the display and format of the text are controlled by the Label Style.

8. Pick the alignment in the drawing editor to display the grips.

9. Select the grip at **PI** number **1** at the northwest corner of the alignment.

10. At the command line, enter **@0,10** to stretch the PI 10 feet north.

11. **[Esc]** to clear the selection and dismiss the context sensitive ribbon.

12. Zoom in and examine the station and offset label. Notice the station and offset values have updated to reflect the changes in the alignment.

### 6.3.4 Creating Polyline Offsets of an Alignment

Offsets can be created with the standard *AutoCAD offset* command. This creates a Polyline on the current layer.

1. Create a new layer named **C-ROAD-L Street-EP**, set the color to **yellow** and set it **current**.

2. Enter **O** at the command line to start the *AutoCAD* **offset** command.

3. Enter **12** for the **offset distance**.

4. Select the **L Street alignment** and offset it to the right and left side of the road.

5. **[Enter]** to end the offset command.

6. Save the drawing.

These offsets are for drafting purposes only. They are not *Civil 3D* objects, displayed in the *Prospector*, or tied to our design in any way. They are simply *AutoCAD polylines*.

The alignment and offsets will look like the graphic below.

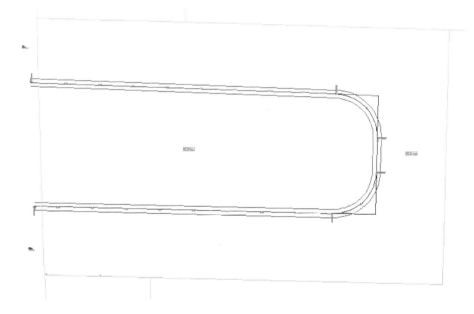

### 6.3.5    Creating Offset Alignments

In this exercise, you will create *Offset Alignments* that define the right of way at a 25' offset. Since the new ROW alignments are created in the same *Site* as the parent, or centerline alignment, two new right of way parcels will be created, one on each side of the centerline.

1.  Pick the alignment **L Street** in the drawing editor to display the context sensitive ribbon.

2.  Select **Ribbon: Alignment: L Street ⇒ Launch Pad ⇒ Offset Alignment**.

This opens the *Create Offset Alignments* dialog box where you define the parameters of multiple alignments that will be created at a dynamic offset from the centerline alignment.

3.  Confirm the **Alignment to offset from** is set to **L Street**.

4.  Confirm the **Number of offsets on left and right** are both set to **1**.

You can create multiple *Offset Alignments* on each side of the parent alignment with this setting.

5.  Set the **Incremental offset on left and right** to **25'**.

6.  Set the **Alignment style** to **ROW**.

7.  Set the **Alignment label set** to **_No Labels**.

This *Alignment Label Set* will not assign any labels to the new *Offset Alignments*. If you decide later that you would like to add labels to the *Offset Alignments* you can always assign the desired *Label Styles* to add stationing or any other labels.

8.  Click **<<OK>>** to create the *Offset Alignments*.

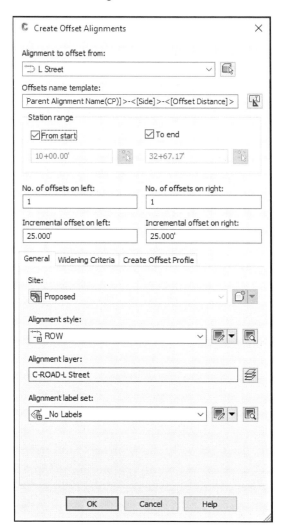

9.  **[Esc]** to clear the selection and dismiss the context sensitive ribbon.

Review the two new *Offset Alignments* that were just created and notice that two new parcels were also created. ROW parcels can also be created with the **Parcel ⇒ Create Right of Way** command on the Home tab. However, parcels created with this command are not dynamic and do not update if the centerline alignment is modified.

## 6.4    Lesson:  Laying Out Parcels

### Introduction

When an alignment is created in the same site as one or more parcels; it automatically splits the parcels it passes through and acts as another parcel line.  When you add the new Offset Alignments, two ROW parcels are created and subtracted from the original parcels.  As you edit the alignment, the parcels are also edited.

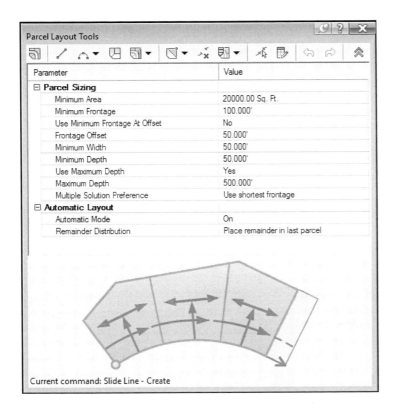

### Key Concepts

Concepts and key terms covered in this lesson are:

- Parcels
- Sites
- Parcel Layout
- Parcel Editing

### Objectives

After completing this lesson, you will be able to:

- Describe how Parcels and Alignments interact within a Site.
- Layout Parcels according to specific parameters.
- Edit and delete Parcels.
- Renumber Parcels.

## Laying Out Parcels

The parcel layout tools can create parcels based on a number of criteria:

- Minimum Area
- Minimum Frontage
- Minimum Frontage at an offset
- Minimum Width
- Minimum Depth
- Maximum Depth

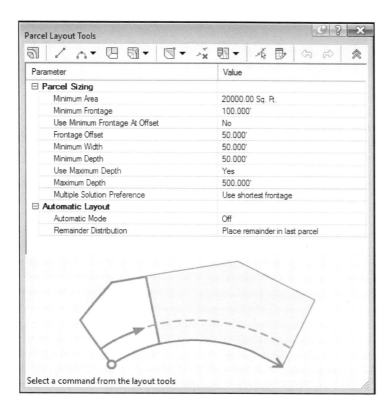

## Editing Parcels

You can stretch or move parcel lines by using standard AutoCAD commands, like grip editing, to edit parcels. You can also create new parcel lines to change the geometry of a parcel. Any time a group of parcel segments from the same Site are closed a parcel will be defined.

Parcels are deleted by erasing a parcel segment or editing a parcel segment so that it is no longer closed. Do not try to delete a parcel by erasing the parcel label; even though it highlights the entire parcel when you select it, nothing will happen when you try to erase it.

## Parcel Layout and Editing Tools

The Parcel Layout Tools toolbar contains many tools for creating, editing and subdividing parcels.

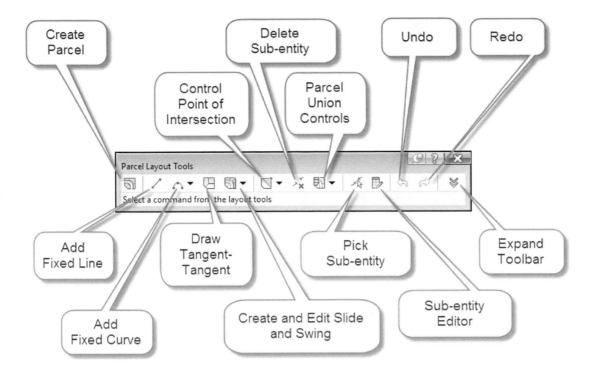

## Exercises: Subdivide and Lay Out Parcels

Parcel layout is interactive and dynamic. In these exercises, you will learn to subdivide a large parcel automatically based on area and frontage criteria. You will also learn how parcels interact with each other when they are part of the same site. This makes editing easier and helps avoid mistakes because parcels are not allowed to overlap. You then edit and renumber parcels.

You do the following:

- Merge the right of way parcels.
- Create parcels with a minimum area and frontage.
- Edit parcels.
- Delete parcels.
- Renumber parcels.

### 6.4.1 Merging Parcels

When creating right of way parcels at least two *Right of Way* parcels are created, one on each side of the alignment or alignment intersection. You may want to merge these parcels together into a single *Right of Way* parcel to make them easier to manage and display. You can do this by editing the parcels and using the Union command.

1. Continue working in the drawing **Design.dwg**.

*Reminder:* You can also open the drawing with this exercise number in the *Chapter Drawings* folder of the dataset if you prefer a fresh start at this point.

2. Select **Ribbon: Home ⇒ Create Design ⇒ Parcel ⇒ Parcel Creation Tools**.

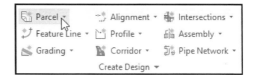

This opens the Parcel Layout Tools toolbar.

3. Click the **Parcel Union** button on the *Parcel Layout Tools* toolbar.

4. Pick the two *ROW* parcels from the drawing editor. It is easiest to select the parcels by picking the parcel label.

5. **[Enter]** to merge the parcels.

The two ROW parcels are now merged together and one of the parcel labels will disappear.

6. Enter **X** at the command line to exit the *Edit Parcel* command.

### 6.4.2 Creating Parcels Manually

Parcels can be laid out and divided by graphically picking the location of the new parcel line.

1. Select **Ribbon: Home ⇒ Create Design ⇒ Parcel ⇒ Parcel Creation Tools**.

This opens the Parcel Layout Tools toolbar.

2. Click the **down arrow** button next to the **Slide Line - Create button** on the *Parcel Layout Tools* toolbar to display the other creation commands.

3. Select ⇒ **Free Form Create**.

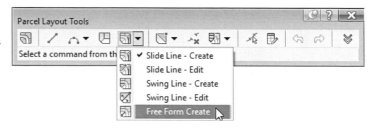

4. Confirm that the **Site** is set to **Proposed**.

5. Set the **Parcel style** to **Single Family**.

The *Parcel Style* controls the display of the parcel lines and optional hatch.

6. Set the **Area Label Style** to **Name Area & Perimeter**.

7. Click **<<OK>>**.

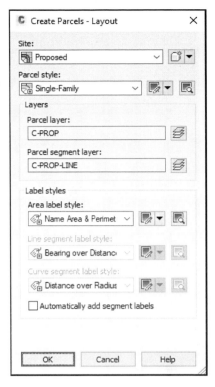

8. Move your cursor into the northwest corner of the main, U-shaped parcel wrapping around the outside of the alignment. You should see a dynamic preview line showing suggestions for the placement of the new parcel line.

9. Pick a location for the new parcel line at about **station 11+50** along the *L Street alignment*.

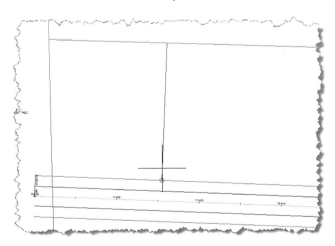

10. **[Enter]** to create the new parcel line perpendicular to the *ROW*.

If you pick a second point graphically it will determine the bearing of the new parcel line.

11. **[Enter]** to end the command.

12. Enter **X** at the command line to exit *the Parcel Layout Tool*.

The new parcel is created and displays with a magenta boundary. This is because it is now using the parcel style *Single Family* that you set in the *Parcel Layout* dialog box. Regen if it does not display properly.

### 6.4.3    Creating Parcels with the Slide Line Tool

In this exercise, you will create the next parcel at an exact size of 20,000 square feet and a minimum frontage of 100 feet.  After entering these parameters *Civil 3D* will find the location of the new parcel line for you rather than you selecting it manually.

1.  Select **Ribbon: Home ⇒ Create Design ⇒ Parcel ⇒ Parcel Creation Tools**.

2.  Expand the **Parcel Layout Tools** toolbar if it is not already expanded by clicking the **chevron** button on the far right of the toolbar.

3.  Set the **Minimum Area** to **20000**.

4.  Confirm that the **Minimum Frontage** is set to **100**.

5.  Set the **Use Minimum Frontage At Offset** option to **No**.

6.  Click the **Slide Line - Create** button on the *Parcel Layout Tools* toolbar.

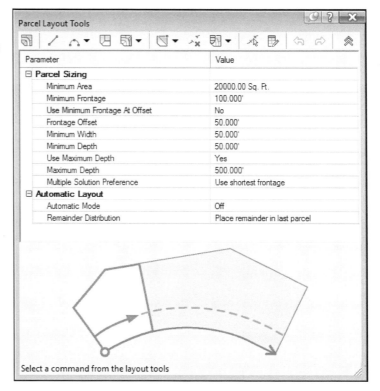

| Parameter | Value |
|---|---|
| ⊟ **Parcel Sizing** | |
| Minimum Area | 20000.00 Sq. Ft. |
| Minimum Frontage | 100.000' |
| Use Minimum Frontage At Offset | No |
| Frontage Offset | 50.000' |
| Minimum Width | 50.000' |
| Minimum Depth | 50.000' |
| Use Maximum Depth | Yes |
| Maximum Depth | 500.000' |
| Multiple Solution Preference | Use shortest frontage |
| ⊟ **Automatic Layout** | |
| Automatic Mode | Off |
| Remainder Distribution | Place remainder in last parcel |

Select a command from the layout tools

7. Confirm that the **Site** is set to **Proposed**.

8. Set the **Parcel style** to **Single Family**.

The *Parcel Style* controls the display of the parcel lines and optional hatch.

9. Set the **Area Label Style** to **Name Area & Perimeter**.

10. Click **<<OK>>**.

11. Select the parcel area label in the large parcel to be subdivided to the right of the parcel you created in the previous exercise.

12. When prompted to **Select start point on frontage** use an **End Point** snap to select the end of the parcel line that you created in the previous exercise where it intersects the ROW.

13. Drag the highlight line along the ROW to a spot near **station 15+00** and click there.

This is tracing a line for the frontage of the new parcel that is longer than will be needed to define a 20,000 s.f. parcel with a minimum 100' frontage.

14. Enter **90** for the **angle** at the frontage.

A preview of the proposed parcel is displayed.

15. **[Enter]** to accept the results of the parcel sizing.

The new parcel is created with an area of 20000 square feet. Depending on the length of parcel frontage you traced on the screen, you may see the preview of another parcel sized in the drawing editor.

16. **[Esc]** to end the command.

17. Enter **X** at the command line to exit the *Parcel Layout Tool*.

### 6.4.4 Creating Parcels with the Slide Line Tool Automatically

The Slide Line command can also be used to divide an entire parcel into as many parcels that fit into it according to the area and frontage parameters that you set.

1. Select **Ribbon: Home ⇒ Create Design ⇒ Parcel ⇒ Parcel Creation Tools**.

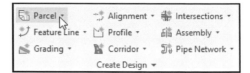

2. Expand the **Parcel Layout Tools** toolbar if it is not already expanded by clicking the **expand** button on the far right of the toolbar.

3. Leave the Parcel Sizing parameters as default and click the **Slide Line - Create** button on the *Parcel Layout Tools* toolbar.

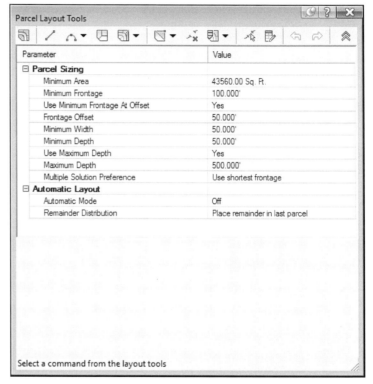

4. Confirm that the **Site** is set to **Proposed**.

5. Set the **Parcel** style to **Single Family**.

6. Set the **Area Label Style** to **Name Area & Perimeter**.

7. Enable the option to **Automatically add segment labels**.

8. Set the **Line Segment Label Style** to **Distance Only**.

9. Confirm the **Curve Segment Label Style** is set to **Distance over Radius & Delta**.

10. Click **<<OK>>**.

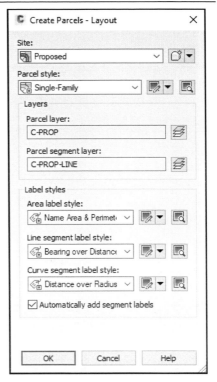

11. Select the parcel area label in the large parcel to be subdivided to the right of the parcel you created in the previous exercise.

12. When prompted to Select start point on frontage use an **End Point** snap to select the end of the parcel line that you created in the previous exercise where it intersects the ROW.

13. Drag the highlight line along the *ROW* to the end of the tangent near **station 32+00** and pick the end of the line.

14. Enter **90** for the **angle** at the frontage.

A preview of the first new parcel is displayed with the default settings.

15. Set the **Automatic Mode** to **On**.

Now a preview of all the parcels created with the default parameters is displayed.

16. Set the default area to **20000**.

17. Confirm that the **Minimum Frontage** is set to **100**.

18. Set the **Use Minimum Frontage At Offset** option to **No**.

19. Confirm that the **Remainder Distribution** will **Place the remainder in the last parcel**.

This will create one larger parcel at the end to use up the left over area that could not complete another 20,000 square foot parcel.

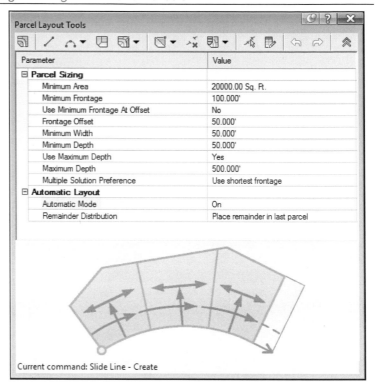

A preview of the proposed parcels is displayed. The last parcel is larger because you used the default option to place the remaining area in the last parcel.

20. **[Enter]** to accept the results of the parcel sizing.

The large parcel is now divided into parcels with a minimum area of 20000 square feet and a minimum frontage of 100 feet with parcel lines perpendicular to the *ROW*.

21. **[Esc]** to end the command.

22. Enter **X** at the command line to exit the *Parcel Layout Tool*.

The newly created parcel segments are automatically labeled with the line and curve segment styles that you selected in the *Create Parcels - Layout* dialog box when you enabled the *Automatically add segment labels* option.

### 6.4.5 Editing Parcels

1. Select that last parcel line created by the automatic layout in the previous exercise. You will see that it only displays a single grip at the *ROW*.

2. Select the grip and drag it along the *ROW* to a position of your choice.

3. Notice that the parcel line stays perpendicular to the *ROW* and that the properties of both parcels are updated.

### 6.4.6 Deleting Parcels

1. Use the *AutoCAD* **erase** command to erase one of the parcel lines that you created during the parcel sizing exercises.

2. Notice that the parcels separated by that line are merged together and that the old parcel is removed from the *Prospector*.

### 6.4.7 Renumbering Parcels

*Civil 3D* makes renumbering parcels easy, by allowing you to trace a path that will select parcels in the order that you would like them to be numbered. So it is best to not worry about parcels that may get numbered incorrectly as you go through the design process of adding, deleting, and editing parcels because you can easily renumber them at any time.

1. Select **Ribbon: Modify ⇒ Design ⇒ Parcel**.

The *Parcel* tab is displayed.

2. Select **Ribbon: Parcel ⇒ Modify ⇒ Renumber/Rename**.

This opens the *Renumber/Rename Parcels* dialog box.

3. Confirm that the **Site** is set to **Proposed**.

4. Confirm that the **Renumber** option is selected.

5. Set the **Starting number** to **101**.

6. Confirm that the **Increment value** is set to **1**.

7. **Enable** the **Use name template in parcel style** option.

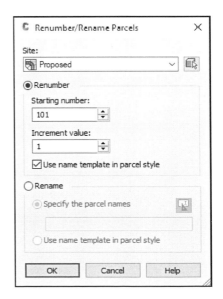

This will use the parcel name template that is defined in the parcel style. In this case it will name the parcels *SINGLE-FAMILY: 101* rather than just *1*.

8. Click **<<OK>>**.

9. Pick a point inside the first parcel that you created in the northwest corner at the beginning of the alignment.

10. Pick a point in the parcel on the northeast corner near **station 20+00** to draw a line that will create a path determining the order that the parcels will be renumbered.

11. Pick a point in the parcel on the southeast corner near **station 23+00**.

12. Pick a point in the parcel in the southwest at the end of the alignment.

13. **[Enter]** to end the path.

14. **[Enter]** again to end the command and renumber the parcels.

15. Zoom in to review the new parcel numbers. You will also see the numbers updated in the *Prospector*. If the parcels are not visible in the *Prospector* right-click on the parcels node and select refresh.

16. Save the drawing.

## 6.5    Lesson:  Working with Parcel Styles and Labels

### Introduction

In this lesson, you will create a new Parcel Style and Parcel Label Style to control the display of the Parcel Lines and the Labeling of the Parcels.

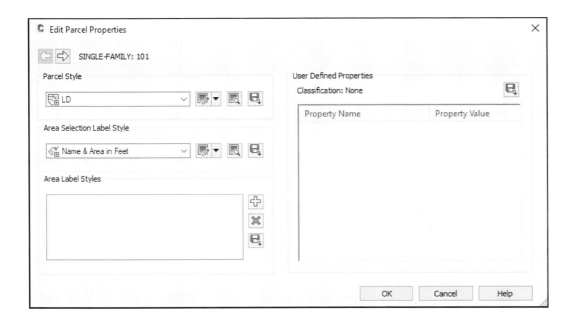

### Key Concepts

Concepts and key terms covered in this lesson are:

- Parcel Styles
- Parcel Area Label Styles
- Parcel Properties

### Objectives

After completing this lesson, you will be able to:

- List the properties of Parcel Styles.
- Create and apply a new Parcel Style.
- Create and apply a new Parcel Area Label Style.
- Describe how Parcels and Parcel Area Label Styles can be applied to multiple Parcels.

## Parcel Display and Labeling

The display and labeling of parcels is controlled by three different styles:

- Parcel Styles
- Parcel Area Label Styles
- Parcel Segment Label Styles

## Parcel Styles

Parcel Styles control the display of the parcel segments and the parcel area fill (hatch). The parcel style also controls the parcel name template. This formats the name of the parcel based on the style that is assigned to it.

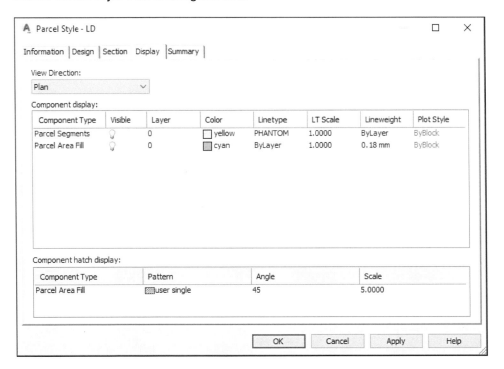

## Parcel Area Label Styles

Parcel Area Label Styles control the display of the parcel are label text. This typically includes things like the parcel name and/or number, area in square feet and/or acres, and perimeter. Parcel Area Labels can be configured to display many other types of information as well, such as tax lot number, address, and user defined fields.

## Parcel Segment Label Styles

Parcel Segment Label Styles control the display of the line and curve labels applied to the perimeter of the parcel.

## Changing Multiple Parcel Properties

The parcel style and area label style of a parcel can be changed in the *Parcel Properties* dialog box. However, this only allows you to select one parcel at a time. You can assign a different style to several parcels at once by using the **Multiple Parcel Properties** command. This command is a two step process.

1. Select **Ribbon: Modify ⇒ Design ⇒ Parcel**.

This displays the *Parcel* tab.

2. Select **Ribbon: Parcel ⇒ Modify ⇒ Multiple Parcel Properties**.

## Exercises: Label Parcels and Control their Display

In these exercises, you create and assign a parcel style to control the display of the parcel geometry. Then you create a parcel area label style to label the parcels with the parcel name and area in square feet. Finally, you change the properties of multiple parcels to assign the new parcel style and parcel area label style.

You do the following:

- Create a new Parcel Style.
- Create a new Parcel Area Label Style.
- Assign the new Parcel Style and Parcel Area Label Style to multiple Parcels.

### 6.5.1 Controlling Parcel Display

1. Continue working in the drawing **Design.dwg**.

*Reminder:* You can also open the drawing with this exercise number in the *Chapter Drawings* folder of the dataset if you prefer a fresh start at this point.

2. Pick the last parcel that you created in the previous exercise by picking the parcel area label to display the context sensitive ribbon.

The parcel is at the end of the alignment, in the southwest corner.

3. Select **Ribbon: Parcel: Property: 119 ⇒ Parcel Properties**

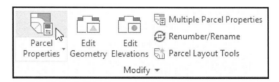

This is the original parcel that you subdivided and it may still be using the original parcel style Property. You could also select the parcel label from the *Prospector* and right-click to select Properties.

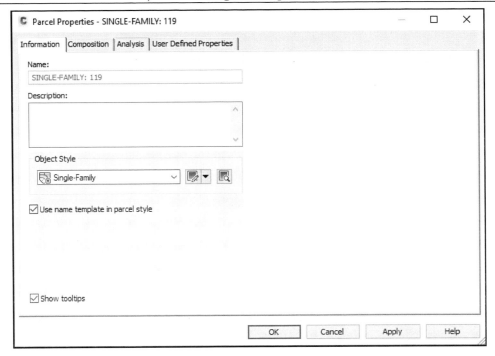

4.  On the *Information* tab, change the **Object Style** to **Single Family**.

5.  Click **<<OK>>** to display the parcel with the new style.

6.  **[Esc]** to clear the selection and dismiss the context sensitive ribbon.

The parcel is now displayed with a magenta boundary line according to the properties of the parcel style. It is also renamed. This is based on the name template in the parcel style.

### 6.5.2    Creating Parcel Styles

Parcel Styles control the display of the parcel segments and the parcel area fill. In this exercise, you will create a new parcel style for Low Density Zoning that will display the parcels with yellow, phantom lines and a crosshatch buffer. You will create the parcel style on the fly through the *Parcel Properties* dialog box. However, you could also create the Parcel Style from the settings tab of the *Toolspace* as you did with the Point Styles in the *Chapter 4.*

1.  Pick the last parcel that you edited in the previous exercise by picking the parcel area label to display the context sensitive ribbon.

The parcel is at the end of the alignment, in the southwest corner.

2.  Select **Ribbon: Parcel: SINGLE-FAMILY: 119 ⇒ Parcel Properties.**

This opens the *Parcel Properties* dialog box.

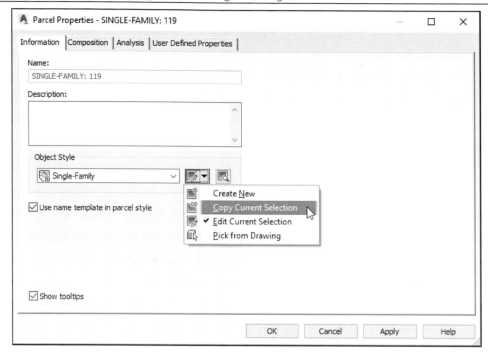

3.  Click the **down arrow** button next to the **Object style** on the *Information* tab of the *Parcel Properties* dialog box to display the other creation commands.

4.  Select ⇒ **Copy Current Selection**.

This style can also be copied, edited, and created on the *Settings* tab of the *Toolspace* along with all other *Civil 3D Styles*.

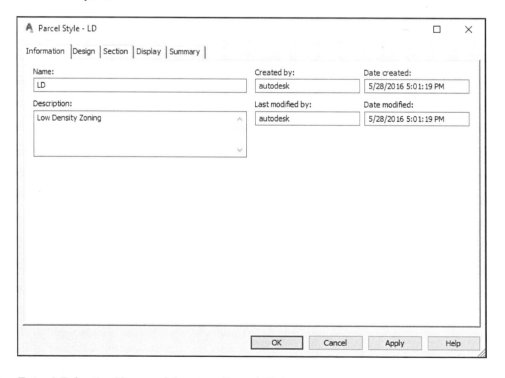

5.  Enter **LD** for the **Name** of the new *Parcel Style*.

6.  Enter **Low Density Zoning** for the **Description** of the new *Parcel Style*.

7.  Select the **Design** Tab of the *Parcel Style* dialog box.

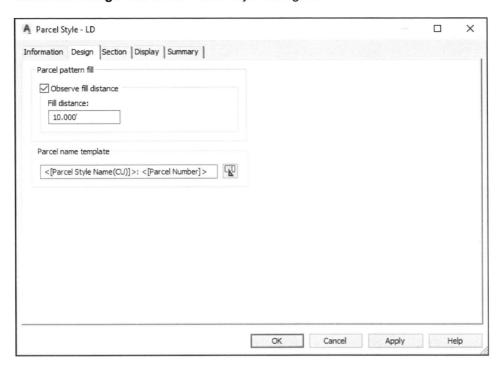

8.  Enable the **Observe fill distance** option.

9.  Set the **Fill distance** to **10**.

This will limit the *Area Fill* component, or hatch, to a 10' buffer around the inside of the parcel boundary.

10. Select the **Display** Tab of the *Parcel Style* dialog box.

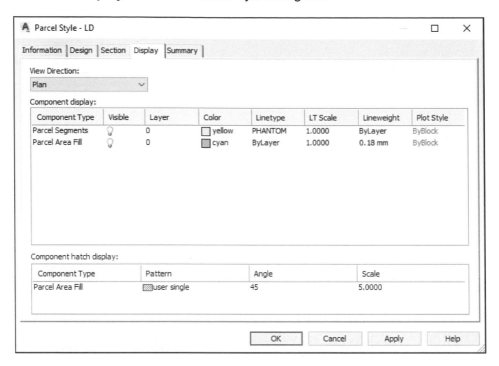

11. Confirm that the **View Direction** is set to **Plan**.

12. Set the color of the **Parcel Segments** component to **Yellow**.

13. Set the *Linetype* of the **Parcel Segments** component to **Phantom**.

14. Turn on the display of the **Parcel Area Fill** component.

15. Set the color of the **Parcel Area Fill** component to **Cyan**.

16. In the *Component hatch display* section set the **Angle** to **45**.

17. In the *Component hatch display* section set the **Scale** to **5**.

This section allows you to set the hatch pattern, angle, and scale for the Parcel Area Fill component that you turned on in the previous steps.

18. Click **<<OK>>** to save the new **Parcel Style** and return to the *Parcel Properties* dialog box.

19. Click **<<OK>>** to close the *Parcel Properties* dialog box and apply the new *Parcel Style*.

20. **[Esc]** to clear the selection and dismiss the context sensitive ribbon.

The parcel is now displayed with a yellow, phantom boundary line according to the properties of the parcel style. It is also renamed *LD: 119*, which is based on the name template in the parcel style. (Your exact parcel number may vary based on the size of the first parcel you created and how many you deleted.)

### 6.5.3   Creating Parcel Area Label Styles

1.   Pick the last parcel that you edited in the previous exercise by picking the parcel area label to display the context sensitive ribbon.

The parcel is at the end of the alignment, in the southwest corner.

2.   Select **Ribbon: Parcel: LD: 119 ⇒ Modify ⇒ Parcel Properties.**

This opens the *Parcel Properties* dialog box.

3.   Select the **Composition** Tab of the *Parcel Properties* dialog box.

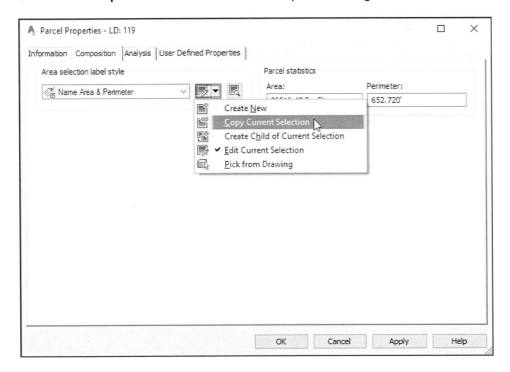

4.   Confirm the *Area selection label style* **Name Area & Perimeter** is set current.

5.   Click the **down arrow** button next to the **Area selection label style** to display the other creation commands.

6.   Select ⇒ **Copy Current Selection**.

This style can also be copied, edited, and created on the *Settings* tab of the *Toolspace* along with all other *Civil 3D Styles*.

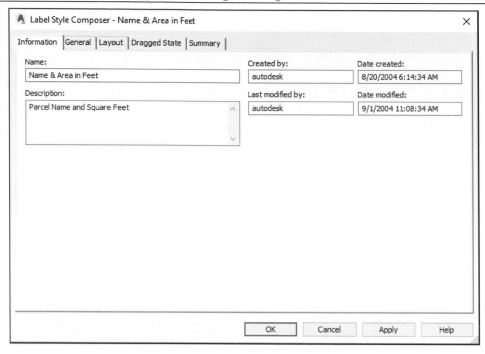

7.  Enter **Name & Area in Feet** for the **Name** of the new *Parcel Label Style*.

8.  Enter **Parcel Name and Square Feet** for the **Description** of the new *Parcel Area Label Style*.

9.  Select the **Layout** tab.

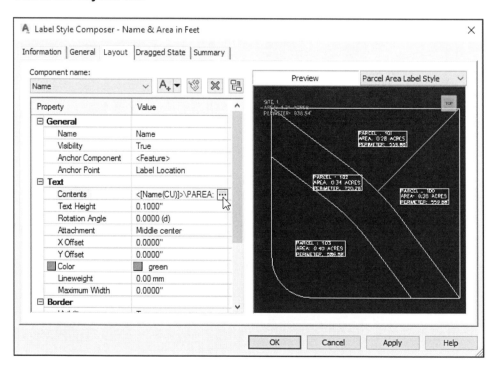

10. Click the **Text Contents** *Value* field to activate the **more <<...>>** button.

11. Click the **more <<...>>** button to open the *Text Component Editor*.

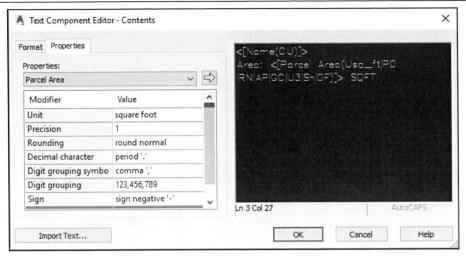

12. Delete the lines starting with **Area** and **Perimeter.**

13. Select **Parcel Area** from the **Properties** drop down list.

14. Confirm that the **Unit** value is set to **square foot**.

15. Set the **Precision** to **1** (no decimal places).

16. Set the **Digit grouping** to **123,456,789**.

17. Click the **right arrow** button to insert the code to display the area of the parcel in square feet.

18. Enter **Area:** in the editor to the left of the code to better describe the label.

19. Enter **SQFT** in the editor to the right of the code to describe the units of the label.

20. Click **<<OK>>** to save the contents of the new component.

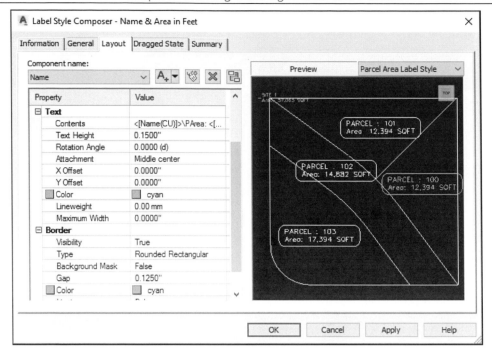

21. Back in the *Label Style Composer* set the **Text Height** to **0.15**.

22. Set the **Color** to **Cyan**.

23. Set the **Border Type** to **Rounded Rectangular**.

24. Set the **Border Gap** to **0.125**.

25. Set the **Border Color** to **Cyan**.

26. Click **<<OK>>** to save the new **Parcel Label Style** and return to the *Parcel Properties* dialog box.

27. Click **<<OK>>** to close the **Parcel Properties** dialog box and apply the new *Parcel Area Label Style*.

28. **[Esc]** to clear the selection and dismiss the context sensitive ribbon.

The parcel is now displayed with a cyan label showing the parcel name and area in square feet according to the properties of the *Parcel Area Label Style*.

### 6.5.4 Changing the Styles of Multiple Parcels

You can change the styles of a parcel in the *Parcel Properties* dialog box. However, this only allows you to select one parcel at a time. In this exercise, you will lean to edit the properties, including the current styles, of several parcels at the same time.

1. Select **Ribbon: Modify ⇒ Design ⇒ Parcel**.

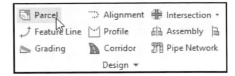

This displays the *Parcel* tab on the *Ribbon*.

2. Select **Ribbon: Parcel ⇒ Modify ⇒ Multiple Parcel Properties**.

You will now select all the newly created parcels to change their parcel style and parcel label style. You will select them by drawing a line that touches all the desired parcels.

3. Pick a point inside the first parcel that you created at the beginning of the alignment, parcel number 101.

4. Pick a point in the parcel on the northeast corner near **station 20+00** to draw a line that will create a path touching all the parcels that you want to select to change the style.

5. Pick a point in the parcel on the southeast corner near **station 23+00**.

6. Pick a point in the parcel at the southwest corner at end of the alignment.

7. **[Enter]** to end the path.

8. **[Enter]** again to complete the selection set and open the *Edit Parcel Properties* dialog box.

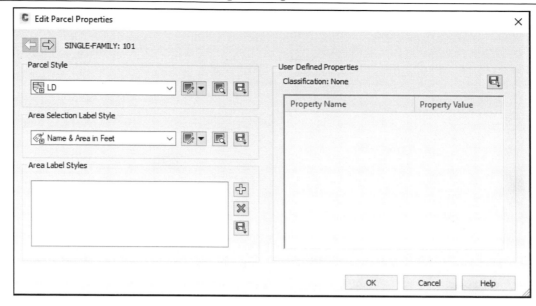

At the top of the *Edit Parcel Properties* dialog box you can cycle through the parcels you selected by using the blue arrow buttons. This allows you to edit the properties of each parcel individually. However, in this exercise you will modify all the selected parcels at the same time.

9. Set the **Parcel Style** to **LD**.

10. Click the **Apply to all selected Parcels** button.

11. Click **<<Yes>>** to apply the new style to all the selected parcels.

12. Set the **Area Selection Label Style** to **Name & Area in Feet**.

13. Click the **Apply to all selected Parcels** button.

14. Click **<<Yes>>** to apply the new style to all the selected parcels.

15. Click **<<OK>>** to close the **Edit Parcel Properties** dialog box

16. Zoom in to review the new parcel style and area label style.

17. Save the drawing.

# Chapter 7

# 7 -   Working with Profiles

In this chapter, you will use the surface and alignment data created in precious chapters to create an existing ground profile.  You will create a *Profile View* to display the profile and explore how to control its display with styles.  You will also layout and edit a finished ground profile that will be used later in the project to create the corridor model.

**Lesson:  Creating Existing Ground Profiles**

In this lesson, you will learn to create existing ground profiles and display them in profile views.

**Lesson:  Creating Finished Ground Profiles**

In this lesson, you will learn the concepts and process of creating and editing finished ground profiles.  You will also learn to work with profile labels and bands.

## 7.1    Lesson:  Creating Existing Ground Profiles

### Introduction

The *Existing Ground Profile* is based on the *Surface* and *Alignment* that you created in earlier.  The *Profile* is an object and is dynamically linked to the *Alignment* and *Surface* so it will automatically update if there are any changes to either of them.

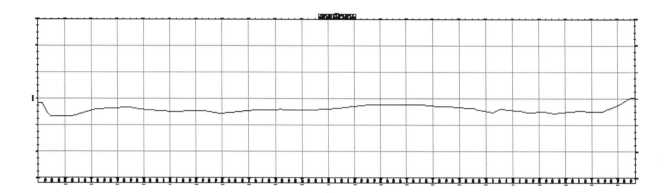

### Key Concepts

Concepts and key terms covered in this lesson are:

- Profiles
- Profile Views
- Profile View Styles

### Objectives

After completing this lesson, you will be able to:

- Describe the relationship between Alignments, Surfaces and Parcels.
- Sample a Profile.
- Create and manage Profile Views.
- Create and apply Profile View Styles.

## Profiles

Profiles provide vertical data along an alignment. They saved under the alignment in the Prospector and cannot exist without the parent alignment. Profiles are viewed within a Profile View. There are two types of profiles:

- Surface Profiles
- Layout Profiles

The dynamic nature of the profile object in Civil 3D allows you to easily make changes to the geometry of the profile. This allows you to approach the design process differently than you may have in the past with other programs. Now you can set a default curve length or K value for the profile and lay out a rough draft in Civil 3D, then modify and revise it in real time either graphically or in a tabular format.

## Surface Profiles

Surface profiles are typically existing ground profiles and are created by sampling a surface along an alignment or at an offset from an alignment. Surface profiles are dynamically linked to the alignment and surface. If either the alignment or surface changes the surface profile is automatically updated.

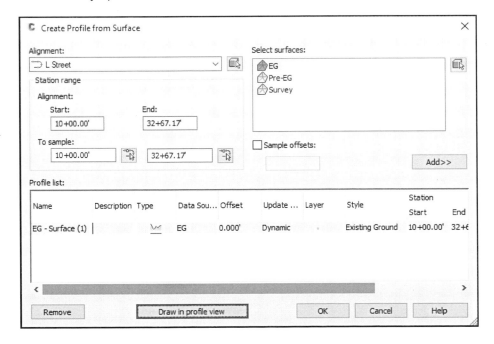

## Layout Profiles

Layout profiles are typically finished ground profiles or design profiles. They are created by drafting the profile into a profile view using the profile layout tools.

## Profile Views

A profile view is an object that acts like a window to display profile data. Typically, it is the grid on which the profile lines are drawn.

- You can create multiple profile views in the same drawing
- Profile views can be moved without changing the profile data
- Erasing a profile view does not erase the profile data
- Display is controlled by Profile View Styles
- Profile View Bands can be added to display rows of data at the bottom or top of the profile view

## Working with Multiple Profile Views

You can create multiple profile views in the same drawing. This gives you the flexibility to separate the design and sheet creation processes and view the profile in many different ways.

For example, you may find it helpful to have a profile view for the entire length of the alignment, that uses a specific style with a certain vertical exaggeration, grid, and labeling for design purposes. However, this is not the information that you would plot according to your organization's standards. In that case you would create several additional profile views (one for each sheet) that use a different style that displays and labels the profiles for plotting according to your standards.

## Profile View Styles

Profile View Styles control the display of the grid on which the profile lines are drawn. This includes:

- Vertical Exaggeration
- The display and labeling of the top, bottom, left and right axis
- The profile view title
- Spacing and display of the grid
- Grid clipping

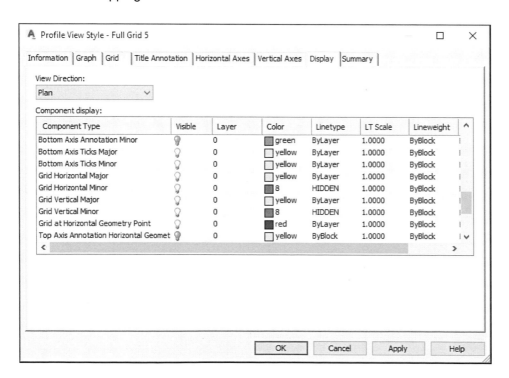

## Exercises: Create an Existing Ground Profile

In these exercises, you sample and display a profile of the existing ground surface. Then you create a new Profile View Style to change the display and vertical exaggeration of the profile grid. Finally, you create multiple Profile Views.

You do the following:

- Sample and display a Profile.
- Create a new Profile View Style.
- Create multiple Profile Views.

### 7.1.1 Sampling and Drawing the Profile

1. Continue working in the drawing **Design.dwg**.

*Reminder:* You can also open the drawing with this exercise number in the *Chapter Drawings* folder of the dataset if you prefer a fresh start at this point.

2. Select **Ribbon: Home ⇒ Create Design ⇒ Profile ⇒ Create Surface Profile**.

This opens the *Create Profile from Surface* dialog box where you can select the alignment, surface(s), and offsets that you would like to use to sample the profile(s).

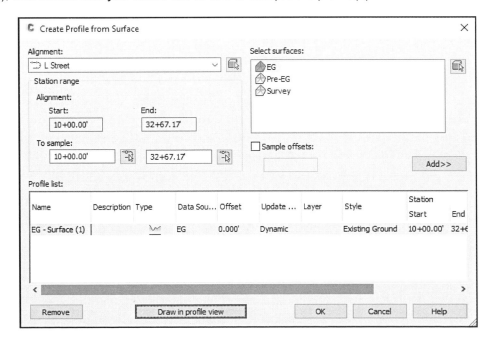

3. Set the **Alignment** to **L Street**.

4. Select the *Surface* **EG**.

5. Click **<<Add>>**.

You can use the *Sample offsets* option to create offset profiles at the offset distance entered in the field below. Multiple offsets can be entered in a comma delimited format. You can also set the layer that the profile will be drawn on, and the style used to display the profile line in, the table at the bottom of the dialog box.

6. Click **<<Draw in profile view>>**.

To display the *Profile* in the drawing you must draw it in a *Profile View*. If you just click <<OK>> the *Profile* will be sampled but not displayed in the drawing.

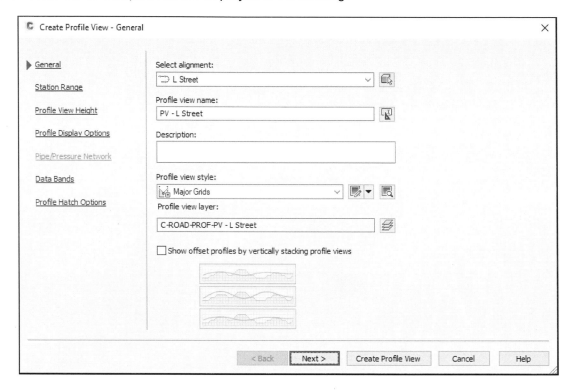

7. Enter a Profile view name of **PV - L Street**.

8. Confirm that the **Profile view style** is set to **Major Grids**.

The *Profile View Style* controls the display of *Profile View* which includes the grid, title, annotation, and vertical exaggeration. You may want to create a *Profile View Style* for each vertical exaggeration that you typically use.

9. Click the **Profile view layer** button to open the *Object Layer* dialog box.

10. Set the **Modifier** to **Suffix**.

11. Enter -* as the **Modifier** *value*.

12. Click **<<OK>> to close the** *Object Layer* dialog box.

You also have an option to *Show offset profiles by vertically stacking profile views*. You will not use this option in this exercise. However, this does automate the process if you need to create offset profile views.

13. Click **<<Next>>** to continue through the wizard.

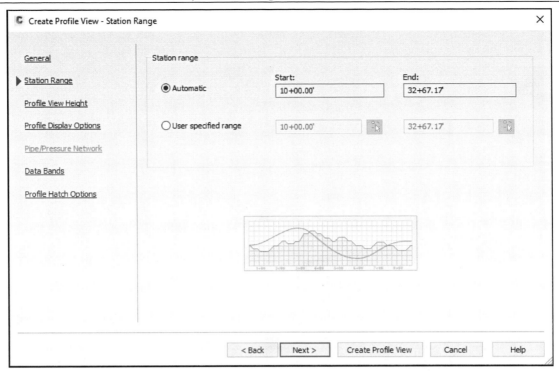

On the *Create Profile View - Station Range* panel of the wizard you can define the length, or station range, of the profile that you wish to display in this *Profile View*. Remember, you have sampled the profile for the entire length of the alignment. This will only determine what is shown in this *Profile View*. You can create multiple *Profile Views* for the same profile showing different, or overlapping, station ranges if you wish.

14. Confirm the **Station range** is set to **Automatic**.

15. Click **<<Next>>** to continue through the wizard.

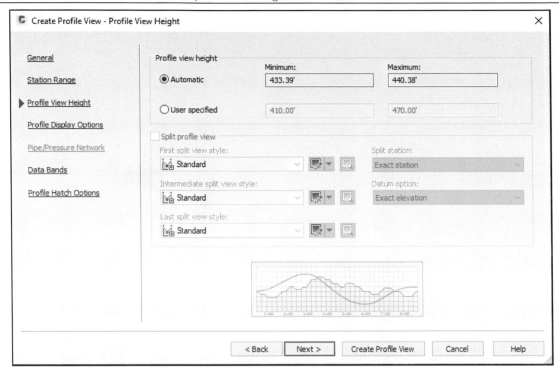

On the *Create Profile View - Profile View Height* panel of the wizard you can define the minimum and maximum elevation of the grid shown for this *Profile View*. You also have the option to split the *Profile View* for profiles that have large changes in elevation. You can even assign different *Profile View Styles* to different sections of a split *Profile View*.

16. Confirm the **Profile view height** is set to **Automatic**.

17. Click **<<Next>>** to continue through the wizard.

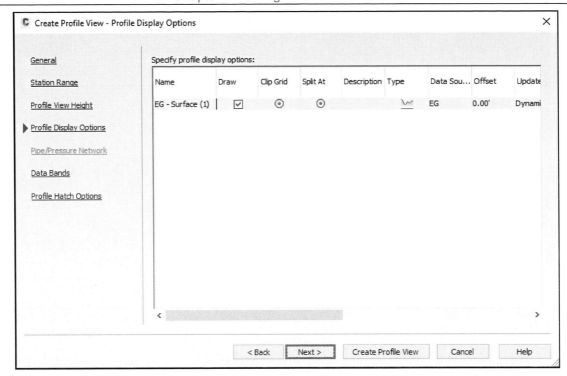

On the *Create Profile View - Profile Display Options* panel of the wizard you can define which profiles are drawn into the *Profile View*, if you have created multiple profiles for this alignment.  For example, you may have sampled left and right offset profiles or you may have already created one or more finished ground profiles.  If you don't want to show all of them in this *Profile View* this is the place to control that.

Since you only have one profile available at this time you will not make any changes.

      18. Click **<<Next>>** to continue through the wizard.

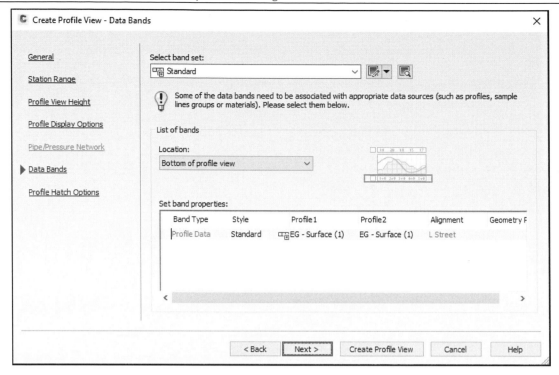

On the *Create Profile View - Data Bands* panel of the wizard you can define the *Band Set* used with this *Profile View*. Band Sets are saved collections of *Profile View Bands*.

*Profile View Bands* are rows of data at the top or bottom of the profile. In *Land Desktop* the standard profile grid was created with bands of labels for stationing and elevations at the bottom of the profile. *Civil 3D* has the ability to create bands labeling station and elevation information as well as other information like the depth of cut or fill at the centerline, geometry information, and superelevation information.

19. Confirm that the **Band set** is set to **Standard**.

20. Click **<<Next>>** to continue through the wizard.

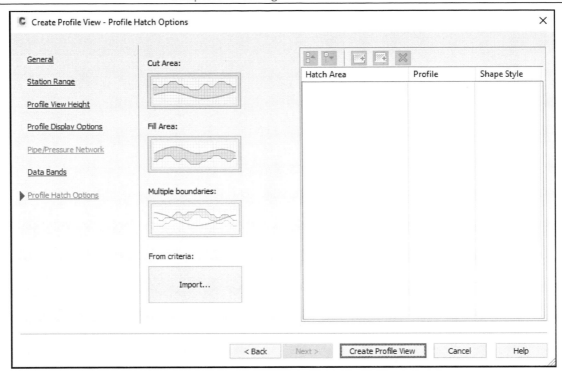

On the *Create Profile View - Profile Hatch Options* panel of the wizard, you can define an optional hatching for the cut area, fill area, or for areas between multiple boundaries. For this exercise, you will not add any hatch areas. However, this is a powerful display option that you can add to the *Profile View* properties at any time if you change your mind.

21. Click **<<Create Profile View>>** to complete the wizard and add the *Profile View* to the drawing.

At the command line prompt *Select the profile view origin*, you can either pick a point on the screen or type in an X,Y coordinate. For this exercise you will type in a coordinate. The *profile view origin* will define the lower left corner of the *Profile View*.

22. At the command line enter **1337900,889300**.

23. **Zoom Extents** to find and review the profile. It should look like the graphic below.

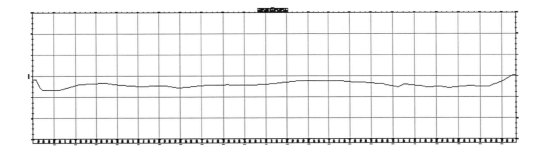

The vertical blue lines display the location of the beginning and end of the horizontal curves. The profile view is a single object and can be moved and erased with *AutoCAD* commands without damaging the profile data. The *Existing Ground Profile* is linked to the alignment. So if you edit the alignment the profile will automatically be updated. This allows you a tremendous amount of flexibility during the design process to make changes and try many alternatives.

### 7.1.2 Changing the Profile View Style

In this exercise, you will change the display of the *Profile View* by selecting a different *Profile View Style*.

1. Pick the **Profile View** in the drawing editor by picking the grid, not the *Profile* line, to display the context sensitive ribbon.

2. Select **Ribbon: Profile View: PV - L Street** ⇒ **Modify View** ⇒ **Profile View Properties**.

You can also access the *Profile View Properties* through the *Prospector*.

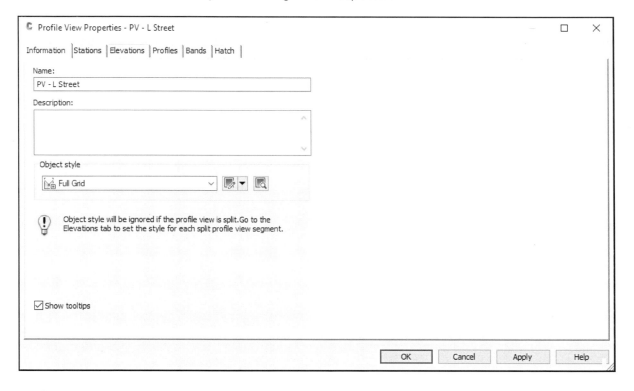

3. On the *Information* tab of the *Profile View Properties* dialog box set the **Object Style** to **Full Grid**.

4. Click **<<OK>>** to apply the new style.

The profile view grid spacing changes and the minor grid lines are added.

5. **[Esc]** to clear the selection and dismiss the context sensitive ribbon.

### 7.1.3 Creating a Profile View Style

In this exercise, you will create a new *Profile View Style* that uses a vertical exaggeration of 5, along with major and minor grid lines at intervals of 50' and 10' horizontally and 10' and 2' vertically.

1. Pick the **Profile View** in the drawing editor to display the context sensitive ribbon.

2. Select **Ribbon: Profile View: PV - L Street** ⇒ **Modify View** ⇒ **Profile View Properties**.

You can also access the *Profile View Properties* through the *Prospector*.

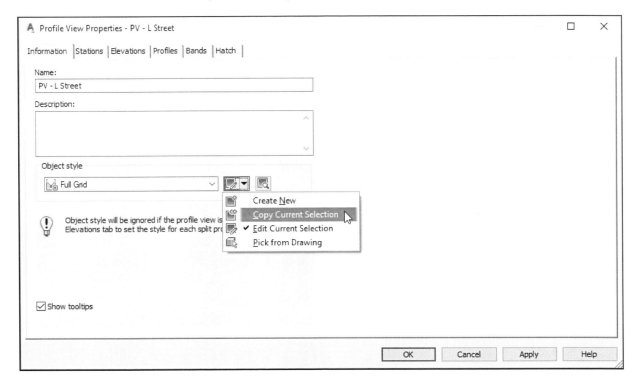

3. Click the **down arrow** button next to the **Object style** on the *Information* tab of the *Profile View Properties* dialog box to display the other creation commands.

4. Select ⇒ **Copy Current Selection**.

This style can also be copied, edited, and created on the *Settings* tab of the *Toolspace* along with all other *Civil 3D Styles*.

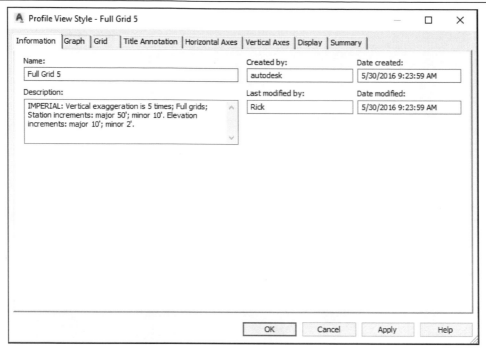

5. On the *Information* tab, name the new style **Full Grid 5**.

6. Enter a description of **IMPERIAL: Vertical exaggeration is 5 times; Full grids; Station increments: major 50'; minor 10'. Elevation increments: major 10'; minor 2'.**

The description is optional so you can be as detailed as you like, or skip it completely.

7. Select the **Graph** tab of the *Profile View Style* dialog box.

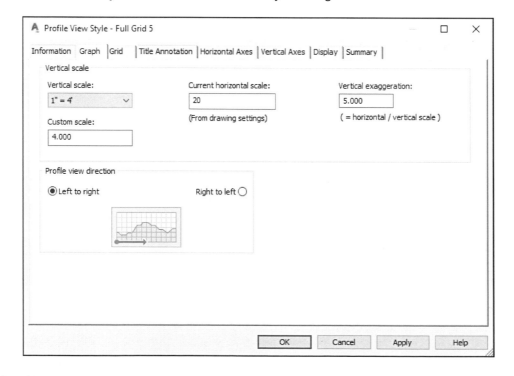

8. Change the **Vertical exaggeration** to **5**.

You can either define the vertical exaggeration by setting the vertical scale as a ratio (such as 1=4') or by entering a vertical exaggeration value.  You also have the option here to change the direction of the *Profile View* if you would prefer for it to be drawn from right to left.

9.  Select the **Grid** tab of the *Profile View Style* dialog box.

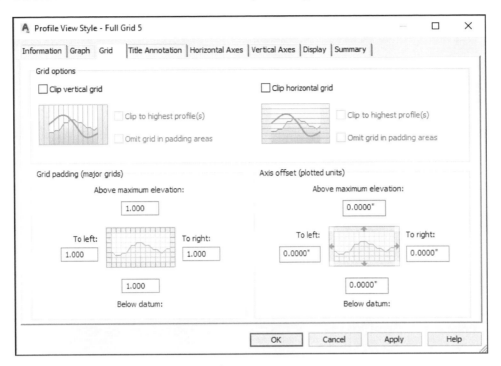

10. Set the *Grid padding* **To left** to **1**.

11. Set the *Grid padding* **To right** to **1**.

This will add spacing for one blank column on the major grid, before and after the profile.  In this example each blank column will be 50 feet.

12. Select the **Title Annotation** tab of the *Profile View Style* dialog box.

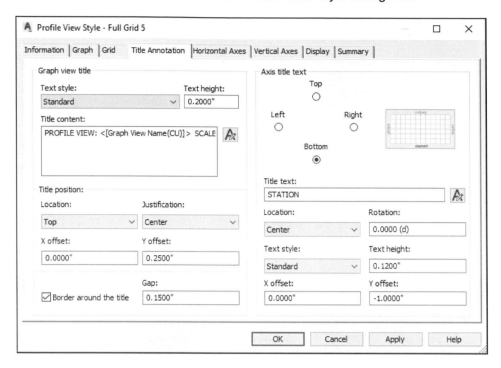

Here you are allowed to define the text contents, location, style, and height for the *Profile View* title as well as the titles of each axis of the *Profile View*. All of these titles are optional and can be turned off on the *Display* tab.

13. For this exercise you will not make any changes to the *Title Annotation* tab.

14. Select the **Horizontal Axes** tab of the *Profile View Style* dialog box.

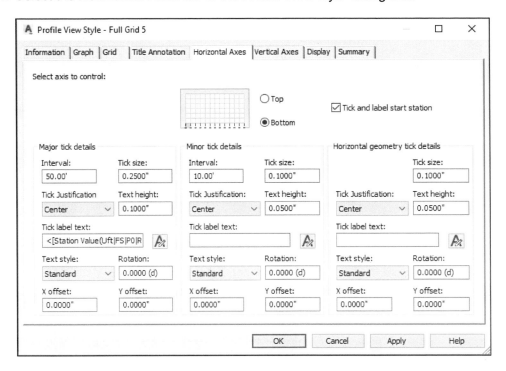

15. Confirm the **Select axis to control** option is set to **Bottom**.

16. Set the **Major tick details Interval** to **50**.

17. Set the **Minor tick details Interval** to **10**.

18. Set the **Select axis to control** option to **Top**.

19. Set the **Major tick details Interval** to **50**.

20. Set the **Minor tick details Interval** to **10**.

The tick interval controls the grid spacing as well as the spacing of the labels.

21. Select the **Vertical Axes** tab of the *Profile View Style* dialog box.

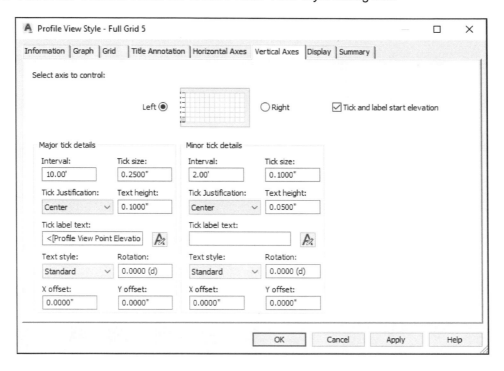

22. Confirm the **Select axis to control** option is set to **Left**.

23. Confirm that the **Major tick details Interval** is set to **10**.

24. Set the **Minor tick details Interval** to **2**.

25. Set the **Select Axis** option to **Right**.

26. Confirm that the **Major tick details Interval** is set to **10**.

27. Set the **Minor tick details Interval** to **2**.

The tick interval controls the grid spacing as well as the spacing of the labels.

28. Select the **Display** tab of the *Profile View Style* dialog box.

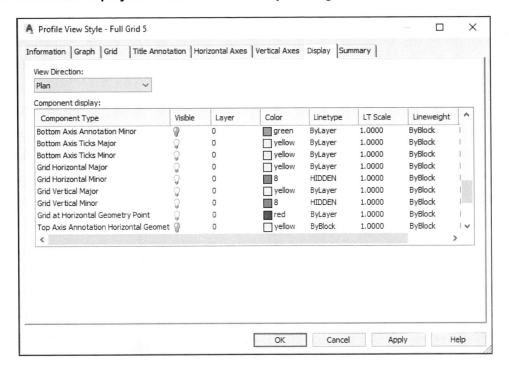

29. Set the color of the **Grid Horizontal Major** component to **Yellow**.

30. Set the color of the **Grid Horizontal Minor** component to **8** and the linetype to **HIDDEN**.

31. Set the color of the **Grid Vertical Major** component to **Yellow**.

32. Set the color of the **Grid Vertical Minor** component to **8** and the linetype to **HIDDEN**.

33. Turn on the **Grid Horizontal Geometry Point** component and set its color to **red**.

34. Click **<<OK>>** to save the new **Profile View Style** and return to the *Profile View Properties* dialog box.

35. Click **<<OK>>** to close the *Profile View Properties* dialog box and apply the new *Profile View Style*.

36. **[Esc]** to clear the selection and dismiss the context sensitive ribbon.

37. Zoom in and examine the changes to the *Profile View* that have been set by the new style.

38. Save the drawing.

### 7.1.4 Creating Additional Profile Views

The main profile setup is now complete. You can copy this *Profile View* to create additional *Profile Views* used for sheets, or any other viewing needs.

1.  Using the *AutoCAD* **copy** command, place a copy of the *Profile View* above the existing *Profile View*.

Be careful to only select the grid and not to select the profile lines, they will automatically appear in the new profile view once it is copied.

2.  Regen if needed to display the profile lines.

Using the AutoCAD Copy command is the most manual way of creating multiple *Profile Views.* It illustrates that *Profile Views* are similar to *Viewports,* in that they are windows used to display profile data the same way *Viewports* are windows that display data from *Model Space* in a *Layout.*

You can also create additional *Profile Views* by selecting *Ribbon: Home* ⇒ *Profile&Section Views* ⇒ *Profile View* ⇒ *Create Multiple Profile Views,* or by using the *Plan Production* tools. Both of these methods are more automated and use a wizard.

Regardless of how you create the *Profile Views,* they are just views, or windows, that display the same *Profile* data. If you edit the *Profile* data in one view it will update in all of the other views as well.

3.  Pick the copy of the **Profile View** in the drawing editor to display the context sensitive ribbon.

4.  Select **Ribbon: Profile View: PV - L Street (1)** ⇒ **Modify View** ⇒ **Profile View Properties**.

5.  In the *Profile View Properties* dialog box, select the **Information** tab.

6.  From the **Object style** list, select **Clipped Grid**.

7.  Select the **Stations** tab.

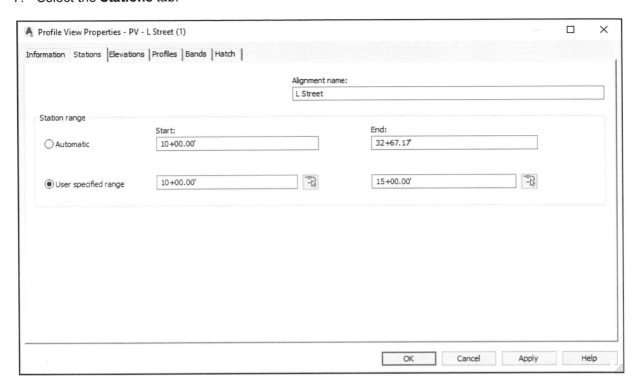

8.  Under **Station range**, select **User specified range**.

9.  Enter **1000** as the starting station.

10. Enter **1500** as the ending station.

11. Click **<<OK>>**.

Notice that the *Profile View* changes to the new style and is only 500' long, according to the station range that you set in the profile view properties.

12. Copy the main *Profile View* three more times, using the following table to modify the appropriate values:

| Style | Start Station | End Station |
|---|---|---|
| Clipped Grid | 15+00 | 20+00 |
| Clipped Grid | 20+00 | 25+00 |
| Clipped Grid | 25+00 | 32+65 |

You may need to reposition the *Profile Views* after modifying their starting and ending stations.

## 7.2    Lesson:  Creating Finished Ground Profiles

### Introduction

Many of the *Profile Layout* and *Editing* commands have a similar look and feel to the *Alignment Layout* and *Editing* tools.  This type of interactive object allows you to approach profile design and modifications differently than you may be used to with other programs like *Land Desktop*.  You may find it faster and more flexible to just sketch in a rough draft of the profile with the profile layout tools, and then refine it either graphically or in a tabular format.  You don't have to lay out the profile perfectly the first time, as this method also allows you to look at many different alternatives quickly and even undo if you want to go back to the previous iteration.  You also do have the option to lay out the profile with precise grades, elevations, and stations.

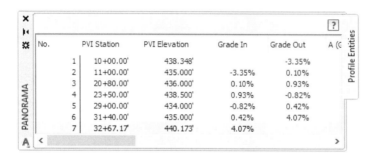

### Key Concepts

Concepts and key terms covered in this lesson are:

- Profile Layout Tools
- Profile Labels
- Profile View Bands

### Objectives

After completing this lesson, you will be able to:

- Layout a finished grade Profile.
- Edit Profile geometry.
- Create and edit Profile Labels.
- Describe the different types of Profile View Bands.

## Layout Profiles

Layout profiles are typically finished ground profiles or design profiles. They are created by drafting the profile into a profile view using the profile layout tools.

## Profile Layout and Editing Tools

The Profile Layout Tools toolbar contains many tools for creating and editing profiles.

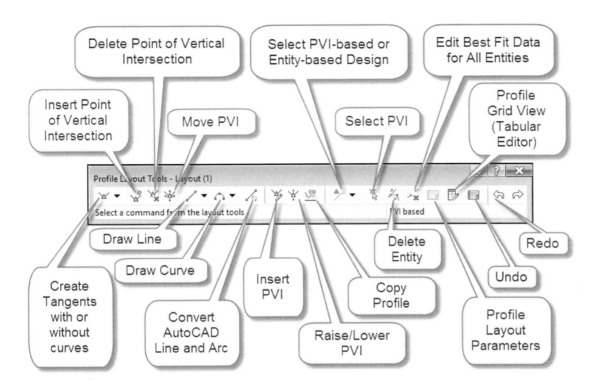

## Editing Profiles

There are two different methods of editing a profile. However, they are not exclusive of one another and can be used together to achieve the most efficient workflow for your project.

- Graphical Editing
- Tabular Editing

## Graphical Editing

- Grip Editing
  - o  Stretch and move PVIs
  - o  Modify curve geometry
  - o  Move tangents
- Commands from the Alignment Layout toolbar
  - o  Insert PVIs
  - o  Delete PVIs
  - o  Delete entities
  - o  Add lines or curves

## Tabular Editing

The profile can be edited in a table by using the Profile Grid View.

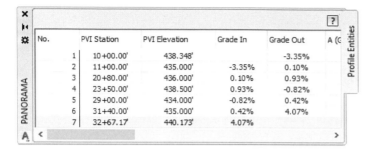

| No. | PVI Station | PVI Elevation | Grade In | Grade Out | A (G |
|-----|-------------|---------------|----------|-----------|------|
| 1 | 10+00.00' | 438.348' | | -3.35% | |
| 2 | 11+00.00' | 435.000' | -3.35% | 0.10% | |
| 3 | 20+80.00' | 436.000' | 0.10% | 0.93% | |
| 4 | 23+50.00' | 438.500' | 0.93% | -0.82% | |
| 5 | 29+00.00' | 434.000' | -0.82% | 0.42% | |
| 6 | 31+40.00' | 435.000' | 0.42% | 4.07% | |
| 7 | 32+67.17' | 440.173' | 4.07% | | |

Try editing the profile graphically first, then once the geometry is close to your desired design use the tabular method to clean up and refine the final geometry.

## Profile Label Sets

Profile labels are controlled by the profile label styles. These styles are originally selected when you select the profile label set in the *Profiles - Create Profile by Layout* command. A profile label set is collection of label styles that can be selected and applied as a group to a profile. For example, a label set may include individual label styles for crest curves, sag curves, and grades. Profile labels can also be edited individually, without using a label set.

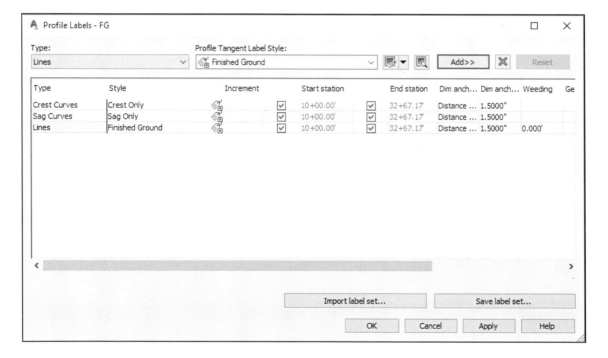

## Profile View Bands

Profile View Bands can be added to display rows of data at the bottom or top of the profile view. Items that can be displayed in profile view bands include:

- Stations
- Elevations
- Cut and Fill
- Depths
- Vertical Geometry
- Horizontal Geometry
- Superelevation
- Section data
- Pipe data

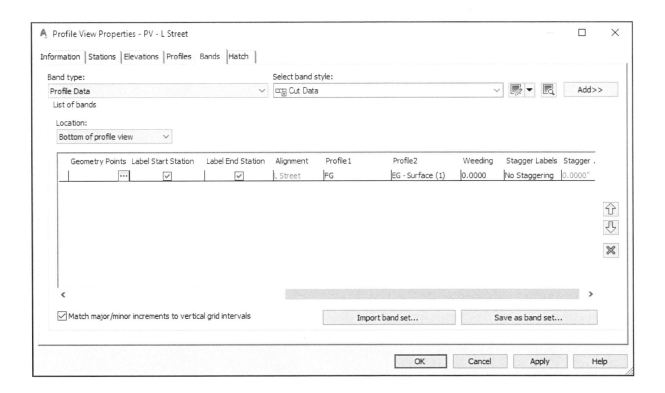

## Exercises: Create a Finished Ground Profile

In these exercises, you lay out a finished grade profile. Then you edit the profile using both graphical (grip editing), and tabular (profile grid view) methods. Next you edit the profile labels. Finally, you create and edit several profile view bands to display station and elevation data as well as horizontal and vertical geometry information.

You do the following:

- Create a Finished Ground Profile.
- Edit a Profile.
- Label a Profile.
- Display Profile Bands.

### 7.2.1 Constructing the Finished Ground Centerline

In this exercise, you will lay out the *Finished Grade Profile* using the transparent commands to enter information by *Grade and Stations* as well as by *Station and Elevation*. If you have difficulty with the transparent commands or if you would rather just sketch in the profile, you can do that as well and then use the *Profile Editing* commands to match the geometry of the exercise. *Civil 3D* is very flexible this way and you should take advantage of that to work the way that you are most comfortable.

1. Continue working in the drawing **Design.dwg**.

2. Select **Ribbon: Home ⇒ Create Design ⇒ Profile ⇒ Profile Creation Tools**.

3. Pick the main **L Street Profile View**.

4. Name the Profile **FG**.

5. Click the **Profile layer** button to open the *Object Layer* dialog box.

6. Set the **Modifier** to **Suffix**.

7. Enter -* as the **Modifier** *value.*

8. Click **<<OK>>** to close the *Object Layer* dialog box.

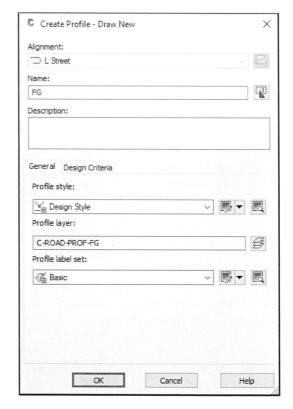

The *Design Criteria Tab* allows you to select design criteria based on minimum design standards. AASHTO standards in both imperial and metric units are included with *Civil 3D*. You also have the option to modify and create your own design standards. Using design criteria is optional and you will not be using it in this exercise.

9. Click **<<OK>>** to save the Profile and open the *Profile Layout Tools* toolbar.

10. Click the **down arrow** next to the *Draw Tangents button* on the *Profile Layout* toolbar to display the other creation commands.

11. Select ⇒ **Curve Settings**.

12. Confirm the **Curve Type** is set to
    **Parabolic**.

13. Set the **K value** to **35** for both the *Crest*
    and *Sag* curves.

14. Click **<<OK>>**.

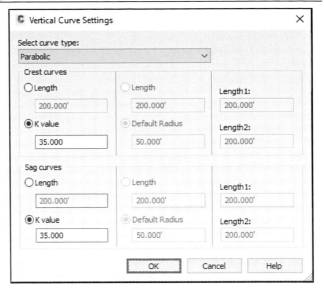

15. Click the **down arrow** next to the *Curve Settings button* on the *Profile Layout* toolbar to display
    the other creation commands.

16. Select ⇒ **Draw Tangents With Curves**.

17. Use an **Endpoint OSNAP** to snap to the beginning of the existing ground profile.

If you close the toolbar without creating the first segment of the profile you will need to delete
the *FG* profile from the *Prospector* and start the exercise again.

18. At the command line enter **'PGS** to change the prompt to specify a Grade and Station on the
    Profile.

Alternatively, you can also select the *Profile Grade Station* button ⌐▟⌐ from the *Transparent*
*Commands* toolbar.

19. Select the *Profile View* when prompted.

20. Enter a **Grade** of **-3**.

21. Enter a **Station** of **1090**.

22. **[Esc]** to end the *Grade and Station* prompt.

23. Enter **'PSE** to change the prompt to specify a Station and Elevation on the Profile.

Alternatively, you can also select the *Profile Station Elevation* button ⌐▟⌐ from the
*Transparent Commands* toolbar.

24. Enter a **Station** of **2040**.

25. Enter an **Elevation** of **436**.

26. Enter a **Station** of **2300**.

27. Enter an **Elevation** of **438**.

28. Enter a **Station** of **2900**.

29. Enter an **Elevation** of **434**.

30. Enter a **Station** of **3140**.

31. Enter an **Elevation** of **435**.

32. **[Esc]** to end the Station and Elevation prompt.

33. Use an **Endpoint** Osnap and snap to the end of the existing ground centerline.

34. **[Enter]** to end the command.

If you did not have exact station and elevation information like we did in this exercise you could simply sketch in the profile using the same command.

Notice the new profile is labeled according to the label set that was assigned to it.

35. Close the **Profile Layout toolbar**.

36. Save the drawing.


**7.2.2    Editing the Profile Graphically**

*Civil 3D Profiles* can be grip edited just like basic *AutoCAD* objects.

1.   Select the **Finished Ground** profile to display the grips.

2.   Zoom in to **PVI number two** at the location of the first vertical curve.

You will see several different types of grips.  The circular grip allows you to drag the curve changing its length and K value.  The triangular grip pointing up allows you to drag the *PVI* to a new location while maintaining the curve properties.  The triangular grips extending from the incoming and outgoing tangents allow you to slide the PVI along the existing grade.  This is a very powerful and useful option.  All of the graphical edits will prevent you from editing the profile in a way that would create overlapping vertical curves.

3.   Select the **triangular grip** extending from the first tangent in the profile.

4.   Drag it along the grade to a new location of your choice.

5.   When you are finished grip editing the profile, press **[Esc]** to clear the grips.

### 7.2.3 Editing the Profile in Grid View

In this exercise, you will edit the profile using a tabular editor.

1. Pick the **Finished Ground Profile** in the drawing editor to display the context sensitive ribbon.

2. Select **Ribbon: Profile: FG** ⇒ **Modify Profile** ⇒ **Geometry Editor**.

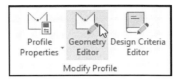

This opens the *Profile Layout Tools* toolbar.

3. Click the **Profile Grid View** button.

4. Change the **Station PVI #2** to **1100**.

The profile will update graphically after each change. Also, you are not allowed to make a change that does not fit the geometry of the profile. So you cannot create overlapping curves.

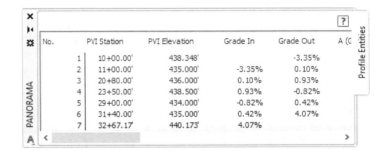

| No. | PVI Station | PVI Elevation | Grade In | Grade Out | A (C |
|-----|-------------|---------------|----------|-----------|------|
| 1 | 10+00.00' | 438.348' | | -3.35% | |
| 2 | 11+00.00' | 435.000' | -3.35% | 0.10% | |
| 3 | 20+80.00' | 436.000' | 0.10% | 0.93% | |
| 4 | 23+50.00' | 438.500' | 0.93% | -0.82% | |
| 5 | 29+00.00' | 434.000' | -0.82% | 0.42% | |
| 6 | 31+40.00' | 435.000' | 0.42% | 4.07% | |
| 7 | 32+67.17' | 440.173' | 4.07% | | |

5. Change the **Elevation PVI #2** to **435**.

6. Change the **Station PVI #3** to **2080**.

7. Change the **Station PVI #4** to **2350**.

8. Change **the Elevation PVI #4** to **438.50**.

9. Confirm the remaining PVI Stations and Elevations match the table above.

You can also modify the curve length, K value, and other properties as needed in this *Profile Grid View*.

10. Close the **Grid View**.

11. Close the **Profile Layout** toolbar.

12. Save the drawing.

### 7.2.4 Working with Profile Labels

Profile labels are controlled by the profile label styles. These styles were originally selected when you selected the profile label set in the *Create Profile* command. In this exercise, you will edit the Profile Curve Label style to add a background mask.

1. Pick the **Finished Ground Profile** in the drawing editor to display the context sensitive ribbon.

2. Select **Ribbon: Profile: FG ⇒ Labels ⇒ Edit Profile Labels**

This opens the Profile Labels dialog box where you can add and modify labels for vertical curves, grades, grade breaks, and other profile geometry.

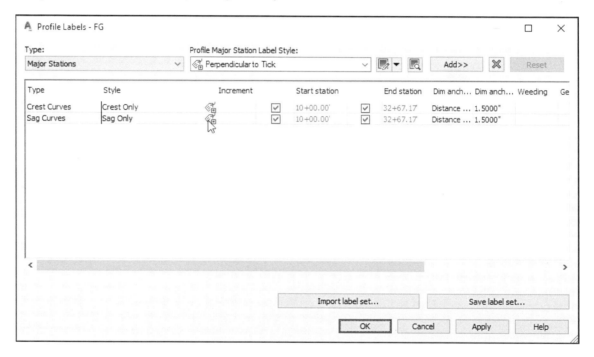

3. Click the symbol in the **Style** field for the **Sag Curves** to display the *Pick Label Style* dialog box.

4. Click the **down arrow**  button next to the **label style.**

5. Select ⇒ **Edit Current Selection**.

6.  Select the **Layout** tab of the *Label Style Composer.*

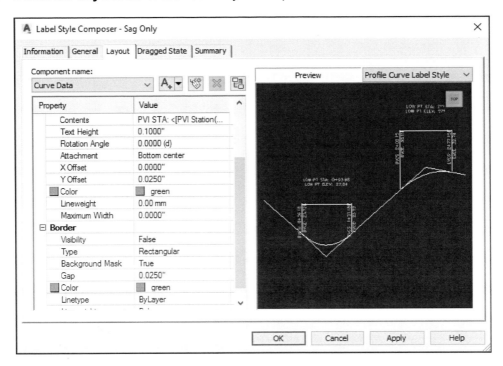

7.  Confirm that the **Component name** is set to **Curve Data.**

8.  Under *Border* set the **Background Mask** to **True.**

9.  Set the **Component name** to **Sag Data.**

10. Set the **Background Mask** to **True.**

11. Click **<<OK>>** to save the changes to the label style.

12. Click **<<OK>>** to return to the *Profile Labels* dialog box.

13. Repeat the process to edit the *Crest Only* label style and enable the **Background Mask** for the **Curve Data** and **Crest Data** components.

14. Click **<<OK>>** to apply the new labels and close the *Profile Labels* dialog box.

15. **[Esc]** to clear the selection and dismiss the context sensitive ribbon.

The profile curve labels will now display with a background mask, making them easier to read.  Regen if the background mask does not display correctly.

### 7.2.5  Adding Profile Labels

Profile labels are controlled by the profile label styles.  These styles were originally selected when you selected the profile label set, in the *Profiles - Create Profile by Layout* command. The profile label set that you used in the previous exercises, when you created the profile, did not include a label style for the line segments. In this exercise you will add a *Profile Line Label* style that labels the grades of the line segments.

    1.   Pick the **Finished Ground Profile** in the drawing editor to display the context sensitive ribbon.

    2.   Select **Ribbon: Profile: FG ⇒ Labels ⇒ Edit Profile Labels**

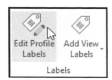

This opens the Profile Labels dialog box where you can add and modify labels for vertical curves, grades, grade breaks, and other profile geometry.

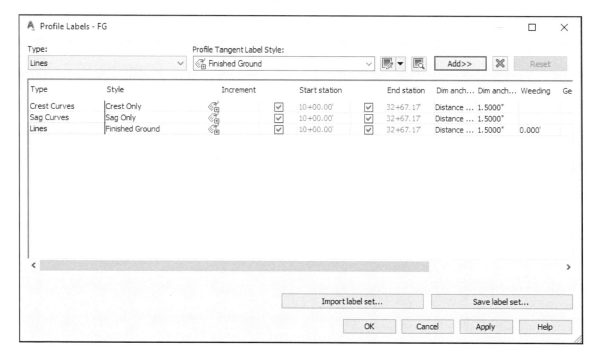

    3.   Set the label **Type** to **Lines**.

    4.   Confirm the **Profile Tangent Label Style** is set to **Finished Ground**.

    5.   Click the **<<Add>>** button.

    6.   Click **<<OK>>** to add the new labels to the profile.

    7.   **[Esc]** to clear the selection and dismiss the context sensitive ribbon.

    8.   Zoom in and examine the new grade labels.  You will find them at the mid points of the profile lines.

### 7.2.6  Working with Profile View Bands

1. Zoom in to the bottom of the profile and examine the band displaying the two elevation values.

These are for the EG and FG profiles. However, currently they are both displaying the same numbers.

2. Pick the **Profile View** in the drawing editor by picking the grid not the *Profile* line to display the context sensitive ribbon.

3. Select **Ribbon: Profile View: PV - L Street** ⇒ **Modify View** ⇒ **Profile View Properties**.

You can also access the *Profile View Properties* through the *Prospector*.

4. Select the **Bands** tab of the *Profile View Properties* dialog box.

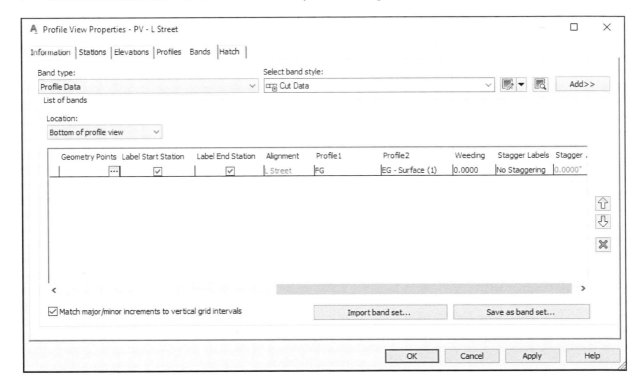

5. Notice there is a band for *Profile Data* already applied to the bottom of the profile view and it is using the style *Standard*.

6. Scroll to the right to find the **Label Start Station** setting for the default band.

7. Enable the **Label Start Station option**.

8. Enable the **Label End Station option**.

9. Set **Profile1** to **FG**.

This band displays the elevations of the EG and FG profiles. By default both profile settings for the band are set to EG. If you do not change this setting the band will display the elevations from the EG profile in both labels.

10. Click **<<OK>>** to update the band.

11. **[Esc]** to clear the selection and dismiss the context sensitive ribbon.

12. Zoom in to the bottom of the profile and examine the band to see the changes.

### 7.2.7 Adding Profile View Bands

*Profile View Bands* can also display other information like the depth of cut or fill at the centerline, geometry information, and superelevation information.

1. Pick the **Profile View** in the drawing editor by picking the grid not the *Profile* line to display the context sensitive ribbon.

2. Select **Ribbon: Profile View: PV-L Street ⇒ Modify View ⇒ Profile View Properties**.

3. Select the **Bands** tab of the *Profile View Properties* dialog box.

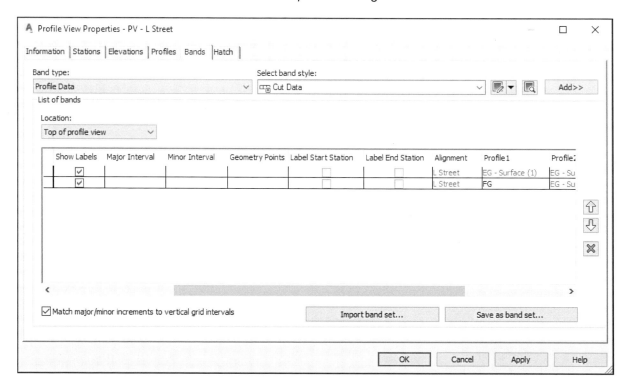

4. Set the **Location** to **Top of profile view**.

5. Set the **Band type** to **Horizontal Geometry**.

6. Set the **Select band style** setting to **Geometry**.

7. Click **<<Add>>**.

8. Set the **Band type** to **Vertical Geometry**.

9. Set the **Select band style** setting to **Geometry**.

10. Click **<<Add>>**.

11. Enable the **Show Labels** option for both new bands.

12. Scroll to the right to find the **Profile1** setting for the *Vertical Geometry* band.

13. Set **Profile1** to **FG**.

14. Click **<<OK>>**.

15. **[Esc]** to clear the selection and dismiss the context sensitive ribbon.

The profile view is now displayed with the original band now showing the elevations of the existing and finished ground profiles. There are also two new bands at the top of the profile view showing the horizontal geometry and vertical geometry information.

The Bands are also controlled by styles that determine the information that is displayed as well as the colors and linetypes.

# Chapter 8

# 8 - Corridor Modeling

In this chapter, you will create an assembly to define the components and geometry of a road. Then you will combine the assembly with, an alignment, profile, and surface that you created in previous chapters to create a corridor model. The corridor model is used to create surfaces and sections that you will plot as well as use for quantity takeoffs. You will conclude the chapter by exporting a corridor surface and merging it with a copy of the existing ground surface to create a surface that represents the final site conditions after the road is built.

### Lesson: Working with Assemblies
In this lesson, you will learn the concepts and process of creating and editing assemblies that will be used in a corridor model.

### Lesson: Working with Corridors
In this lesson, you will learn to create and edit a corridor. You will also learn to create surfaces that are linked to the corridor and extract points from the corridor for staking.

### Lesson: Working with Sections
In this lesson, you will learn to create sample lines and sections. Then you will learn to create sheets of sections with the plan production tools. Finally you will learn to preform volume calculations and create a surface representing the final site conditions.

### Lesson: Plan Production
In this lesson, you will learn to use the Plan Production tools to automate the creation of Plan and Profile sheets.

## 8.1    Lesson: Working with Assemblies

### Introduction

An *Assembly* is a collection of *Subassemblies* that make up the components of a road or any other design based on an *Alignment*. *Assemblies* are combined with *Alignments* and *Profiles* to create a *Corridor* model of your design.

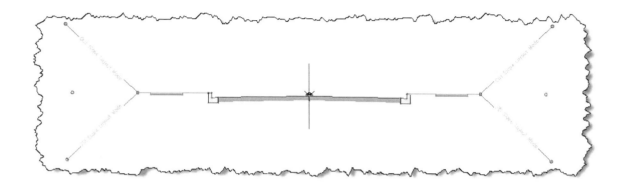

### Key Concepts

Concepts and key terms covered in this lesson are:

- Assemblies
- Subassemblies

### Objectives

After completing this lesson, you will be able to:

- Describe the relationship between Assemblies and Subassemblies.
- Create an Assembly.

## Subassemblies

The Civil 3D tool palette and catalogs include a large selection of predefined subassemblies, such as lanes, curbs, shoulders, and ditches.

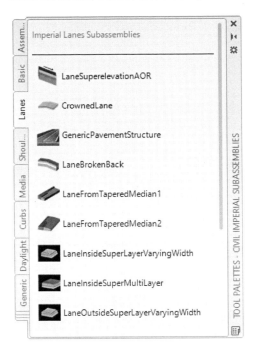

## Assemblies

An Assembly is a collection of subassemblies, such as lanes, curbs, shoulders, and ditches, which form the typical sections of a corridor.

Assemblies can be copied within a drawing, between drawings, or to tool palettes for later use; or the copies can be modified to easily create similar assemblies without starting from scratch.

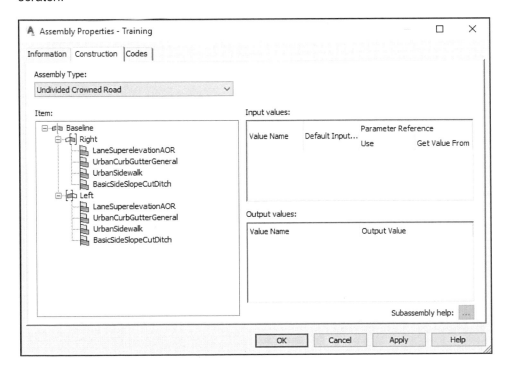

## Exercise: Create an Assembly

In this exercise, you use the subassemblies that come with Civil 3D to create an assembly that will be used later when creating the corridor.

You do the following:

- Create an Assembly.

### 8.1.1 Creating an Assembly

In this exercise, you will create a basic *Assembly* using the *Subassemblies* from the *Tool Palette*. The *Assembly* you create in this exercise is symmetrical. So you will only create the right side of the *Assembly*, and then use the *Mirror Subassembly* command to create the left side.

1. Continue working in the drawing **Design.dwg**.

*Reminder:* You can also open the drawing with this exercise number in the *Chapter Drawings* folder of the dataset if you prefer a fresh start at this point.

2. Select **Ribbon: Home ⇒ Create Design ⇒ Assembly ⇒ Create Assembly**.

This opens the *Create Assembly* dialog box where you can name the new assembly and select the styles and layers it will use.

3. Name the *Assembly* **Training**.

4. Set the **Assembly Type** to **Undivided Crowned Road**.

5. Click **<<OK>>** to create the *Assembly* using the default styles and layer.

6. Select a location for the assembly in a blank area of the drawing.

Civil 3D will automatically zoom in to the *Assembly* displayed as a red vertical line with a white point representing the connection to the baseline.

If you have trouble finding the *Assembly,* you can select it in the *Prospector* and use the **Zoom to** command.

> 7. Select **Ribbon: Home ⇒ Palettes ⇒ Tool Palettes**.

This opens the *Tool Palettes* window, where you will find many of the Civil 3D subassemblies preloaded from the content browser.

> 8. Select the **Lanes** tab.
>
> 9. Click the **LaneSuperelevationAOR** tool to open the *Properties* window displaying the *Parameters* that you can configure for this subassembly.

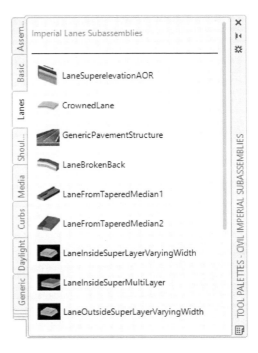

10. Confirm the **Side** is set to **Right**.

11. Set the **Width** to **14**.

12. Pick the **vertical line** on the *Assembly* to add the *Subassembly* to the *Assembly*.

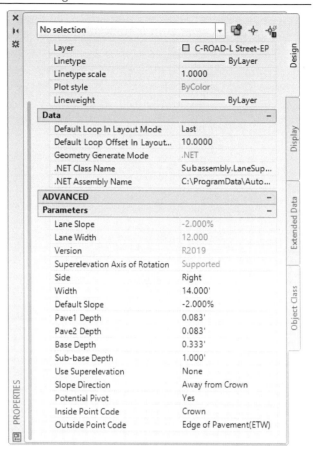

| | |
|---|---|
| Layer | ☐ C-ROAD-L Street-EP |
| Linetype | ByLayer |
| Linetype scale | 1.0000 |
| Plot style | ByColor |
| Lineweight | ByLayer |
| **Data** | **−** |
| Default Loop In Layout Mode | Last |
| Default Loop Offset In Layout... | 10.0000 |
| Geometry Generate Mode | .NET |
| .NET Class Name | Subassembly.LaneSup... |
| .NET Assembly Name | C:\ProgramData\Auto... |
| **ADVANCED** | **−** |
| **Parameters** | **−** |
| Lane Slope | -2.000% |
| Lane Width | 12.000 |
| Version | R2019 |
| Superelevation Axis of Rotation | Supported |
| Side | Right |
| Width | 14.000' |
| Default Slope | -2.000% |
| Pave1 Depth | 0.083' |
| Pave2 Depth | 0.083' |
| Base Depth | 0.333' |
| Sub-base Depth | 1.000' |
| Use Superelevation | None |
| Slope Direction | Away from Crown |
| Potential Pivot | Yes |
| Inside Point Code | Crown |
| Outside Point Code | Edge of Pavement(ETW) |

Notice the *LaneSuperelevationAOR* subassembly added to the right side of the *Assembly*. This *Subassembly* uses four polygons to represent the road material. The depth of each road layer can be configured in the properties palette.

13. Select the **Curbs** tab.

14. Click the **UrbanCurbGutterGeneral** tool to open the *Properties* window displaying the *Parameters* that you can configure for this subassembly.

Imperial Curbs Subassemblies

- UrbanCurbGutterGeneral
- UrbanCurbGutterValley1
- UrbanCurbGutterValley2
- UrbanCurbGutterValley3
- UrbanReplaceCurbGutter1
- UrbanReplaceCurbGutter2
- UrbanReplaceSidewalk
- UrbanSidewalk

The parameters of the *UrbanCurbGutterGeneral* subassembly are displayed in the Properties window.

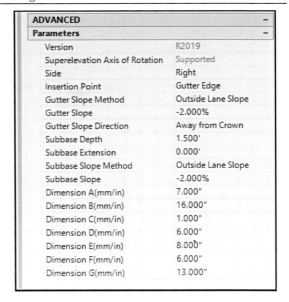

15. Change the **Subbase Extension** to **0**.

16. Pick the connection point on the Right edge of pavement. You don't need to use object snaps, just pick the circle.

17. Click the **UrbanSidewalk** tool from the tool palette.

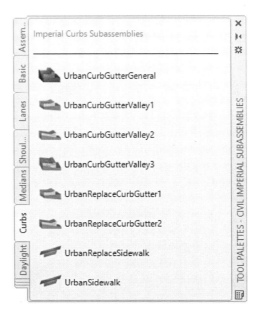

18. Set the **Inside Boulevard Width** to **4**.

19. Confirm the **Sidewalk Width** to **5.**

20. Set the **Outside Boulevard Width** to **2**.

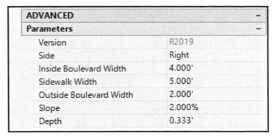

21. Pick the connection point on the Right back of curb.

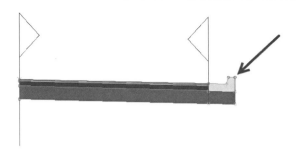

22. Select the **Basic** tab of the tool palette.

23. Click the **BasicSideSlopeCutDitch** tool.

BasicSideSlopeCutDitch

24. Set the slopes to **3:1** by entering **3** in the four appropriate fields, as shown.

| ADVANCED | − |
|---|---|
| **Parameters** | − |
| Version | R2019 |
| Side | Right |
| Daylight Link | Include Daylight link |
| Cut Slope | 3.000:1 |
| Fill Slope | 3.000:1 |
| Foreslope Slope | 3.000:1 |
| Foreslope Width | 4.000' |
| Bottom Width | 2.000' |
| Backslope Slope | 3.000:1 |
| Backslope Width | 4.000' |
| Rounding Option | None |
| Rounding By | Length |
| Rounding Parameter | 1.500' |
| Rounding Tessellation | 6 |
| Place Lined Material | None |
| Slope Limit 1 | 1.000:1 |
| Material 1 Thickness | 1.000' |
| Material 1 Name | Rip Rap |
| Slope Limit 2 | 2.000:1 |
| Material 2 Thickness | 0.500' |
| Material 2 Name | Rip Rap |
| Slope Limit 3 | 4.000:1 |
| Material 3 Thickness | 0.333' |
| Material 3 Name | Seeded Grass |

25. Pick the connection point on the Right back of sidewalk.

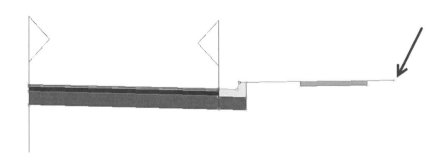

26. **[Enter]** to end the command.

The *Assembly* should now look like the one below.

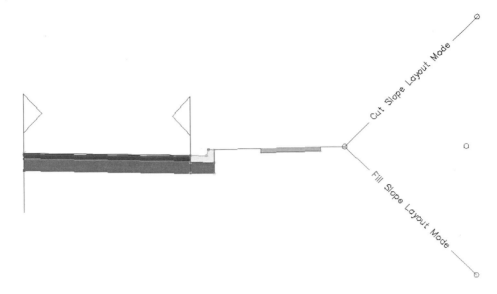

27. Close the Tool Palette.

Next you will use the *Mirror Subassembly* command to create the left side of the *Assembly*.

28. Select the **Assembly** by picking the red vertical line in the drawing editor to display the context sensitive ribbon.

29. Select **Ribbon: Assembly: Training ⇒ Modify Subassembly ⇒ Mirror.**

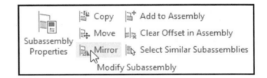

30. At the command prompt you are asked to **Select Subassembly.** Select all four Subassemblies with a crossing window. Then **[Enter].**

31. At the command prompt you are asked to **Select marker point within assembly for the mirrored subassemblies**. Pick the red vertical line.

The *Subassemblies* are now mirrored to create the left side of the *Assembly* as shown below.

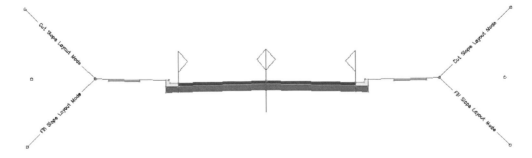

The *Subassemblies* have been added to your *Assembly* and configured according to the parameters you entered in the *Properties* dialog box. You can modify any of those parameters by right-clicking on the *Assembly* in the *Prospector* and selecting ⇒ *Properties*.

Be sure not to erase the Assembly or you will lose it. You may want to freeze the layer so that it is not accidentally selected and deleted.

## 8.2    Lesson: Working with Corridors

### Introduction

The *Corridor* dynamically links the *Alignment*, *Profile*, *Surface*, and *Assembly* together to model your design.

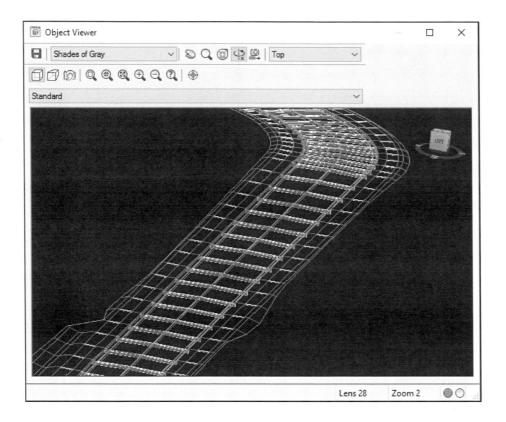

### Key Concepts

Concepts and key terms covered in this lesson are:

- Corridors
- Corridor Surfaces
- Targets
- Frequency
- Regions
- Baselines

### Objectives

After completing this lesson, you will be able to:

- Describe the components needed to create a Corridor.
- Create a Corridor.
- Edit a Corridor.
- Create Surfaces that are linked to a Corridor.
- Export Corridor Points for staking.

## Corridor Models

A corridor is a cross section based model that dynamically link alignments, profiles, assemblies, surfaces, other targets. Key components of a corridor that you should become familiar with are:

- Baselines
- Regions
- Targets
- Frequency

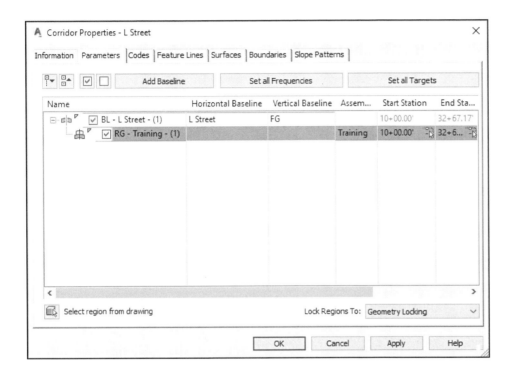

## Baselines

Each corridor will contain at least one baseline. The baseline is the alignment that includes a profile and is attached to the assembly. This is typically the centerline of the road, but it does not have to be. Baselines can also represent curb returns in an intersection, or other features.

## Regions

Each baseline will contain at least one region. A region is a station range along a baseline that is assigned a specific assembly, targets and frequency. Adding multiple regions to a baseline allows you to select a different assembly, targets and frequency for a specific part of the corridor.

## Targets

Targets are objects that can be attached to different locations on subassemblies. When you create an assembly you should take note of the target points on the subassemblies that you use. Different targets can be assigned to different regions within the same corridor.

Targets allow you to stretch assemblies to add features like widening and turning lanes without then need for additional assemblies with different geometry.

---

## Frequency

The frequency setting controls the distance between sections that are created within the corridor. You can assign different frequencies to tangents, curves, spirals and profile curves. You can also create additional sections automatically at horizontal and vertical geometry points and target geometry points. Sections can also be added manually at any important location.

With all the components of the road design dynamically linked together in the Corridor object, you have the flexibility to experiment with many design alternatives, review the way that they impact the model, and even undo the changes to try something else.

## Corridor Surfaces

Surfaces can be created and linked to the *Corridor* model. These surfaces display along with your other surfaces in the *Prospector*. Since they are linked to the *Corridor* model they, are automatically updated and rebuilt any time that the *Corridor* is rebuilt.

If you grip edit the alignment or the profile, the corridor will show as out of date in the *Prospector*. If you set the corridor option to *Rebuild Automatic*, the corridor will automatically be rebuilt after each edit. This is a nice feature, but may be inconvenient because you will have to wait for the corridor to rebuild and redisplay after each edit. If this option is disabled, you can make several changes and rebuild when you are ready to review them.

## Exercises: Create a Corridor

In these exercises, you create and edit a corridor. Next you create surfaces that are dynamically linked to the corridor. Then, you view the corridor cross sections. Finally, you export points based on the corridor geometry for staking.

You do the following:

- Create a Corridor.
- Edit a Corridor.
- Create Corridor Surfaces.
- View Corridor Sections.
- Export Corridor Points.

### 8.2.1 Creating a Corridor

1. Continue working in the drawing **Design.dwg**.

*Reminder:* You can also open the drawing with this exercise number in the *Chapter Drawings* folder of the dataset if you prefer a fresh start at this point.

2. Select **Ribbon: Home ⇒ Create Design ⇒ Corridor ⇒ Corridor**.

3. Name the corridor **L Street**.

4. Click the **Corridor layer** 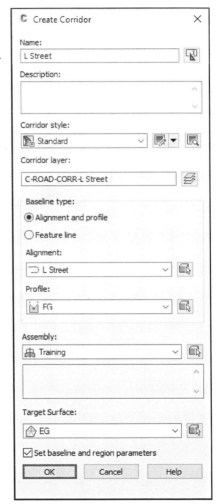 button to open the *Object Layer* dialog box.

5. Set the **Modifier** to **Suffix**.

6. Enter -* as the **Modifier** *value.*

7. Click **<<OK>> to close the** *Object Layer* dialog box.

8. Confirm the **Alignment** is set to **L Street.**

You can also use a *Feature line* here as the baseline for the corridor.

9. Set the **Profile** to **FG**.

10. Set the **Assembly** to **Training**.

11. Set the **Target Surface** to **EG**.

12. Confirm the **Set baseline and region parameters** option is enabled.

13. Click **<<OK>>**.

The *Baseline and Region Parameters* dialog box opens. Here you can add baselines and regions and also set the frequency and targets for each region.

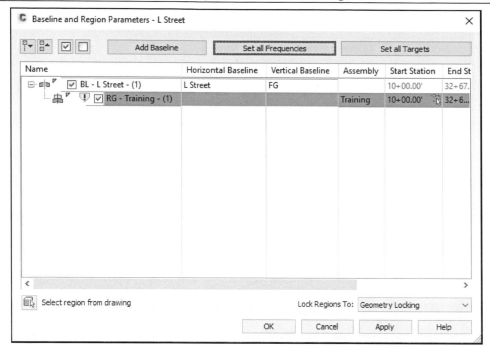

The *Corridor* model is based on *Sections* that it samples and updates as you make changes to the design. You can control the frequency of these *Sections* when you create the *Corridor*.

14. Click **<<Set all Frequencies>>**.

15. Confirm that the frequency **Along tangents** is set to **25**.

16. Set the frequency **Along curves** to **At an increment**.

17. Set the **Curve increment** to **10**.

There are not any spirals in your alignment, so this setting does not matter for this exercise. However, you can control the frequency that the spirals are modeled in the corridor, if needed. You can also specify additional stations by picking the blue plus sign button.

18. Set the frequency **Along vertical curves** to **10**.

19. Click **<<OK>>** to return to the *Baseline and Region Parameters* dialog box.

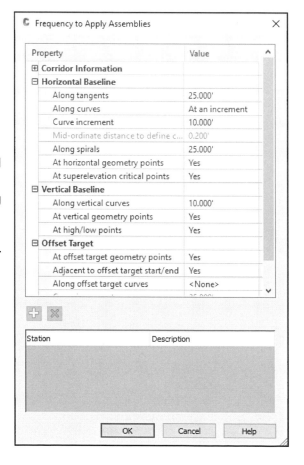

20. Click **<<Set all Targets>>**.

The *Target Mapping* dialog box is where you attach subassemblies to surfaces, alignments, and profiles. If a subassembly was designed to attach to one of these objects, it will display in the *Target* list.

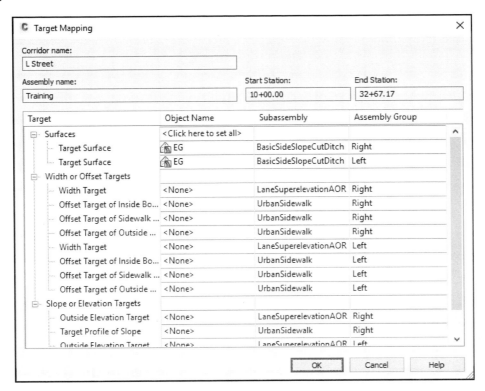

The surface *EG* has been assigned as a target for the *Basic Side Slope Cut Ditch* subassembly previously in the *Create Corridor* dialog box. If you wanted to assign *Width or Offset Targets* to transition the assembly horizontally, or if you wanted to add *Slope or Elevation Targets* to transition the assembly vertically, you could assign them here. For this exercise you will not assign any additional targets.

21. Click **<<OK>>** to return to the *Baseline and Region Parameters* dialog box.

22. Click **<<OK>>** to create the corridor.

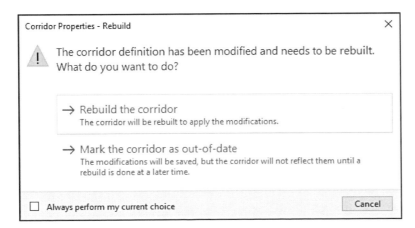

23. Click **Rebuild the corridor** to finish creating the corridor.

24. Zoom to the alignment **L Street** and you will see the corridor has been created along it.

Once the corridor is built, it will look like the graphic below.

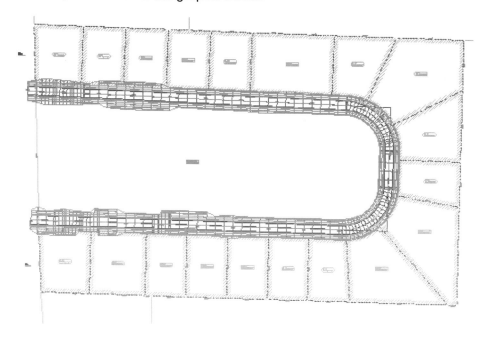

25. Save the drawing.

## 8.2.2   Editing a Corridor

In this exercise, you will make a change to the profile, rebuild the corridor and review the changes, then undo back to the original state.

1. Select **Ribbon: View** ⇒ **Model Viewports** ⇒ **Viewport Configuration** ⇒ **Two: Horizontal**.

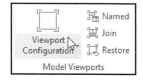

Two viewports are now created in model space, each showing the entire model.

2. Zoom in the top viewport to the profile.

3. Zoom in the bottom viewport to the alignment and corridor.

4. Select **Ribbon: Analyze** ⇒ **Inquiry** ⇒ **Station Tracker** ⇒ **All Viewports**.

5. Move your cursor along the alignment and notice the vertical line that moves along the profile view marking the corresponding station.

6. Now move your cursor along the profile and notice the line that moves perpendicularly along the alignment marking the corresponding station.

The Station Tracker is a great tool to let you know where you are working along the corresponding alignment or profile.

7. Select the **FG** profile line, to display the grips.

8. Select one of the grips and stretch a **PVI** to a new location.

9. Notice how the corridor is displayed in the *Prospector*, it will have the orange out of date symbol next to it.

10. On the *Prospector* tab of the *Toolspace*, right-click on the *Corridor* **L Street** and select ⇒ **Rebuild**.

11. Review the changes to the corridor.

12. **Undo** twice to return the corridor and the profile to their original states.

You may need to undo more than 2 times if you have zoomed or issued any other commands during the process.

Editing the alignment or the assembly will also make the corridor out of date.

13. Select **Ribbon: Analyze** ⇒ **Inquiry** ⇒ **Station Tracker** ⇒ **Off**.

14. Select **Ribbon: View** ⇒ **Model Viewports** ⇒ **Viewport Configuration** ⇒ **Single**.

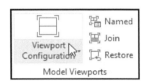

15. Now that you are back to a single viewport and the *Station Tracker* is off **zoom to the corridor**.

### 8.2.3   Creating Corridor Surfaces

1.   On the *Prospector* tab of the *Toolspace,* right-click on the *Corridor* **L Street** and select ⇒ **Properties**.

2.   Select the **Surfaces** tab.

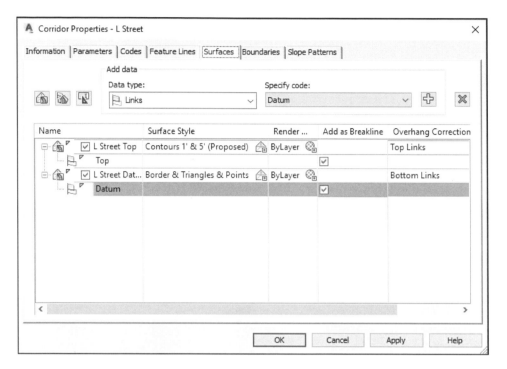

3.   Click the **Create Corridor Surface** button.

4.   Confirm that the **Data type** is set to **Links**.

5.   Confirm that **Specify Code** is set to **Top**.

6.   Click the **Add Surface Item** button.

7.   Rename the surface to **L Street Top**.

8.   Set the **Surface Style** to **Contours 1' & 5' (Proposed)**.

9.   Enable the **Add as Breakline** option.

This will create breaklines in the surface from the selected links in the assembly, rather than just adding points to the surface based on the endpoints of the links.  Adding the links as breaklines will ensure more accurate triangulation in the surface.

10.   Set the **Overhang Correction** to **Top Links**.

11.   Click the **Create Corridor Surface** button.

12.   Confirm that the **Data type** is set to **Links**.

13.   Set the **Specify Code** option to **Datum**.

---

14. Click the **Add Surface Item** button.

15. Rename the surface to **L Street Datum**.

16. Set the **Surface Style** to **Border & Triangles & Points**.

17. Enable the **Add as Breakline** option.

18. Set the **Overhang Correction** to **Bottom Links**.

19. Click the **Boundaries** tab.

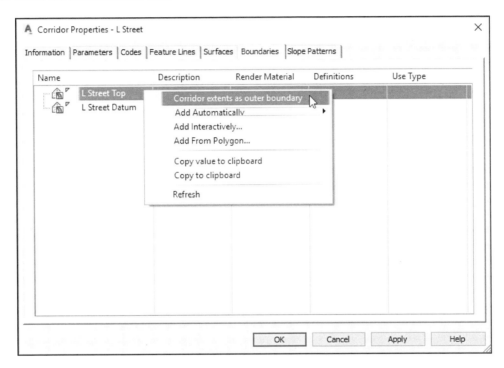

20. Right-click on the surface **L Street Top** and select ⇒ **Corridor extents as outer boundary**.

This will use the daylight line as the boundary for the top surface. Without a boundary the surface would triangulate outside of the extents of the corridor.

21. Right-click on the surface **L Street Datum** and select ⇒ **Corridor extents as outer boundary**.

22. Click **<<OK>>** to add the surfaces to the corridor.

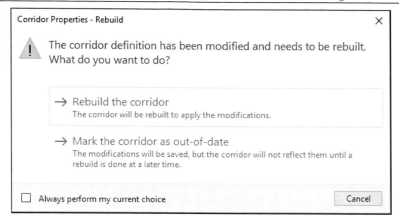

23. Click **Rebuild the corridor** to rebuild the corridor and add the surfaces.

The new surfaces linked to the corridor now display contours for the top surface and triangles for the datum surface. These surfaces are linked to the corridor model so they are automatically updated any time the corridor is changed. The surfaces are also displayed in the *Prospector* under the *Surface* node.

24. Save the drawing.

## 8.2.4   Viewing and Editing Corridor Sections

In this exercise, you will view the *Corridor* one section at a time. You also have the option to edit the individual *Corridor Sections* through this command.

1. **Thaw** the layer **C-TOPO-EG**.

Thawing the existing ground surface layer will allow the existing ground to display in the *View/Edit Section* command.

2. On the *Prospector* tab of the *Toolspace*, expand **Corridors**.

3. Right-click on the *Corridor* **L Street** and select ⇒ **Corridor Section Editor**.

This displays the first cross section in the corridor in the drawing editor. It also opens a new ribbon that allows you to display any section in the corridor, along with tools to edit individual sections.

4. Select **Ribbon: Section Editor ⇒ Station Selection ⇒ Select a Station** to scroll through several of the sections and review them on the screen.

5. Select **Ribbon: Section Editor** ⇒ **Corridor Edit Tools** ⇒ **Parameter Editor.**

This opens the *Corridor Parameters* window which includes a grid listing of the subassemblies and their values applied to the current corridor section. You can edit the parameters of each assembly, section by section, to refine the corridor model.

6. Close the *Corridor Parameters* window without making any changes.

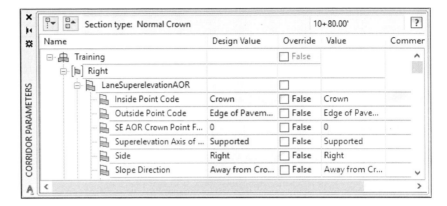

7. One you are finished reviewing the corridor sections, select **Ribbon: Section Editor** ⇒ **Close** ⇒ **Close** to close the *Section Editor* ribbon tab and return to the plan view.

### 8.2.5    Exporting Corridor Points

In this exercise, you will create points based on the corridor model. These points may be used for reports, or for staking purposes.

1. Select **Ribbon: Home** ⇒ **Create Ground Data** ⇒ **Points** ⇒ **Point Creation Tools**.

Before you create the points, it is best to set the defaults that control the layer the points are created on, as well as the numbers of the points.

2. Select the **Chevron** button on the right of the *Create Points* toolbar to expand it and show the point settings.

3. Expand the **Default Layer** parameters.

4. Select the **Layer Value** field and click the more **<<...>>** button.

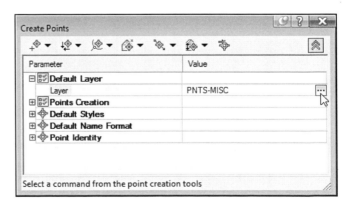

5. In the *Layer Selection* dialog box click **<<New>>**.

6. Enter **PNTS-L STREET CORRIDOR** for the new layer name.

7. Set the option to **Freeze** the layer to **No**.

8. Click **<<OK>>** to create the new layer.

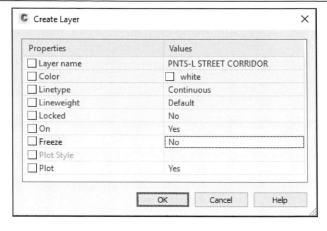

9. Click **<<OK>>** to select the new layer and close the *Layer Selection* dialog box.

10. Expand the **Point Identity** parameters.

11. Set the **Next Point Number** to **5000**.

This will number the new points that you create from the corridor, starting at point number 5000. This way, the new design points are numerically separated from the survey points.

12. Close the **Create Points** toolbar.

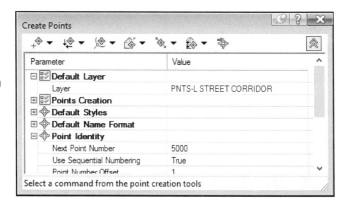

13. Select **Ribbon: Home ⇒ Create Ground Data ⇒ Points ⇒ Create COGO Points from Corridor**.

If there are multiple *Corridors* in your drawing you will be prompted at the command line to select a *Corridor*. If there is only one *Corridor* in the drawing, as should be the case in this exercise, you are taken directly to the *Export COGO Points* dialog box.

14. Select the option to create points **For entire corridor range**.

If needed, you can run this command several times as you specify specific ranges and make changes to the point group name and codes used.

15. Enter the **New point group** name **L Street Corridor**.

Creating a new point group for these points will keep the new design points separate from the other points in the drawing, and make them easily selectable for creating reports, editing, or exporting.

16. Disable all the *Point Codes* with the exception of **Back_Curb, Daylight_Cut,** and **Daylight_Fill**.

The list of *Point Codes* displayed in the *Export COGO Points* dialog box is dependent on the subassemblies used to create the Assembly in Corridor model. This is only for example purposes; you may want more information than this if you were creating points to stake the project. *Civil 3D* gives you the flexibility to select exactly the information you want without forcing you to create more points than you need.

17. Click **<<OK>>** to create the points.

18. On the *Prospector* tab of the *Toolspace,* click on the *Point Group* **L Street Corridor** and review the list of points in the preview window.

If the points are not displayed in the drawing confirm that the layer *PNTS-L STREET CORRIDOR* is on and thawed.

19. Save the drawing.

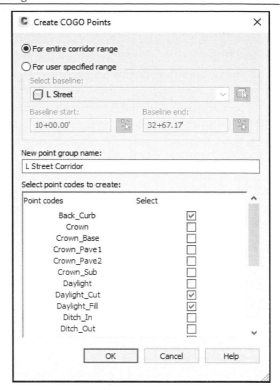

## 8.3    Lesson: Working with Sections

### Introduction

Sections can be sampled from regular *Surfaces* as well as *Corridor Surfaces* and *Assemblies*. These *Sections* are used for output and can be plotted in *Section Views* as well as used for *Quantity Takeoffs*. These *Sections* are not used for design; the design of the model is handled by the *Corridor*.

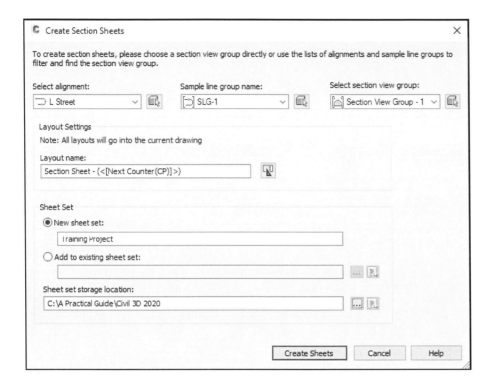

### Key Concepts

Concepts and key terms covered in this lesson are:

- Sample Lines
- Sample Line Groups
- Sections
- Section Views
- Quantity Takeoff Criteria
- Mass Haul Diagrams

### Objectives

After completing this lesson, you will be able to:

- Describe the difference between Sections and Corridors.
- Create Sample Lines.
- Create Section Views.
- Calculate Earthwork Quantities.
- Create a Mass Haul Diagram.

## Sample Lines

Sample lines are objects that determine the location that section data is sampled. They are associated with an alignment and are collected in Sample Line Groups. The data stored in these sample line groups can be used to create:

- Section Views
- Earthwork Volumes
- Material Volumes
- Mass Haul Diagrams

## Section Views

To display the Sections in the drawing you must create Section Views. A section view is an object that acts like a window to display section data. Typically, it is the grid on which the section lines are drawn.

- You can create multiple section views in the same drawing
- Section views can be moved without changing the section data
- Erasing a section view does not erase the section data
- Display is controlled by Section View Styles
- Section View Bands can be added to display rows of data at the bottom or top of the section view

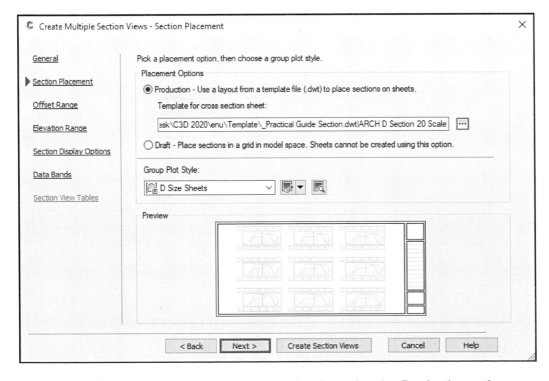

Once you have created *Section Views* in your drawing using the *Production* option, you can use the *Plan Production Tools* to automate the process of creating section sheets.

## Section View Styles

Section View Styles are similar to profile view styles and control the display of the grid on which the section lines are drawn. This includes:

- Vertical Exaggeration
- The display and labeling of the top, bottom, left and right axis
- The section view title
- Spacing and display of the grid
- Grid clipping

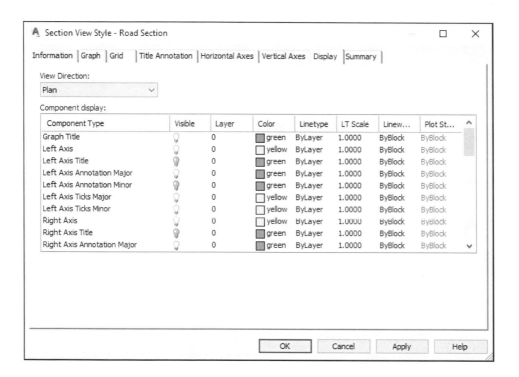

## Section Based Volumes

Volumes can be calculated from the sample line group data for earthworks as well as material quantities from the assemblies in the corridor. This is a two-step process. First you Compute Materials, then you can display the volumes by creating a volume table or by generating a volume report.

## Mass Haul Diagrams

Once section volumes have been calculated you can create a *Mass Haul Diagram* to display the volumes along the alignment. This helps designers and contractors see where material movements will occur along the alignment.

A change to any of the corridor data updates the sample lines and all Section Views, Volume Tables, and Mass Haul Diagrams.

## Exercises: Work with Sections

In these exercises, you create sample lines and sample sections of the existing ground, corridor surfaces, and assembly. Then you create section views and section sheets. Next you calculate earthwork volumes and display a mass haul diagram. Finally, you create a surface representing the finished site conditions with the new road.

You do the following:

- Create Sample Lines and a Sample Line Group.
- Create a Section Group Plot Style.
- Create Section Views.
- Create Section Sheets.
- Perform Volume Calculations.
- Paste Surfaces to create a Surface representing finished site conditions.

### 8.3.1   Creating Sample Lines

In this exercise, you will create *Sample Lines* that sample *Sections* for selected *Surfaces* at a specified interval.

1.   Continue working in the drawing **Design.dwg**.

*Reminder:* You can also open the drawing with this exercise number in the *Chapter Drawings* folder of the dataset if you prefer a fresh start at this point.

2.   **Freeze** the layer **PNTS-L STREET CORRIDOR.**

3.   Select **Ribbon: Home ⇒ Profile & Section Views ⇒ Sample Lines**.

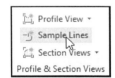

4.   When asked to *Select an alignment* at the command line, **[Enter]** to select it from a list.

You also have the option to pick it graphically from the screen.

5.   Select the Alignment **L Street**.

6.   Click **<<OK>>** to define the *Sample Line Group*.

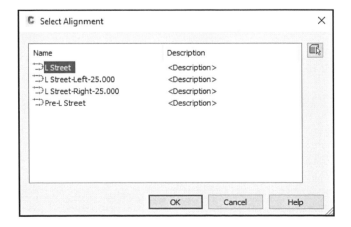

---

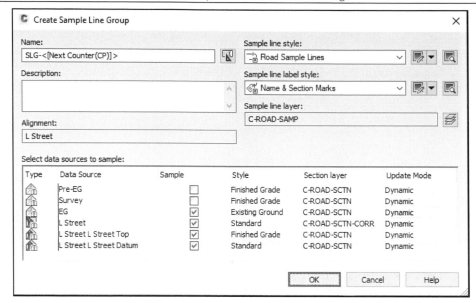

7. Leave the **Name** of the *Sample Line Group* unchanged. This will automatically name it according to the counter.

The Sample Line Group will be displayed under the Alignment L Street in the *Prospector* so a unique name does not help for descriptive purposes.

8. **Disable** the options to Sample Surfaces **Pre-EG** and **Survey**.

You will sample the *Surface EG* and the *Top* and *Datum* corridor surfaces along with the assemblies in the corridor sections.

9. Set the **Style** for **EG** to **Existing Ground**.

10. Confirm the **Style** for **L Street** is set to **Standard**.

11. Confirm the **Style** for **L Street Top** is set to **Finished Grade**.

12. Set the **Style** for **L Street Datum** to **Standard**.

This style controls the display of the section lines in the *Section Views*.

13. Click **<<OK>>** to open the *Sample Line Tools* toolbar.

14. Click the **down arrow** next to the *At a Station* button to display the other options.

15. Select ⇒ **By range of stations**…

16. Confirm the **Alignment** is set to **L Street**.

17. Set the **Left Swath Width** to **50**.

18. Set the **Right Swath Width** to **50**.

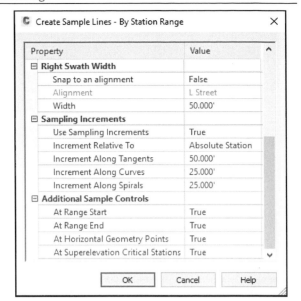

This will sample sections 100' wide along the corridor.

19. Set the **Increment Along Tangents** to **50**.

20. Set the **Increment Along Curves** to **25**.

21. Set the **Increment Along Spirals** to **25**.

22. Under Additional Sample Controls set **At Range Start** to **True**.

23. Set **At Range End** to **True**.

24. Set **At Horizontal Geometry Points** to **True**.

25. Set **At Super Elevation Critical Stations** to **True**.

26. Click **<<OK>>** to sample the sections and return to the *Sample Line Tools* toolbar.

You can add critical sections at any point along the alignment by selecting it graphically or typing the station at the command line.

27. Close the *Sample Line Tools* toolbar.

You will see the sample lines created in plan view along your corridor at the interval and width you specified in the previous steps.

### 8.3.2    Creating a Section Group Plot Style

In this exercise, you will create a *Section Group Plot Style* that places three rows of 4 *Section Views* in an area that will fit on a D sized sheet.  This *Section Group Plot Style* is yet another example of a style that should be saved as part of your drawing template so that it does not need to be created from scratch in every project.

1. On the **Settings** tab of the *Toolspace*, expand the **Section View** node, and then expand the **Group Plot Styles** node under it.

2. Under the **Group Plot Styles** node, right-click on **Plot By Page** and select ⇒ **Copy**.

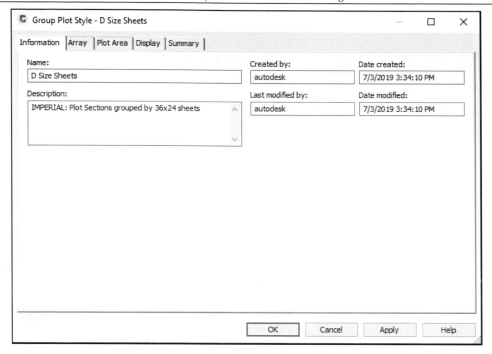

3.  Enter **D Size Sheets** for the **Name** of the new Group Plot Style.

4.  Enter **IMPERIAL: Plot Sections grouped by 36x24 sheets** for the **Description**.

5.  Select the **Array** tab of the *Group Plot Style* dialog box.

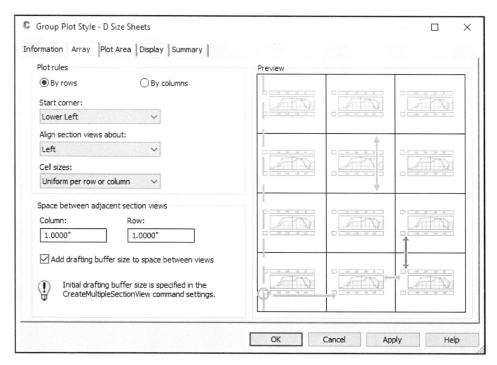

6.  In the *Space between adjacent section views* area, set the **Column** distance to **1**.

7.  In the *Space between adjacent section views* area, set the **Row** distance to **1**.

8. Select the **Plot Area** tab of the *Group Plot Style* dialog box.

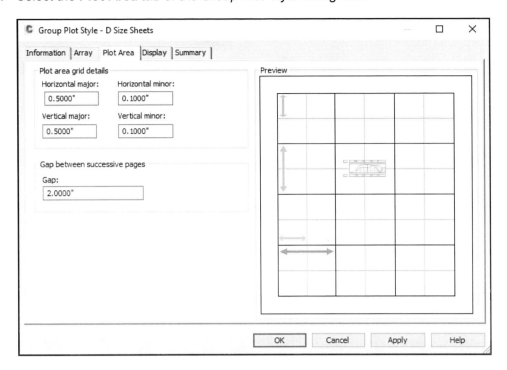

The grid details are in plotted units and will update based on the *Viewport* scale. The visibility, color and other display details are controlled on the *Display* tab. In this exercise the grid will not be displayed.

9. Select the **Display** tab of the *Group Plot Style* dialog box.

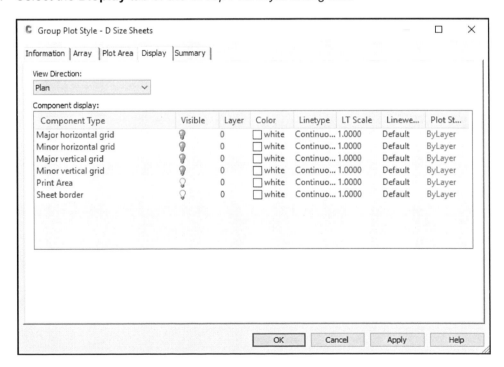

In this style only the *Print Area* and the *Sheet border* will be displayed.

10. Click **<<OK>>** to save the new *Group Plot Style*.

### 8.3.3 Creating Section Views

To display the *Sections* in the drawing you must create *Section Views*. *Section Views* are similar to *Profile Views*; they use styles to control the vertical exaggeration, grid, and labeling, as well as bands to display information along the top or bottom of the *Section View*.

1. Select **Ribbon: Home ⇒ Profile & Section Views ⇒ Section Views ⇒ Create Multiple Views**.

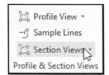

This will start the *Create Multiple Sections Views* wizard.

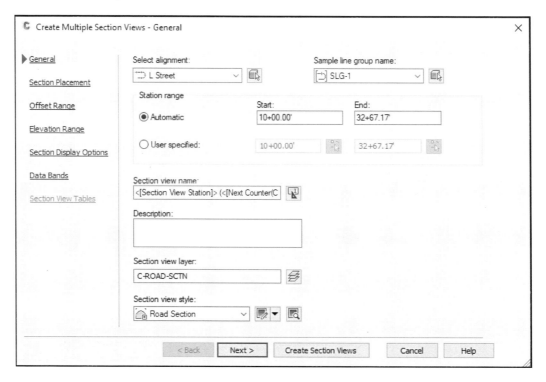

2. Confirm the **Alignment** is set to **L Street**.

3. Confirm the **Sample Line Group** is set to **SLG-1**.

The *Alignment* and *Sample Line Group* should be set correctly by default since you only have one *Sample Line Group* in this drawing. In more complex drawings that contain multiple *Sample Line Groups* you will need to be sure the desired one is selected.

4. Leave the **Name** of the Section Views unchanged. This will automatically name each section view according to the counter.

Each *Section View* will be displayed under the corresponding *Sample Line* in the *Prospector* so a unique name does not help a lot for descriptive purposes.

5. Click **<<Next>>** to continue through the wizard.

On the *Create Multiple Section Views - Section Placement* panel of the wizard you can control the layout and grouping of the *Section Views* so they fit properly on a sheet.

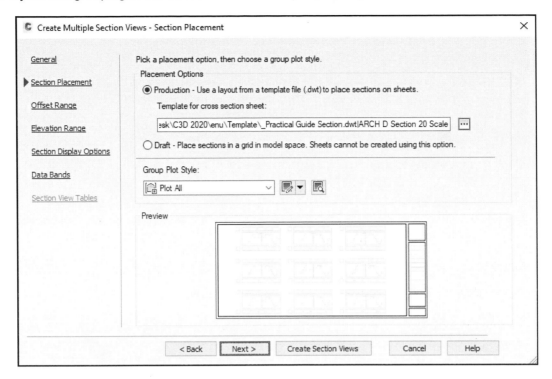

6. In the *Placement Options* section, choose **Production**.

7. To specify the **Template for the Cross Section sheet**, click the **more <<...>>** button.

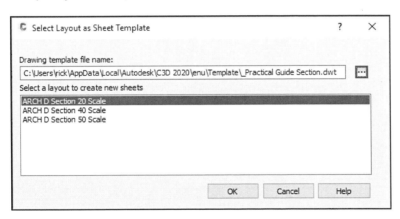

8. In the *Select Layout as Sheet Template* dialog box, click more **<<...>>** button.

9. In *the Select Layout as Sheet Template* dialog box, browse to the **Template** folder.

10. Select **_Practical Guide Section.dwt** and click **<<Open>>**.

11. From the **Layout** list, select **ARCH D Section 20 Scale**.

12. Click **<<OK>>** to assign the template and return to the *Create Multiple Section Views - Section Placement* panel of the wizard.

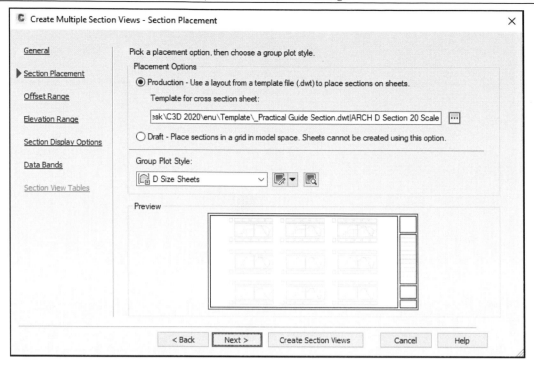

13. Set the **Group Plot Style** to **D Size Sheets**.

This is the section group plot style that you created in the previous exercise and it will group the section views for plotting on a D sized sheet.

14. Click **<<Next>>** to continue through the wizard.

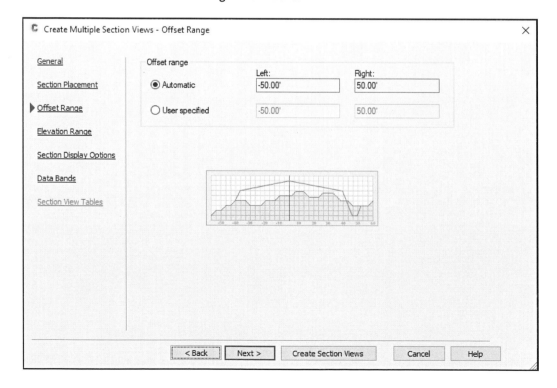

On the *Create Multiple Section Views - Offset Range* panel of the wizard you can define the width of the *Section Views.* Remember, you have sampled the sections at a width defined by the *Sample Lines.* This will only determine what is shown in the *Section Views.*

15. Confirm the **Offset range** is set to **Automatic**.

16. Click **<<Next>>** to continue through the wizard.

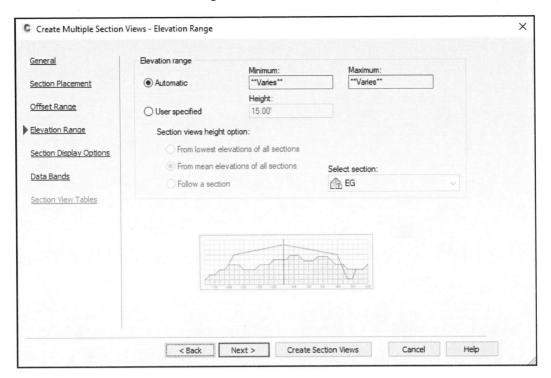

On the *Create Multiple Section Views - Elevation Range* panel of the wizard you can define the height of the *Section Views.* Using a user specified height will give you a consistent height for all of your *Section Views.* However, if the height you specify is not large enough you could cut off the display of some of the taller sections.

17. Confirm the **Elevation range** is set to **Automatic**.

18. Click **<<Next>>** to continue through the wizard.

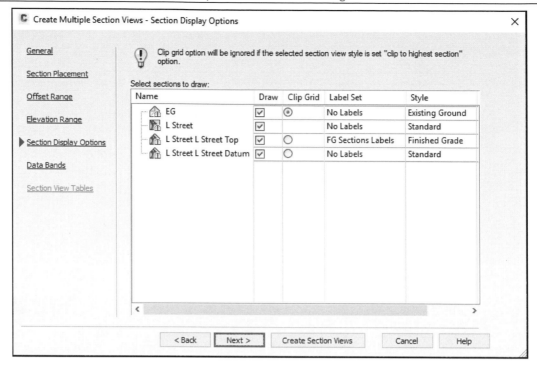

On the *Create Multiple Section Views - Section Display Options* panel of the wizard you can define which sections are drawn into the *Section Views*, if you have sampled multiple sections for this sample line group.  For example, you may have sampled the existing ground, the top surface of the corridor, and the datum surface of the corridor.  If you don't want to show all of them in the *Section Views* this is the place to control that.

The labeling of the section lines can be controlled here as well.  Each section line uses a Style to display the line and a Label Style to add text to the section.  These can each be created and configured in style editors similar to ones you have used in previous exercises.

19. Set the **Change Labels** field for the **EG, L Street** and **L Street Datum** sections to the **No Labels** *Label Set.*

20. Set the **Change Labels** field for the **L Street Top** sections to the **FG Section Labels** *Label Set.*

21. Click **<<Next>>** to continue through the wizard.

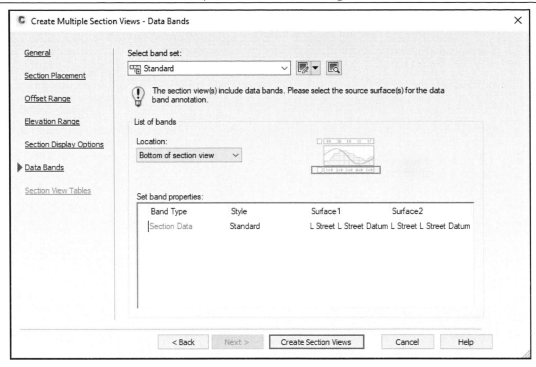

On the *Create Multiple Section Views* panel of the wizard you can define the *Bands* used with the Section *Views*. *Section View Bands* are rows of data at the top or bottom of the sections similar to profile bands.

22. Confirm that the **Band Style** is set to **Standard**.

23. Click **<<Create Section Views>>**.

24. Select a blank area in the drawing to create the sections.

The *Section Views* will be created up and to the right of the point you pick.

25. Zoom in and examine the sections.

26. Save the drawing.

### 8.3.4 Creating Section Sheets

1. Select **Ribbon: Output** ⇒ **Plan Production** ⇒ **Create Section Sheets**.

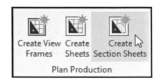

This opens the Create Section Sheets dialog box.

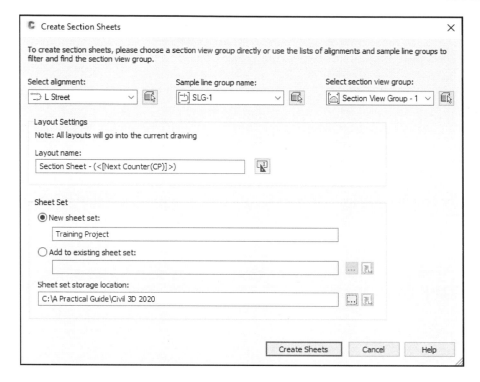

2. Confirm the **Alignment** is set to **L Street**.

3. Confirm the **Sample Line Group** is set to **SLG-1**.

4. Confirm the **Section View Group** is set to **Section View Group-1**.

The *Alignment*, *Sample Line Group* and *Section View Group* should be set correctly by default since you only have one *Section View Group* in this drawing. In more complex drawings that contain multiple *Section View Group* you will need to be sure the desired one is selected.

5. In the *Sheet Set section*, confirm **New sheet set** is selected.

6. Name the new sheet set **Training Project**.

7. Set the **Sheet set storage location** to: **C:\A Practical Guide\Civil 3D 2020**

8. Click **<<Create Sheets>>** to create the section sheets.

9. Click **<<OK>>** to save the drawing before proceeding.

A *Layout* is now created for each section sheet.

10. Select one of the *Layouts* and review the results.

11. Select the **Model** tab to return to *Model Space*.

## 8.3.5 Volume Calculations

In this exercise, you will calculate earthwork volumes based on the sections you sampled in the previous exercises. The sections do not need to be displayed in *Section Views* to calculate volumes; they only need to be sampled.

1. Select **Ribbon: Analyze ⇒ Volumes and Materials ⇒ Compute Materials**.

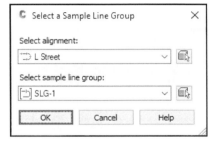

This opens the *Select a Sample Line Group* dialog box where you select the alignment and sample line group that you want to use for the volume calculations.

2. Confirm that the **alignment** is set to **L Street**.

3. Confirm that the **sample line group** is set to **SLG-1**.

4. Click **<<OK>>**.

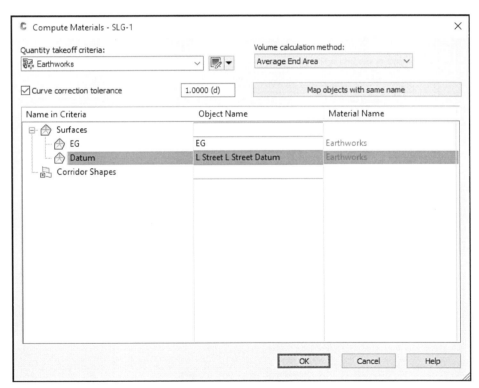

5. Set the **Quantity Takeoff Criteria** to **Earthworks**.

6. Confirm the **Calculation Method** is set to **Average End Area**.

7. Set the **EG Surface** option to **EG**.

8. Set the **Datum Surface** option to **L Street Datum**.

9. Click **<<OK>>** to calculate the volume.

The earthwork volume has now been calculated.  However, the results have not yet been displayed.  You can choose to display the results of the volume calculation as a table in the drawing, or you can export it to a report.  In the following steps you will create a table in the drawing to display these results.  This table is dynamically linked to the section data and will update if there are changes to the design.

10.  Select **Ribbon: Analyze** ⇒ **Volumes and Materials** ⇒ **Total Volume Table**.

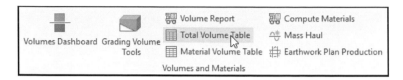

This opens the *Create Total Volume Table* dialog box.

11.  Set the **Table style** to **Cut and Fill**.

12.  Confirm that the **alignment** is set to **L Street**.

13.  Confirm that the **sample line group** is set to **SLG-1**.

14.  Confirm that the **Select material list** option is set to **Material List (1)**.

This is the material list you created in the previous steps.

15.  Click **<<OK>>**.

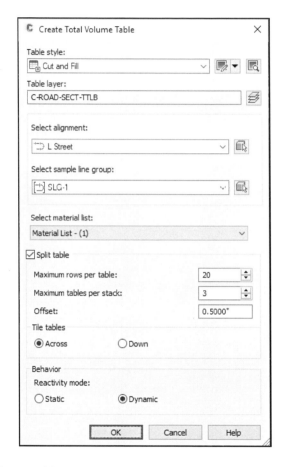

16.  Select a blank area in the drawing to create the volume table.

The tables will be created down and to the right of the point you pick.

17.  Zoom in and examine the volume table.

18.  Save the drawing.

This volume table will update if there are changes to the corridor model.

### 8.3.6    Creating a Mass Haul Diagram

1. Select **Ribbon: Analyze ⇒ Volumes and Materials ⇒ Mass Haul**.

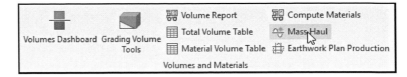

This starts the *Create Mass Haul Diagram* wizard.

2. Confirm that the **alignment** is set to **L Street**.

3. Confirm that the **Sample line group** is set to **SLG-1**.

4. Set the **Mass haul view style** to **Basic**.

5. Click **<<Next>>** to continue through the wizard.

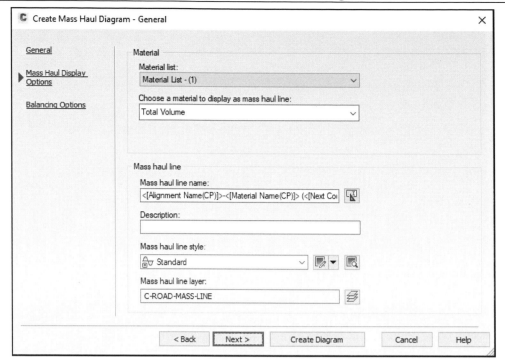

On the *Create Mass Haul Diagram - Mass Haul Display Options* panel of the wizard you can select the material that you will display in the mass haul diagram and select the style to use to display the mass haul line.

6.  Confirm the **Material list** is set to **Material List - (1)**.

7.  Confirm the **material to display as mass haul line** is set to **Total Volume**.

8.  Click **<<Next>>** to continue through the wizard.

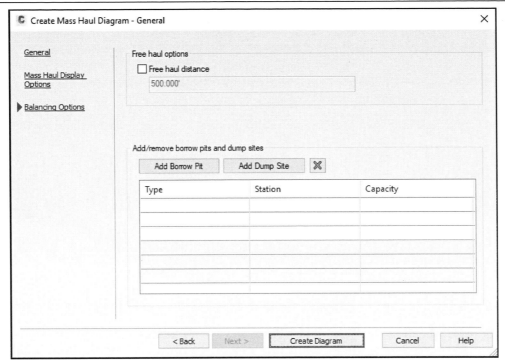

On the *Create Mass Haul Diagram - Balancing Options* panel of the wizard you can add borrow pits and dump sites. You also have the option to set a free haul distance.

    9.  Click **<<Create Diagram>>**.

    10.  Select a blank area in the drawing to create the *Mass Haul Diagram*.

The *Mass Haul Diagram* will be created to the right of the point you pick.

    11.  Zoom in and examine the *Mass Haul Diagram*.

    12.  Save the drawing.

### 8.3.7 Editing a Corridor to Update Surfaces, Sections, and Volumes

In previous exercises, you have explored how the corridor is dynamically linked to the alignment, profile, and assembly. In this exercise, you will make a change to the profile, rebuild the corridor and review the changes that it makes to the surfaces, sections, and volume table that have been created from the corridor.

1. Zoom to the profile and select the **FG** profile line to display the grips.

2. Select one of the grips and stretch a PVI to a new location.

3. Notice how the corridor is displayed in the *Prospector*. It will have the orange out of date symbol next to it.

4. On the *Prospector* tab of the *Toolspace*, right-click on the *Corridor* **L Street** and select ⇒ **Rebuild**.

5. Review the changes to the corridor, surfaces, sections, volume table and mass haul diagram.

This will allow you to look at many different design alternatives quickly and easily, while also updating the surfaces, sections, and volume calculations. You can also undo and go back to a previous design if you do not like the changes.

6. **[Esc]** to clear the selected objects.

### 8.3.8 Creating a Surface Showing Final Site Conditions

In this exercise, you will make a new surface that represents the final site with the new road. You will paste the surfaces *EG* and *L Street Top* into the new surface called *Final*. You can use this surface to display contours of the finished project, and also as the target surface for grading or pipe networks.

1. Set layer **0** current.

2. Freeze the layers **C-ROAD-CORR-L Street, C-ROAD-L Street, C-ROAD-SAMP, C-ROAD-SAMP-LABL, C-TOPO-EG, C-TOPO-L Street Surface - (1),** and **C-TOPO-L Street Surface - (2).**

3. On the *Prospector* tab of the *Toolspace,* right-click on **Surfaces** and select ⇒ **Create Surface**.

4. Confirm that **TIN surface** is selected as **Type**.

5. Enter **Final** for the **Name**.

6. Set the **Style** to **Border & Triangles & Points**.

7. Confirm the *Surface layer* is set to **C-TOPO-Final**.

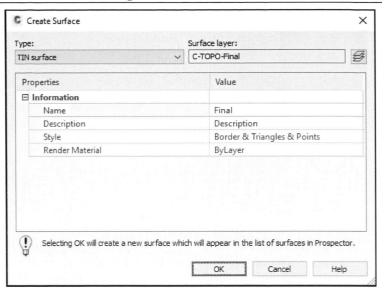

This layer name that includes the surface name as a suffix was setup in an earlier exercise through the Drawing Settings command.

8. Click **<<OK>>** to close the *Create Surface* dialog box and create the surface.

At this time the surface has not been given any data so it is not displayed. However, it has been created and you will see it in the *Prospector*. This is where you will access the surface definition commands and add data to the surface.

9. Expand the *Surface* **Final** on the *Prospector* tab of the *Toolspace*.

10. Expand the **Definition** node under *Surface* **Final**.

Be sure that you are under the surface *Final* in the *Prospector*. As you continue to add surfaces to your drawing it can become easy to have the wrong surface expanded and edit the wrong surface.

11. Right-click on **Edits** under the *Definition* **node,** and select ⇒ **Paste Surface**.

12. Select *Surface* **EG**.

13. Click **<<OK>>** to paste the surface *EG* into the surface *Final*.

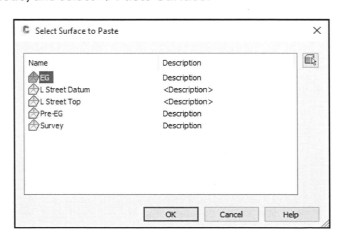

The surface *Final* will now be displayed as triangles, according to the style you selected earlier. By pasting the surface *EG* into the surface *Final* there is a dynamic link created. If the surface *EG* is updated at any time, the surface Final will become out of date. When the surface *Final* is rebuilt it will be built using the current version of the surface *EG*.

Next you will paste the surface *L Street Top* into the surface *Final*.

14. Right-click on **Edits** under the *Definition* node of the surface *Final*, and select ⇒ **Paste Surface**.

15. Select *Surface* **L Street Top**.

16. Click **<<OK>>** to paste the surface *L Street Top* into the surface *Final*.

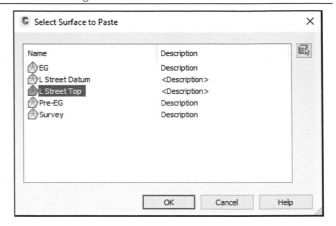

The surface *L Street Top* has now been pasted into the surface *Final*. You will see the triangles have updated along the corridor where the new surface was pasted.

17. On the *Prospector* tab of the *Toolspace*, right-click on the *Surface* **Final** and select ⇒ **Surface Properties**.

18. On the *Information* tab of the *Surface Properties* dialog box, select **Border & Contours** from the **Surface style** list.

19. Click **<<OK>>** to display the *Surface* **Final** as contours.

Notice how the top surface from the corridor has been merged with the copy of the existing ground model. You can now see the contours of the final site conditions including the new road. You can also review the surface in the Object Viewer to see the results of combining the surfaces.

20. Save the drawing.

## 8.4    Lesson:  Plan Production

### Introduction
The *Plan Production* tools allow you to automate the process of creating *Plan and Profile*, *Plan only* or *Profile only* sheets along an alignment.

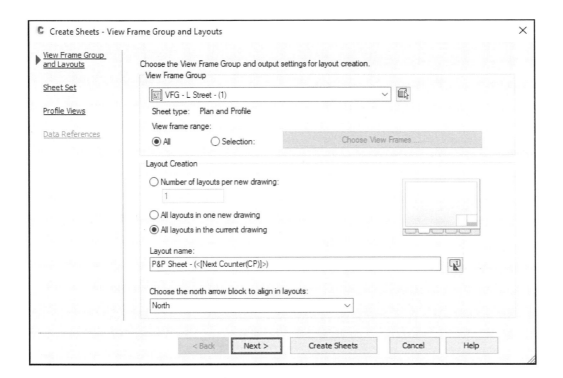

### Key Concepts
Concepts and key terms covered in this lesson are:

- View Frames
- View Frame Groups
- Match Lines

### Objectives
After completing this lesson, you will be able to:

- Create View Frames.
- Edit View Frame location and rotation.
- Create Plan and Profile Sheets

## View Frames

*View Frames* are rectangles created along an alignment that determine the position of the plan view in a viewport when creating sheets with the *Plan Production* tools.

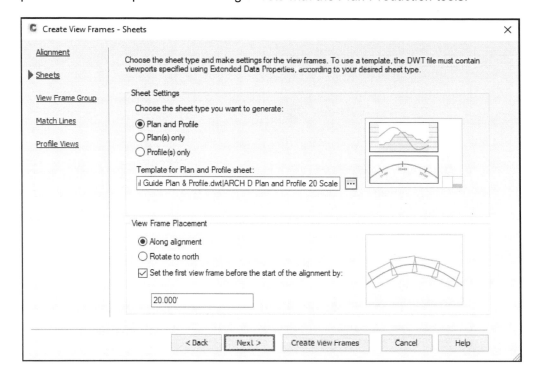

When creating *View Frames* you will specify if they are used for *Plan and Profile*, *Plan only* or *Profile only* sheets along the alignment. You will also select a layout from a drawing template. The size and scale of the plan viewport in that layout will determine the size of the *View Frame*.

## Match Lines

*Match Lines* can be created between each *View Frame* to display and label the overlap between each sheet.

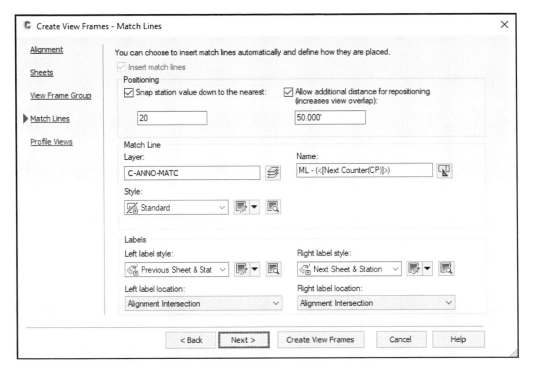

You can specify if you want the *Match Lines* to snap to an even station value along with the amount of overlap between sheets for repositioning on the *Match Lines*.

The *Match Line Labels* can be configured to show a variety of information including the station and sheet number.

## Exercises: Create Plan and Profile Sheets

In these exercises, you create and edit *View Frames* along the alignment. Then you will edit the *Match Lines*. Finally, you will create *Plan and Profile* sheets.

You do the following:

- Create View Frames.
- Edit View Frame location and rotation.
- Edit Match Lines.
- Create Plan and Profile sheets.

### 8.4.1 Creating View Frames

In this exercise, you will create *View Frames*. These *View Frames* will determine the location of the plan view shown in each sheet.

1. Continue working in the drawing **Design.dwg**.

*Reminder:* You can also open the drawing with this exercise number in the *Chapter Drawings* folder of the dataset if you prefer a fresh start at this point.

2. **Thaw** the layer **C-ROAD-L Street**.

3. Select **Ribbon: Output ⇒ Plan Production ⇒ Create View Frames**.

This will start the *Create View Frames* wizard.

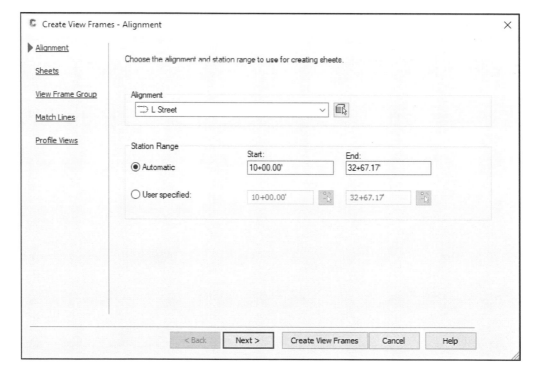

4. Confirm the **Alignment** is set to **L Street**.

5. Confirm the **Station range** is set to **Automatic**.

6. Click **<<Next>>** to continue through the wizard.

On the *Create View Frames - Sheets* panel of the wizard you specify the type of sheets you will create along with selecting a layout from a drawing template to use for the sheets. You also set how the *View Frames* are rotated along the alignment and where the first *View Frame* starts relative to the beginning of the alignment.

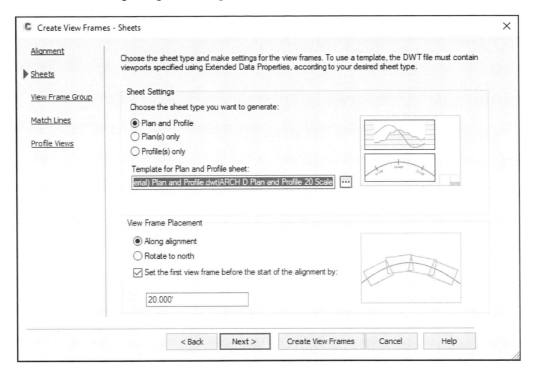

7. Confirm the **Sheet Type** is set to **Plan and Profile**.

8. To specify the **Template for Plan and Profile sheet**, click the **more <<...>>** button.

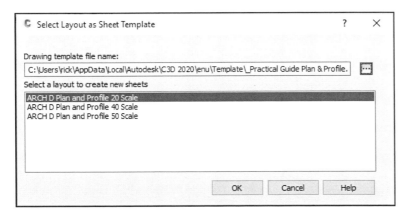

9. In the *Select Layout as Sheet Template* dialog box, click more **<<...>>** button.

10. In *the Select Layout as Sheet Template* dialog box, browse to the **Template** folder.

11. Select **_Practical Guide Plan & Profile.dwt** and click **<<Open>>**.

12. From the **Layout** list, select **ARCH D Plan and Profile 20 Scale**.

13. Click **<<OK>>** to assign the template and return to the *Create View Frames - Sheets* panel of the wizard.

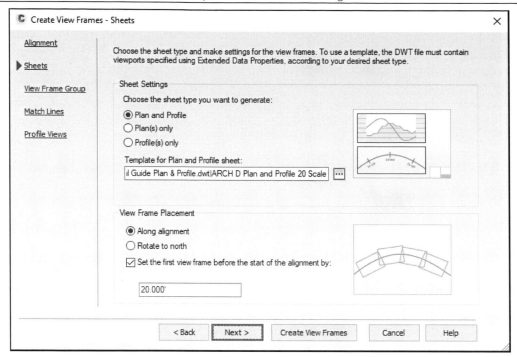

14. Confirm the **View Frame Placement** is set to **Along alignment**.

15. Enable the **Set the first view frame before the start of the alignment by** option and set it to **20**.

16. Click **<<Next>>** to continue through the wizard.

On the *Create View Frames - View Frame Group* panel of the wizard you specify how the *View Frames* are named and labeled.

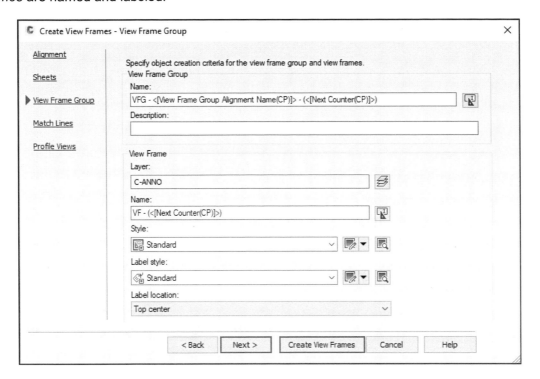

17. Set the **Label Location** of the *View Frame* to **Top center**.

18. Click **<<Next>>** to continue through the wizard.

On the *Create View Frames - Match Lines* panel of the wizard you specify the positioning, style and labeling for the *Match Lines*.

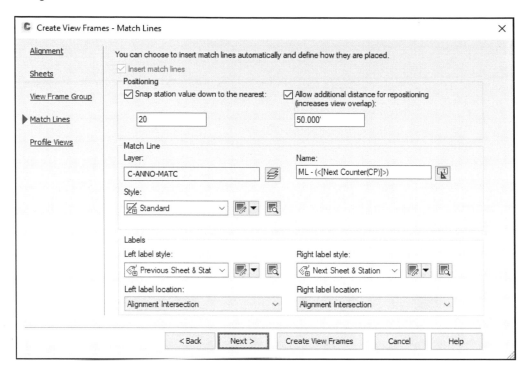

19. Enable the **Snap station value to nearest** option and set it to **20**.

20. Enable the **Allow additional distance for repositioning** option and set it to **50**.

21. Set the **Left label style** to **Previous Sheet & Station**.

22. Set the **Right label style** to **Next Sheet & Station**.

23. Set the **Left label location** to **Alignment Intersection**.

24. Set the **Right label location** to **Alignment Intersection**.

25. Click **<<Next>>** to continue through the wizard.

On the *Create View Frames - Profile Views* panel of the wizard you select the *Profile View Style* and *Band Set* that will be used to create the *Profile Views* that will be displayed in the sheets.

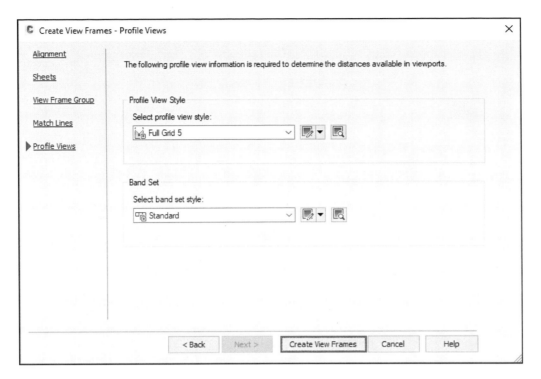

26. Set the **Profile View Style** to **Full Grid 5**.

27. Click **<<Create View Frames>>**.

The *View Frames* are now created along the alignment according to your settings. Each *View Frame* represents the location of the plan view on a sheet that you will create in a future exercise.

28. Save the drawing.

## 8.4.2 Editing View Frames

In this exercise, you will edit the location and rotation of a *View Frame*.

1. Continue working in the drawing **Design.dwg**.

2. Select the *View Frame* named **VF - (3)** in the drawing.

3. Notice the different shaped grips.

   - The **Circular** grip rotates the *View Frame*.
   - The **Diamond** grip slides the *View Frame* along the alignment.
   - The **Square** grip moves the *View Frame* freely to any position.

4. Use the grips to reposition the *View Frame* as desired, making sure to keep the alignment displayed on the sheet.

5. Save the drawing.

## 8.4.3 Editing Match Lines

In this exercise, you will edit the location and length of a *Match Line*.

1. Continue working in the drawing **Design.dwg**.

2. Select the *Match Line* at station **19+20**.

3. Notice the different shaped grips.

   - The **Circular** grip rotates the *Match Line*.
   - The **Diamond** grip slides the *Match Line* along the alignment.
   - The **Triangle** grip extends or shortens the *Match Line*.

4. Use the grips to reposition the *Match Line* as desired.

5. Save the drawing.

### 8.4.4 Creating Plan and Profile Sheets

In this exercise, you will create *Plan and Profile* sheets from the *View Frames*.

1. Continue working in the drawing **Design.dwg**.

2. Select **Ribbon: Output ⇒ Plan Production ⇒ Create Sheets**.

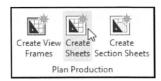

On the *Create Sheets - View Frame Group and Layouts* panel of the wizard you select a *View Frame Group* and which *View Frames* you will use to create sheets. Then you determine if the sheets will be created in a new drawing or the current one. This is also where you can name the layouts that will be created and select a north arrow block from the template that was selected when you created the *View Frames*.

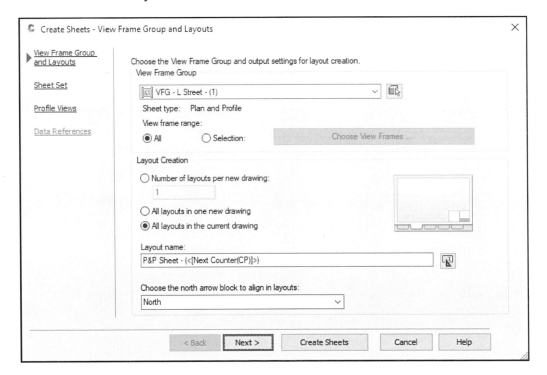

3. Select the **Layout Creation** option to **All layouts in the current drawing**.

4. Add **P&P** to the **Layout Name** so it reads **P&P Sheet - (<[Next Counter(CP)]>)**.

5. Set the **North Arrow Block** to **North**.

This list of block names comes from the template selected when the *View Frames* were created.

6. Click **<<Next>>** to continue through the wizard.

On the *Create Sheets - Sheet Set* panel of the wizard you name a new *Sheet Set* that will be created or select an existing one to add the new sheets to.

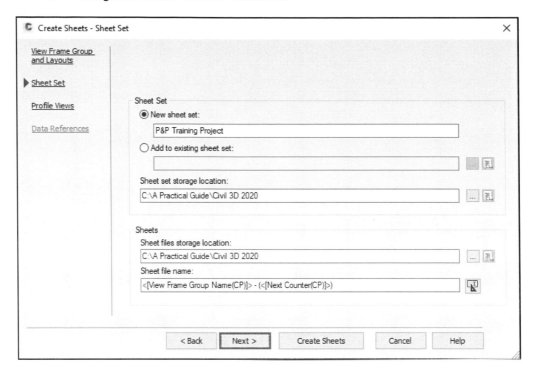

7.  Name the new sheet set **P&P Training Project**.

8.  Set the **Sheet set storage location** to: **C:\A Practical Guide\Civil 3D 2020**

9.  Click **<<Next>>** to continue through the wizard.

On the *Create Sheets - Profile Views* panel of the wizard you can set additional *Profile View* options and specify how the plan and profile viewports are aligned on the sheet.

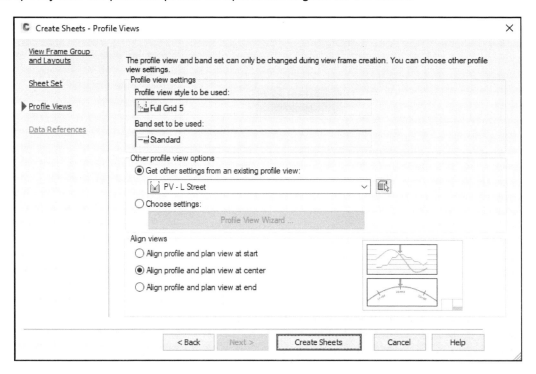

10. Select the **Align views** option to **Align profile and plan view at center**.

11. Click **<<Create Sheets>>** to create the section sheets.

12. Click **<<OK>>** to save the drawing before proceeding.

13. Select a blank area in the drawing above the *Section Views* to create the *Profile Views* that will be created for the new sheets.

The *Profile Views* will be created to the right of the point you pick.

A *Layout* is now created for each Plan and Profile sheet.

14. Select one of the *Layouts* and review the results.

15. Notice how the plan view is shaded outside of the *Match Lines*.

16. In the *Layer Properties Manager* set the **Transparency** of layer **C-ANNO-MATC** to **50**.

The shading outside the *Match Lines* is now transparent so you can see the design through it.

17. Select the **Model** tab to return to *Model Space*.

18. Save the drawing.

# Chapter 9

# 9 -   Pipes

In this chapter, you will design a sanitary sewer extension.  You will lay out the pipe network in plan view and explore several methods of editing the geometry and the display.  You will conclude the gravity pipe design by working with the pipe network in a profile view.  Next you will create a pressure network to represent a water line.  You will lay out the pressure network in plan view and add fittings and additional pipes.  Finally, you will create a profile view to display the water line and edit it to follow the surface at a specified depth.

## Lesson:  Working with Pipe Networks in Plan
In this lesson, you will learn to lay out and edit a pipe network in plan view.

## Lesson:  Working with Pipe Networks in Profile
In this lesson, you will learn to add a pipe network to a profile view.  Then you will learn to edit and label the pipe network in the profile view.

## Lesson:  Working with Pressure Networks in Plan
In this lesson, you will create a pressure network. You will learn how to layout a pressure network in plan view, add fittings and additional pipes.

## Lesson:  Working with Pressure Networks in Profile
In this lesson you will draft the pressure network into a *Profile View*.  You will also explore editing the network in the *Profile View* to follow a *Surface* at a specified depth.

## 9.1 Lesson: Working with Pipe Networks in Plan

### Introduction

In this lesson, you will create a pipe network to represent a proposed sanitary sewer extension. You will learn how to layout a pipe network in plan view and grip edit pipes and structures.

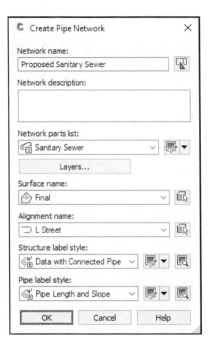

### Key Concepts

Concepts and key terms covered in this lesson are:

- Pipes
- Structures
- Network Parts List
- Pipe Labels
- Structure Labels

### Objectives

After completing this lesson, you will be able to:

- Describe a Network Parts List.
- Lay out a Pipe Network in plan view.
- Edit a Pipe Network in plan view.

## Pipe Networks

Pipe networks are made up of pipes and structures. These pipes and structures (or parts) are selected from a Network Parts List. The pipe network can be associated with alignments and surfaces. An associated alignment will provide stationing for labels while an associated surface will be used to determine the rim elevation of the structures along with depth and cover checks.

## Network Parts List

A part list is a collection of pipes and structures that will be used in a particular pipe network. Styles, Rules, Render Materials, and Pay Items can be individually assigned to each part.

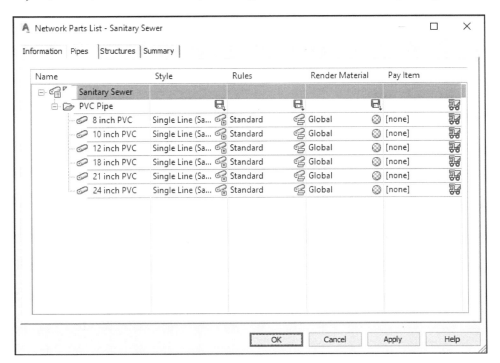

 When creating Part lists you may decide to create a part list for a specific utility, such as sanitary sewer or storm sewer, or a municipality, depending on the specifications. The part list will contain parts specific to that utility, municipality or client.

## Pipe Network Layout and Editing Tools

The Network Layout Tools toolbar contains many tools for creating and editing pipe networks.

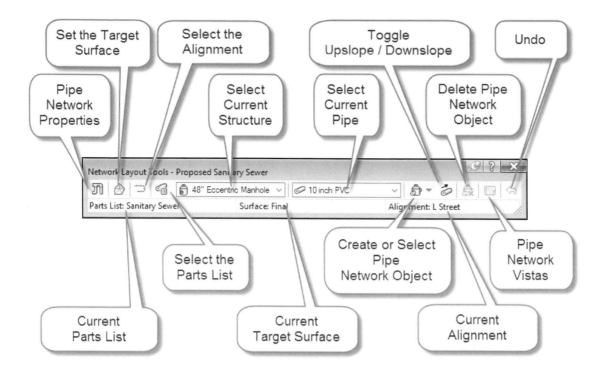

## Editing a Pipe Network in Plan View

When editing a pipe network in plan view there are some best practices you should keep in mind:

- Move the structures and the pipes will follow
- Move the pipes and they will become disconnected from the structures
- Turn off object snaps, they are 3D and can change the elevations of the pipes or structures

## Exercises: Create a Pipe Network

In these exercises, you create a pipe network in plan view. Then you edit the pipe network in plan view.

You do the following:

- Create a Pipe Network.
- Lay out the Pipe Network in Plan View.
- Edit the Pipe Network in Plan View.

### 9.1.1 Laying Out a Pipe Network

In this exercise, you will lay out a pipe network along the first half of the L Street alignment.

1. Continue working in the drawing **Design.dwg**.

*Reminder:* You can also open the drawing with this exercise number in the *Chapter Drawings* folder of the dataset if you prefer a fresh start at this point.

2. Zoom to the beginning of the L Street alignment.

3. Select **Ribbon: Home ⇒ Create Design ⇒ Pipe Network ⇒ Pipe Network Creation Tools**.

This opens the *Create Pipe Network* dialog box where you can name and setup your pipe network.

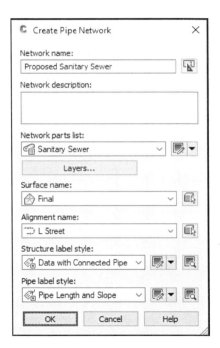

4. In the *Create Pipe Network* dialog box, for **Network name** enter **Proposed Sanitary Sewer**.

5. From the **Network parts** list, select **Sanitary Sewer**.

6. From the **Surface name** list, select **Final**.

7. From the **Alignment name** list, select **L Street**.

8. From the **Structure label** style list, select **Data with Connected Pipes**.

9. From the **Pipe label** style list, select **Pipe Length and Slope**.

10. Click **<<OK>>**.

This opens the *Network Layout Tools* toolbar.

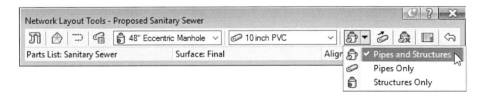

11. From the *Network Layout Tools* toolbar, **Structure** list, select **48" Eccentric Manhole**.

12. From the **Pipe** list, select **10 inch PVC**.

13. Set the **Upslope / Downslope** toggle to ⬆ **upslope**.

14. Click the **Draw** button and select ⇒ **Pipes and Structures**.

15. At the **Specify the structure insertion point:** command prompt, enter **'SO** to change the prompt and enter locations by station and offset.

Alternatively, you can also select the *Station Offset* button from the *Transparent Commands* toolbar.

16. At the **Select Alignment** prompt pick the **L Street** alignment from the screen.

17. Enter the stations and offsets in the following table to lay out the pipe run.

| Station | Offset |
|---------|--------|
| 1000 | 5 |
| 1300 | 5 |
| 1600 | 5 |
| 1900 | 5 |
| 2100 | 5 |

18. Press **[Enter]** to end the Station and Offset prompt.

Pipe networks can also be drawn by just graphically selecting locations, using object snaps, or typing in coordinates.

19. Press **[Enter]** to end the command.

20. Close the *Network Layout Tools* toolbar.

21. Zoom in and examine the new pipe network.

Notice the pipes and structures have been labeled according to the styles selected earlier in the exercise.

22. Save the drawing.

### 9.1.2    Editing a Pipe Network in Plan

1. Zoom to **Structure - (5)**.

2. Pick **Structure - (5)**.

Note the structure has two grips; a square grip at the structure insertion point and a circular grip on a line extending from the square grip. The circle grip is the structure rotation grip. The square grip is the structure location grip.

3. Pick the structure **rotation grip (circular grip)**.

This grip allows you to rotate the structure. This is useful for correctly orienting structures containing text (e.g. "S" for a sanitary sewer manhole) or an outfall structure.

4. Move the cursor around the structure noting the effect on the structure rotation.

5. Select a new rotation angle for the structure.

6. **[Esc]** to clear the selection.

7. Zoom to **Structure - (4)**.

8. Pick **Structure - (4)**.

9. Select the **square grip**.

The square grip allows you to move the structure location and pipes connected to it.

10. At the command line enter **'SO** to change the prompt and enter locations by station and offset.

Alternatively, you can also select the *Station Offset* button from the *Transparent Commands* toolbar.

11. At the **Select Alignment** prompt pick the **L Street** alignment from the screen.

12. Enter **1950** for the **Station**.

13. Enter **-5** for the **Offset**.

The structure is now moved to the new location and the connected pipes are also updated along with all of the labels.

14. **[Esc]** to clear the selection.

15. Save the drawing.

## 9.2   Lesson:  Working with Pipe Networks in Profile

### Introduction

In this lesson, you will draft the pipe network into a *Profile View*.  You will also explore editing the network in the *Profile View* both graphically and by entering specific values in a dialog box.

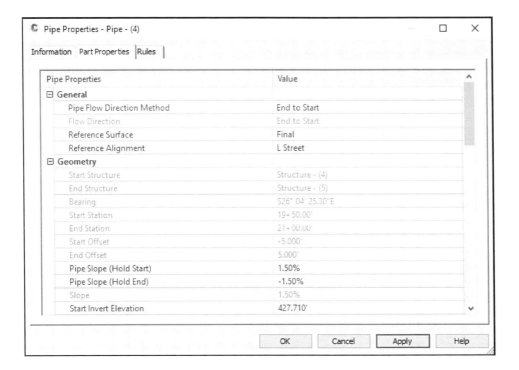

### Key Concepts

Concepts and key terms covered in this lesson are:

- Pipes
- Structures
- Pipe Labels
- Structure Labels

### Objectives

After completing this lesson, you will be able to:

- Draw a Pipe Network into a Profile View.
- Edit a Pipe Network in Profile View.
- Label a Pipe Network in Profile View.

# Pipe Networks in Profile

Parts from a pipe network, or the entire pipe network, can be drawn into any profile view in the drawing. This command is a two-step process.

1. Select **Ribbon: Modify ⇒ Design ⇒ Pipe Network**.

The *Pipe Networks* tab is displayed.

2. Select **Ribbon: Pipe Networks ⇒ Network Tools ⇒ Draw Parts in Profile**.

## Is it a profile of the Pipe or Alignment?

When you draw a pipe network into a profile view you can choose to align the pipe network with any alignment. For example, you could choose between the street centerline, projecting the pipes onto it obliquely, or aligning the profile with this pipe network itself.

Options include:

- Projected
- Pipe centerline

## Projected Pipe Network Profiles

A pipe network can be drawn into any profile view. If the alignment associated with this profile view is not drawn down the centerline of the pipe, then the pipe network will be projected onto the profile view. In this case the lengths of the pipes will be labeled correctly; however, the lengths will not measure accurately in the profile since the pipe network is projected, or oblique, rather than parallel to the alignment.

## Pipe Centerline Profiles

When an alignment is created down the center of the pipes, then a pipe network drawn into this profile view will be an actual profile of the pipe, as opposed to an oblique projection.

## Editing a Pipe Network in a Profile View

When editing a pipe network in profile view there are some best practices you should keep in mind:

- Move the pipes and the structures will follow
- Move the structures and they will become disconnected from the pipes

## Exercises: Work with a Pipe Network in Profile

In these exercises, you add a pipe network to a profile view. Then you edit the pipe network in profile. Finally, you label the pipe network in profile.

You do the following:

- Add a Pipe Network to a Profile View.
- Edit the Pipe Network in Profile.
- Label the Pipe Network in Profile.

### 9.2.1  Adding a Pipe Network to a Profile

1. Continue working in the drawing **Design.dwg**.

*Reminder:* You can also open the drawing with this exercise number in the *Chapter Drawings* folder of the dataset if you prefer a fresh start at this point.

2. Select **Ribbon: Modify ⇒ Design ⇒ Pipe Network**.

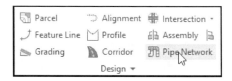

The *Pipe Networks* tab is displayed.

3. Select **Ribbon: Pipe Networks ⇒ Network Tools ⇒ Draw Parts in Profile**.

4. Select any part of the pipe network in plan view.

If you only want to draw some of the pipes and structures in the profile view, rather than the entire network, then enter S at the command line for the *Selected parts only* option. Then select the desired pipes and structures.

5. **[Enter]** end the selection.

6. Select the main profile view that displays the entire length of the profile.

7. Zoom in to review the pipes and structures that are now displayed in the *Profile View*.

The *Profile View* will update automatically and expand vertically to display the *Pipe Network*. This could be a large change, a small amount, or no change at all to the *Profile View*, it depends on the depth of the pipes and structures.

## 9.2.2    Editing a Pipe Network in Profile

1.  Zoom in to **Pipe 4** in the *Profile View* near station 20+00.

2.  Pick Pipe 4.

Notice the pipe has seven grips. Three grips are located on each end, one at each of the following locations; pipe crown (diamond), pipe centerline (triangle), and pipe invert (diamond). A square grip is located at the middle of the pipe.

The endpoint grips are for modifying the respective pipe elevations. Modifying one of these endpoints grips changes the slope of the pipe.  The square grip at the pipe midpoint maintains the pipe slope and moves the pipe vertically.

3.  Select one of the grips on the upstream end of the pipe and drag it down to pick a new elevation for the start of the pipe.

Notice the structure updates to match the pipe in the profile view.

4.  Press **[Esc]** to clear the pipe grips.

5.  Pick Pipe 4 to display the context sensitive ribbon.

6.  Select **Ribbon: Pipe Networks: Proposed Sanitary Sewer ⇒ Modify ⇒ Pipe Properties**.

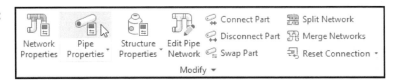

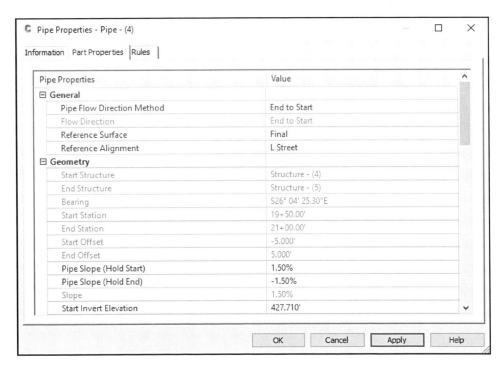

7.  Select the **Part Properties** tab.

8.  Change the **Pipe Slope (Hold Start)** to **1.50%.**

9.  Click **<<OK>>** to save the changes and update the pipe.

### 9.2.3   Labeling a Pipe Network in Profile

In this exercise, you will add pipe labels to the *Profile View*.

1.   Select **Ribbon: Annotate** ⇒ **Labels & Tables** ⇒ **Add Labels**

This will display the *Add Labels* dialog box where you can select the feature, type of label, and label styles that you would like to use.

2.   In the *Add Labels* dialog box, from the **Feature** list, select **Pipe Network**.

3.   From the **Label type** list, select **Entire Network Profile**.

4.   From the **Pipe label style** list, select **Pipe Length and Slope**.

5.   From the **Structure label style** list, select **Profile Data with Connected Pipes**.

6.   Click **<<Add>>**.

7.   Pick a pipe or structure from the network to be labeled.

8.   In the *Add Labels* dialog box, click **<<Close>>**.

9.   Zoom in and examine the labels.

## 9.3 Lesson: Working with Pressure Networks in Plan

### Introduction

In this lesson, you will create a pressure network to represent a proposed water line. You will learn how to layout a pressure network in plan view, add fittings and additional pipes.

### Key Concepts

Concepts and key terms covered in this lesson are:

- Pressure Pipes
- Fittings
- Appurtenances
- Pressure Pipe Labels
- Fitting Labels
- Appurtenance Labels

### Objectives

After completing this lesson, you will be able to:

- Describe a Pressure Network Parts List.
- Lay out a Pressure Network in plan view.
- Add a Fitting to a Pressure Network.

## Pressure Networks

Pressure networks are made up of pressure pipes, fittings and appurtenances. These pressure pipes, fittings and appurtenances (or parts) are selected from a Pressure Network Parts List. The pressure network can be associated with alignments and surfaces. An associated alignment will provide stationing for labels while an associated surface will be used to determine the depth of the pressure pipes.

## Pressure Network Parts List

A part list is a collection of pressure pipes, fittings and appurtenances that will be used in a particular pressure network. Styles and Render Materials can be individually assigned to each part.

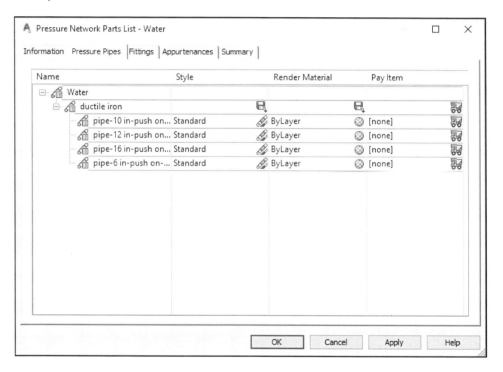

 When creating Part Lists you may decide to create a part list for a specific utility, such as water, or a municipality, depending on the specifications. The part list will contain parts specific to that utility, municipality or client.

## Pressure Network Layout and Editing Tools

A special tab on the ribbon is displayed when laying out or editing a pressure network in plan view.

A special tab on the ribbon is displayed when laying out or editing a pressure network in profile.

## Exercises: Create a Pressure Network

In these exercises, you create a pressure network in plan view.

You do the following:

- Create a Pressure Network.
- Lay out the Pressure Network in Plan View.
- Add a Fitting and a Lateral to the Pressure Network.

### 9.3.1   Laying Out a Pressure Network

In this exercise, you will lay out a pressure network for a water line along the L Street alignment.

1.   Continue working in the drawing **Design.dwg**.

*Reminder:*  You can also open the drawing with this exercise number in the *Chapter Drawings* folder of the dataset if you prefer a fresh start at this point.

2.   Zoom to the beginning of the *L Street* alignment.

3.   Select **Ribbon: Home ⇒ Create Design ⇒ Pipe Network ⇒ Pressure Network Creation Tools**.

This opens the *Create Pressure Pipe Network* dialog box where you can name and setup the pressure network.

4. In the *Create Pressure Pipe Network* dialog box, for **Network name** enter **Water**.

5. From the **Parts List**, select **Water**.

6. From the **Surface name** list, select **Final**.

7. From the **Alignment name** list, select **L Street**.

8. From the **Pressure Pipe Label Style** list, select **Nominal Diameter and Material**.

9. From the **Fitting Label Style** list, select **Nominal Diameter Bend Angle and Material**.

10. From the **Appurtenance Label Style** list, select **Nominal Diameter Valve Type**.

11. Click **<<OK>>**.

This opens the *Pressure Network Plan Layout* tab on the ribbon.

12. Go to **Ribbon: Pressure Network Plan Layout: Water ⇒ Network Settings**.

13. Confirm the **Surface** is set to **Final**.

14. Confirm the **Alignment** is set to **L Street**.

15. Confirm the **Parts List** is set to **Water**.

16. Set the **Cover** to **3.5**.

17. Go to **Ribbon: Pressure Network Plan Layout: Water ⇒ Layout**.

18. Confirm the **Size and Material** is set to **pipe - 10 in - push on - ductile iron**.

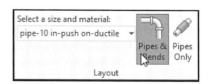

19. If the command is not already selected, select **Ribbon: Pressure Network Plan Layout: Water ⇒ Layout ⇒ Pipes & Bends**.

20. At the **Specify first pressure pipe point:** command prompt, enter **'SO** to change the prompt and enter locations by station and offset.

Alternatively, you can also select the *Station Offset* button ⬚ from the *Transparent Commands* toolbar.

21. At the **Select Alignment** prompt pick the **L Street** alignment from the screen.

22. Enter the stations and offsets in the following table to lay out the pipe run.

| Station | Offset |
| --- | --- |
| 1000 | -10 |
| 1400 | -10 |
| 1800 | -10 |
| 2030 | 14 |
| 2135 | -14 |

23. Press **[Enter]** to end the Station and Offset prompt.

Pressure networks can also be drawn by just graphically selecting locations, using object snaps, or typing in coordinates. Notice the graphical compass that shows the available angles in the fitting as you draw the pressure network.

24. Press **[Enter]** to end the command.

25. Select **Ribbon: Pressure Network Plan Layout: Water ⇒ Close**

26. Zoom in and examine the new pressure network.

Notice the pipes and fittings have been labeled according to the styles selected earlier in the exercise.

27. Save the drawing.

### 9.3.2   Adding a Lateral to a Pressure Network

In this exercise, you will add a tee and a lateral to the water line.

1. Zoom to **Station 14+50**.

2. Select the pressure pipe to display the context sensitive tab on the ribbon.

3. Select **Ribbon: Pressure Network: Water** ⇒ **Modify** ⇒ **Edit Network** ⇒ **Plan Layout Tools**.

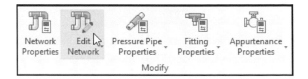

This opens the *Pressure Network Plan Layout* tab on the ribbon.

4. Go to **Ribbon: Pressure Network Plan Layout: Water** ⇒ **Insert**.

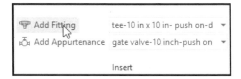

5. Set the **Fitting** to **tee - 10 in x 10 in push on - ductile iron**.

6. Select **Ribbon: Pressure Network: Water** ⇒ **Insert** ⇒ **Add Fitting**.

7. Move your cursor over the pressure pipe at station 14+50.

8. Notice the tooltip indicating that the pipe will be broken to insert the new fitting.

9. Click the desired location for the fitting on the pressure pipe at station 14+50.

The pressure pipe is now broken and the Tee fitting is inserted between the two pressure pipes.

10. Press **[Enter]** to end the command.

11. Zoom in to examine the new fitting.

12. Select the fitting.

13. Notice the different grips on the fitting.

These grips can move the fitting to a new position along the pipes, flip the direction of the fitting, and add new pipes to open connections.

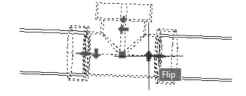

14. Click the arrow shaped grip to flip the fitting so the Tee points north.

15. Click the plus shaped grip at the open end of the fitting on the north side to continue the layout by adding a new pressure pipe.

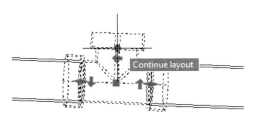

16. Pick an endpoint for the new pressure pipe about 100' to the north.

The exact location of this pipe is not important for this exercise.

17. Press **[Enter]** to end the command.

18. Select **Ribbon: Pressure Network Plan Layout: Water ⇒ Close**

19. Zoom in to review the new pressure pipe that has been added to the fitting.

20. Save the drawing.

## 9.4 Lesson: Working with Pressure Networks in Profile

### Introduction

In this lesson, you will draft the pressure network into a *Profile View*. You will also explore editing the network in the *Profile View* to follow a *Surface* at a specified depth.

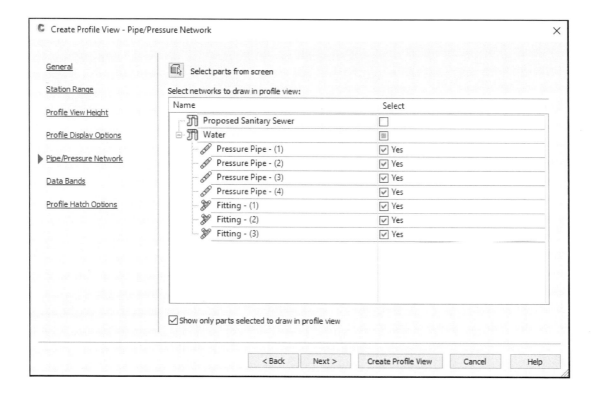

### Key Concepts

Concepts and key terms covered in this lesson are:

- Pressure Pipes
- Fittings
- Appurtenances

### Objectives

After completing this lesson, you will be able to:

- Draw a Pressure Network into a Profile View.
- Edit a Pressure Network in Profile View.

# Pressure Networks in Profile

Parts from a pressure network, or the entire pressure network, can be drawn into any profile view in the drawing. This command is a two-step process.

1. Select **Ribbon: Modify ⇒ Design ⇒ Pressure Pipe Network**.

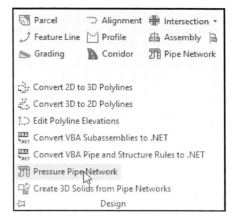

The *Pressure Networks* tab is displayed.

2. Select **Ribbon: Pressure Networks ⇒ Network Tools ⇒ Draw Parts in Profile**.

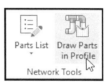

Pressure networks can also be added to new profile views when the profile view is created. The entire pressure network, or just the desired parts from the network, can be selected on the *Pipe Network Display* panel of the *Create Profile View* wizard.

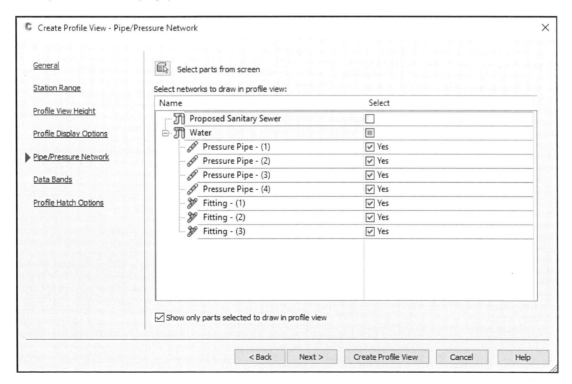

## Is it a profile of the Pipe or Alignment?

When you draw a pressure network into a profile view you can choose to align the pressure network with any alignment. For example, you could choose between the street centerline, projecting the parts onto it obliquely, or aligning the profile with this pressure network itself.

Options include:

- Projected
- Pipe centerline

## Projected Pressure Network Profiles

A pressure network can be drawn into any profile view. If the alignment associated with this profile view is not drawn down the centerline of the pipe, then the pressure network will be projected onto the profile view. In this case the lengths of the pipes will be labeled correctly; however, the lengths will not measure accurately in the profile since the pressure network is projected, or oblique, rather than parallel to the alignment.

## Network Centerline Profiles

When an alignment is created down the center of the pipes, then a pressure network drawn into this profile view will be an actual profile of the network, as opposed to an oblique projection.

## Exercises: Work with a Pressure Network in Profile

In these exercises, you create a new profile view to display the pressure network. Then you edit the pressure network in profile to follow the surface at a specified depth.

You do the following:

- Create a Profile View and display the Pressure Network in it.
- Edit the Pressure Network in Profile to follow the Surface.

### 9.4.1 Creating a Profile View with a Pressure Network

In this exercise, you will create a new Profile View that includes the parts from the pressure network representing the water line.

1. Continue working in the drawing **Design.dwg**.

2. Select **Ribbon: Home ⇒ Profile & Section Views ⇒ Profile View ⇒ Create Profile View**.

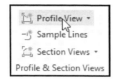

Since profile data has already been sampled for the *L Street* alignment you can go directly to the *Create Profile View* command.

This starts the *Create Profile View* wizard.

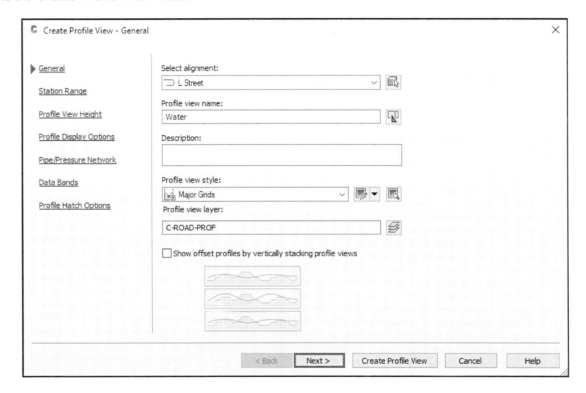

3. Set the **Alignment** to **L Street**.

4. Enter **Water** as the **Profile view name**.

5. Confirm the **Profile view style** is set to **Major Grids**.

6. Click **<<Next>>** to continue through the wizard.

7. On the *Create Profile View - Station Range* panel of the wizard, confirm the **Station range** is set to **Automatic**.

8. Click **<<Next>>** to continue through the wizard.

9. On the *Create Profile View - Profile View Height* panel of the wizard, confirm the **Profile view height** is set to **Automatic**.

10. Click **<<Next>>** to continue through the wizard.

11. On the *Create Profile View - Profile Display Options* panel of the wizard, confirm both the **EG** and **FG** profiles have the **Draw** option enabled.

12. Click **<<Next>>** to continue through the wizard.

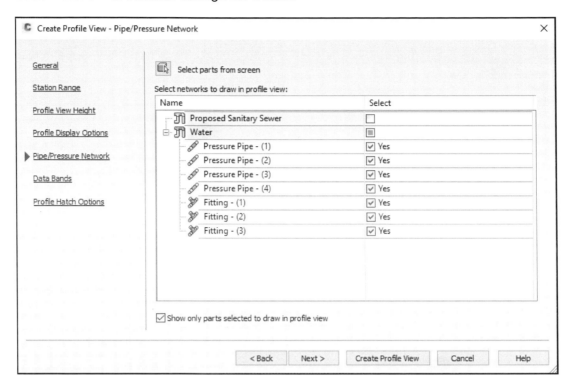

On the *Create Profile View - Pipe Network Display* panel of the wizard you can select the network you want to display in the profile view. You can even select individual parts that you want to add to the profile view.

13. Click the **Select Parts from Screen**  button.

14. At the command line enter **S** to select a **Series of Parts**.

15. Now, in the drawing editor, select the first water pipe in the network near station 11+00.

16. Next select the last water pipe in the network near station 21+00. Notice that all the pipes in the network between the two you selected are highlighted. However, the lateral near station 14+50 is not selected.

17. **[Enter]** to end the selection prompt and return to the *Create Profile View* wizard.

18. Click **<<Next>>** to continue through the wizard.

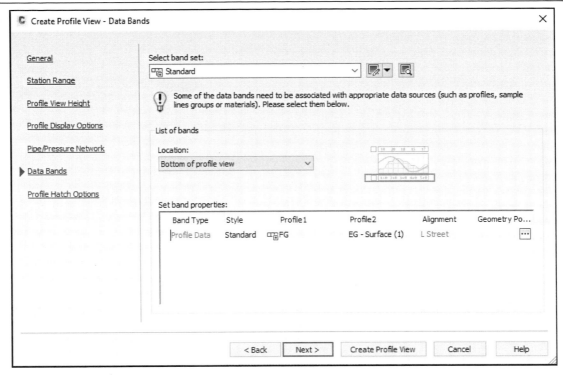

19. On the *Create Profile View - Data Bands* panel of the wizard, confirm that the **Band set** is set to **Standard**.

20. Set **Profile 1** to **FG**.

21. Confirm **Profile 2** is set to **EG**.

22. Click **<<Next>>** to continue through the wizard.

On the *Create Profile View - Profile Hatch Options* panel of the wizard, you will not make any changes.

23. Click **<<Create Profile View>>** to complete the wizard and add the new *Profile View* to the drawing.

24. In a blank area of the drawing, pick a point to represent the lower left corner of the *Profile View*.

25. Zoom in to review the new *Profile View* with the pressure network displayed.

26. Save the drawing.

### 9.4.2 Editing a Pressure Network in Profile

1. Zoom to the Profile View that contains the water line.

Some of the pipes may not follow the surface at the desired depth. The pressure pipes can be edited in the *Profile View* graphically by using the grips, or in a more automated way by using the *Follow Surface* command.

2. Select **Ribbon: Modify ⇒ Design ⇒ Pressure Pipe Network**.

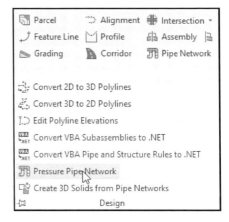

The *Pressure Networks* tab is displayed.

3. Select **Ribbon: Pressure Network ⇒ Modify ⇒ Edit Network ⇒ Profile Layout Tools**.

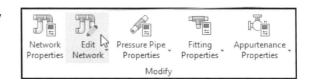

4. Select the pressure pipe network named **Water**.

5. Click **<<OK>>**.

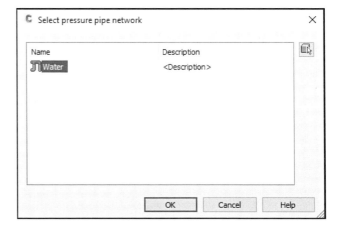

This opens the *Pressure Network Plan Layout* tab on the ribbon.

6. Go to **Ribbon: Pressure Network Profile Layout: Water ⇒ Modify ⇒ Follow Surface**.

7. Select the first pressure pipe in the *Profile View*, and then select the last pressure pipe in the *Profile View* and press **[Enter]**.

All of the connected pressure pipes will be highlighted in the *Profile View*; you do not need to select each one individually.

8.  Enter **3.5** for the **depth below surface**.

The pipes are now updated to follow the surface.

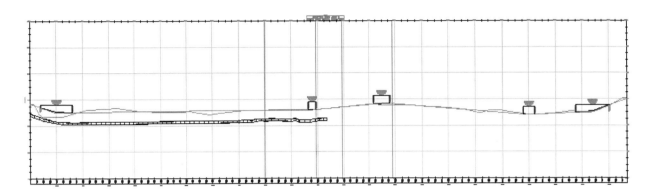

# 10 - Grading

In this chapter, you will create a grading group to grade a pond. The grading group will be dynamically linked to a surface so that the surface is updated automatically each time that you add a grading object to the grading group or edit a grading object within the group. Finally, you will create *Grid* and *TIN Volume* surfaces to calculate the volume of the pond and explore ways to use surface styles to display the volume surfaces showing depths of cut and fill.

## Lesson: Working with Grading Groups

In this lesson, you will learn to create a grading group, link it to a surface, and then create grading objects based on grading criteria.

## Lesson: Volume Calculations

In this lesson, you will learn to calculate volumes between two surfaces using both the *Grid Surface* and *TIN Surface* methods. You will also learn to analyze and display the results of these volume calculations.

## 10.1 Lesson: Working with Grading Groups

### Introduction

*Grading Groups* are a collection of *Grading* objects that interact with each other. *Grading Groups* are components of a *Site* and interact with other *Grading Groups*, *Alignments*, and *Parcels* contained in the same *Site*.

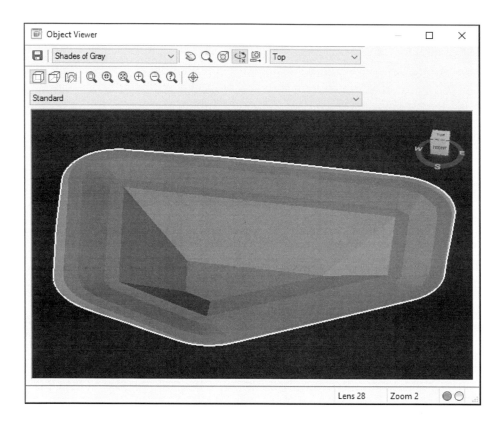

### Key Concepts

Concepts and key terms covered in this lesson are:

- Grading Groups
- Grading Objects
- Grading Infill
- Stage Storage Calculations

### Objectives

After completing this lesson, you will be able to:

- Create a Grading Group and link it to a Surface.
- Create Grading Objects to represent your design.
- Preform Stage Storage Calculations.

## Grading Groups

A grading group is a collection of grading objects that interact with each other and can be used to automatically create and update a surface. Grading groups are contained within a Site.

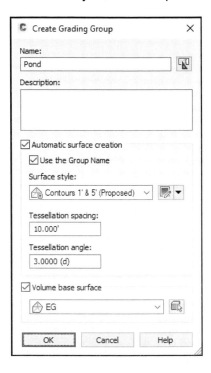

## Grading Criteria

Grading criteria are methods of grading that include parameters like the grading target and projection method. Collections of grading criteria are saved in a Grading Criteria Set. Examples of grading criteria include:

- Grading to a surface
- Grading to a horizontal distance
- Grading to an absolute elevation
- Grading to a relative elevation

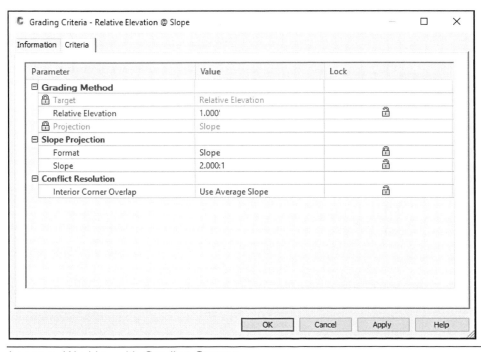

## Grading Tools

The Grading Creation Tools toolbar contains many tools for creating and editing grading objects.

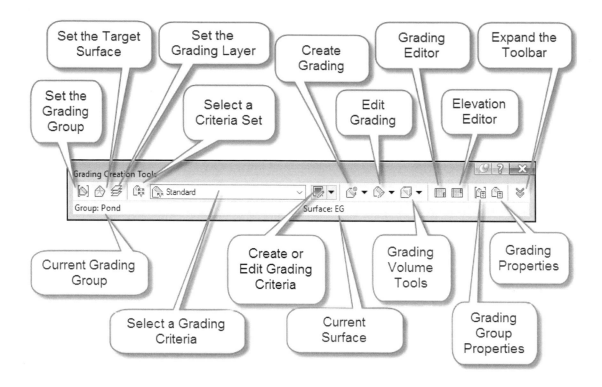

## Exercises: Grading a Detention Pond

In these exercises, you create a site and a grading group that will contain the grading objects used in your design. Then you create grading objects to grade a detention pond. Next, you create infill to finish the grading and close the hole at the bottom of the pond. Finally, you perform a stage storage calculation to determine the capacity of the pond.

You do the following:

- Create a Site.
- Create a Grading Group in the new Site.
- Create Grading Objects to grade the pond.
- Create Infill.
- Perform a Stage Storage Calculation.

## 10.1.1  Creating a Grading Group

In this exercise, you will create a new *Site* and a *Grading Group*.  This *Grading Group* will be used later to grade a detention pond.

    1.   Continue working in the drawing **Design.dwg**.

*Reminder:*  You can also open the drawing with this exercise number in the
*Chapter Drawings* folder of the dataset if you prefer a fresh start at this point.

    2.   **Freeze** the layers **C-ANNO-MATC** and **C-ANNO-VFRM** .

    3.   On the *Prospector* tab of the *Toolspace*, right-click on **Sites** and select ⇒ **New**.

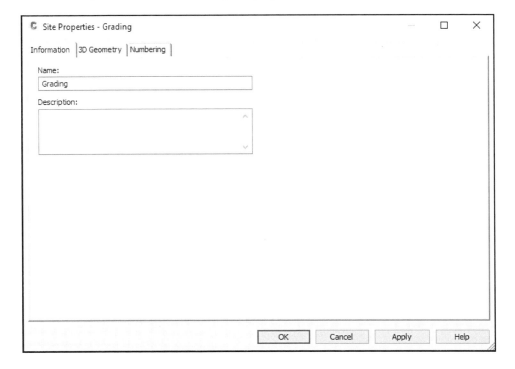

    4.   Enter **Grading** for the **Name**.

    5.   Click **<<OK>>** to create the *Site*.

    6.   On the *Prospector* tab of the *Toolspace*, expand the **Sites** node.

    7.   Expand the *Site* **Grading**.

    8.   Right-click on **Grading Groups** under the *Site* **Grading** and select ⇒ **New**.

9.  Enter **Pond** for the **Name** of the *Grading Group*.

10. **Enable** the **Automatic Surface Creation** option.

11. Set the **Surface style** to **Contours 1' & 5' (Proposed)**.

12. Enable the **Volume base surface** option.

13. Set the **Volume base surface** to surface **EG**.

14. Click **<<OK>>** to create the *Grading Group* and open the *Create Surface* dialog box.

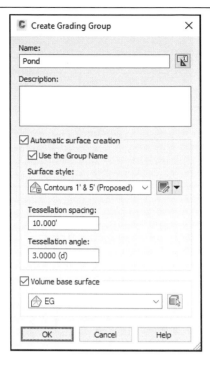

15. Confirm that the surface **Name** is set to **Pond**.

16. Confirm that the surface **Style** is set to **Contours 1' & 5' (Proposed)**.

17. Click **<<OK>>** to create the new surface based on the grading group.

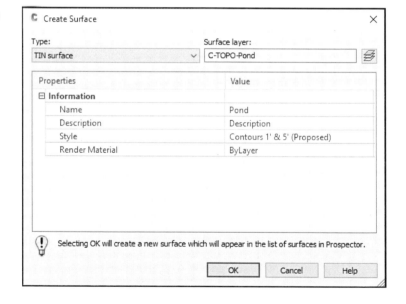

### 10.1.2 Creating a Grading Object

In this exercise, you will insert a block that contains a polyline that you will use as the outline of a pond. This is just a 2D polyline with an elevation assigned to it. You will create several Grading objects and offsets based on this polyline.

1. Continue working in the drawing **Design.dwg**.

*Reminder:* You can also open the drawing with this exercise number in the *Chapter Drawings* folder of the dataset if you prefer a fresh start at this point.

2. Select **Ribbon: Insert ⇒ Block ⇒ Insert ⇒ Blocks from Other Drawings**.

This opens the *Blocks* palette.

3. Select the [ ... ] button to load a drawing into the **Blocks Palette**.

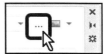

The **Select Drawing File...** dialog box appears.

4. Browse to **C:\A Practical Guide\Civil 3D 2020\Drawings\pond.dwg**

5. Click **<<Open>>**.

The drawing appears in the **Blocks** palette.

6. In the *Insertion Options* section of the **Blocks** palette, confirm that the settings are as shown:

7. **Disable** the **Insertion Point** option.

8. Confirm the **Insertion Point** is set to **0,0**.

9. **Enable** the option to **Explode** the block.

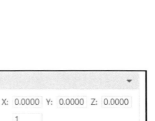

10. Right-click on the drawing **Pond** and select **Insert**.

11. Zoom in to the red polyline representing the pond outline in the northeast corner of the site.

This is a 2D polyline that was created at elevation 437 to represent the top of the berm around the pond. If needed it could have been drawn as a 3D polyline or a feature line.

12. Select **Ribbon: Home ⇒ Create Design ⇒ Grading ⇒ Grading Creation Tools**.

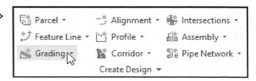

This will display the *Grading Creation Tools* toolbar.

At the bottom of the *Grading Creation Tools* toolbar you will see that the *Grading Group* is set along with the target *Surface*.

    13. Click the **Select a Criteria Set**  button on the *Grading Creation Tools* toolbar.

    14. Select the **Basic Set** grading criteria.

Selecting a *Grading Criteria Set* populates the list in the middle of the toolbar with different grading methods (criteria).

    15. Click **<<OK>>**.

    16. Set the **Grading Criteria** to **Surface @ 3-1 Slope**.

    17. Click the **Create Grading** button.

    18. Pick the Pond Outline.

Since the pond outline is a polyline and not a *Feature Line*, Civil 3D opens the *Create Feature Lines* dialog box where you can control the settings for how the polyline will be converted to a *Feature Line*. Civil 3D can only create grading objects from *Feature Lines*.

                                    Lesson: Working with Grading Groups

19. Confirm that the **Site name** is set to **Grading**.

20. Confirm that the *Conversion option* to **Erase existing entities** is enabled.

If the *Erase existing entities* option is not enabled the new feature line will be created on top of the existing polyline.

21. Confirm that the *Conversion option* to **Assign elevations** is disabled.

22. Confirm that the *Conversion option* to **Weed points** is disabled.

You also have options to apply a feature line style to the object and control the layer of the new object.

23. Click **<<OK>>** to create the feature line.

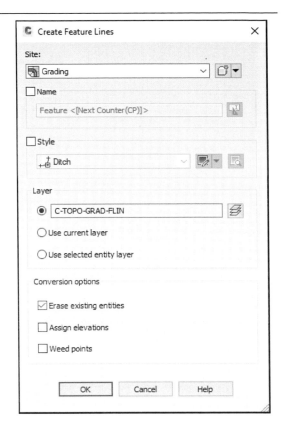

24. Pick a point outside of the pond outline to grade to the outside.

25. At the command line **[Enter]** to apply the grading to the entire length of the feature line.

The *Grading Object* is now created and daylights to the surface *Final* at a 3:1 slope according to the grading criteria.

26. **[Esc]** to end the command when asked to select another feature.

The surface *Pond* is now rebuilt with the information from the grading group and displayed as 1 foot contours according to the surface style.

27. Set the **Grading Criteria** to **Distance @ Grade**.

28. Click the **Create Grading** button.

29. Pick the interior pond outline. This is the same feature line that you just graded to the surface.

30. Pick a point inside of the pond outline you just selected to grade to the inside.

31. At the command line **[Enter]** to apply the grading to the entire length of the feature line.

32. Enter **5** for the **Distance**.

33. Enter **-1** for the **Grade**.

The *Grading Object* is now created projecting down at -1% into the center of the pond for a horizontal distance of 5 feet, according to the grading criteria.

> 34. **[Esc]** to end the command when asked to select another feature.

The surface *Pond* is now rebuilt with the information from the grading group and displayed as 1 foot contours according to the surface style.

> 35. Set the **Grading Criteria** to **Relative Elevation @ Slope**.
>
> 36. Click the **Create Grading** button.
>
> 37. Pick the inner most feature line created during the last grading command.
>
> 38. At the command line **[Enter]** to apply the grading to the entire length of the feature line.
>
> 39. Enter **-2** for the **Relative Elevation**.
>
> 40. Enter **5** for the **Slope**.

The *Grading Object* is now created projecting down 2 feet into the center of the pond at a 5:1 slope, according to the grading criteria.

> 41. **[Esc]** to end the command when asked to select another feature.

The surface *Pond* is now rebuilt with the information from the grading group and displayed as 1 foot contours according to the surface style.

> 42. Set the **Grading Criteria** to **Distance @ Grade**.
>
> 43. Click the **Create Grading** button.
>
> 44. Pick the inner most feature line created during the last grading command.
>
> 45. At the command line **[Enter]** to apply the grading to the entire length of the feature line.
>
> 46. Enter **5** for the **Distance**.
>
> 47. Enter **-1** for the **Grade**.

The *Grading Object* is now created projecting down at -1% into the center of the pond for a horizontal distance of 5 feet, to create a bench, according to the grading criteria.

> 48. **[Esc]** to end the command when asked to select another feature.

The surface *Pond* is now rebuilt with the information from the grading group and displayed as 1 foot contours according to the surface style.

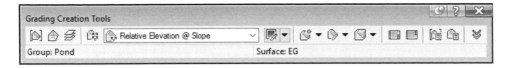

49. Confirm that the **Grading Criteria** is set to **Relative Elevation @ Slope**.

50. Click the **Create Grading** button.

51. Pick the inner most feature line created during the last grading command.

52. At the command line **[Enter]** to apply the grading to the entire length of the feature line.

53. Enter **-12** for the Relative Elevation.

54. Enter **2** for the Slope.

The *Grading Object* is now created projecting down 12 feet into the center of the pond at a 2:1 slope, according to the grading criteria.

55. **[Esc]** to end the command when asked to select another feature.

The surface *Pond* is now rebuilt with the information from the grading group and displayed as 1 foot contours according to the surface style.

56. Close the *Grading Creation Tools* toolbar.

57. Save the drawing.

### 10.1.3 Creating a Grading Infill

In a grading group, areas between individual grading objects have no data. This creates blank or void areas in the surface that is created from the grading group. These blank areas can be filled in by creating an Infill. The Infill fills the gap between the individual grading objects in the group with a straight slope.

In this exercise, you will create an Infill in the Pond grading group to fill the hole at the bottom of the pond.

1. Review the Surface Pond with the Object Viewer to see the blank area representing the hole at the bottom of the surface.

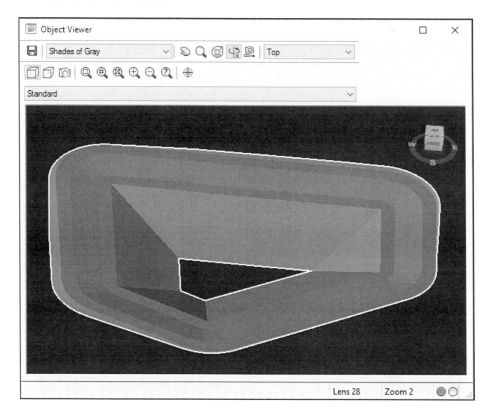

2. Select **Ribbon: Home ⇒ Create Design ⇒ Grading ⇒ Create Grading Infill**.

3. The command line will prompt you to Select an area to infill. Move your cursor over the flat bottom of the pond. You will see the extents of the flat area highlight.

4. Pick any point in the flat, highlighted, area to create the Infill.

5. **[Enter]** to end the command.

The surface *Pond* is now rebuilt with the information from the infill and displayed as 1 foot contours according to the surface style.

6. Review the surface with the *Object Viewer* to confirm that the blank area at the bottom of the pond is now filled in.

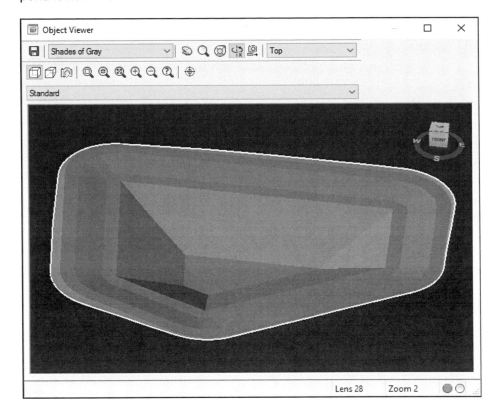

7. Close the *Object Viewer*.

8. Save the drawing.

## 10.1.4 Reviewing Grading Group Properties

1. On the *Prospector* tab of the *Toolspace*, expand **Sites, Grading, and Grading Groups.**

If the grading group named Pond is not displayed in the *Prospector*, right-click on *Grading Groups* and select ⇒ *Refresh*

2. Right-click on *Grading Group* **Pond** under the *Site* **Grading** and select ⇒ **Properties.**

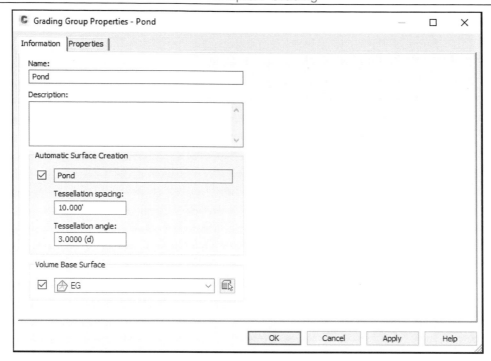

On the *Information* tab of the *Grading Group Properties* dialog box you can control the name, the surface created from the grading group, and the volume base surface. For this exercise you will not make any changes to the *Information* tab.

    3.   Select the **Properties** tab.

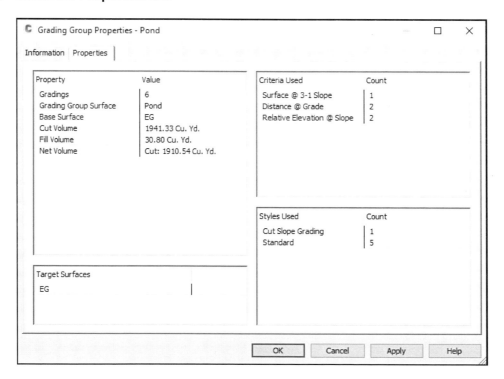

On the *Properties* tab of the *Grading Group Properties* dialog box you can review the current volume of the grading group along with the grading criteria and styles used.

    4.   Click **<<Cancel >>** to close the *Grading Group Properties* dialog box without making any changes.

## 10.1.5  Calculating Stage Storage

In this exercise, you will calculate the incremental and cumulative volumes of a basin using the *Stage Storage* command.  This will create a report based on the pond surface you created in the previous exercises showing the capacity of the pond at different elevations.

1. Select **Ribbon: Analyze ⇒ Design ⇒ Stage Storage.**

This opens the *Stage Storage* dialog box where you define the basin and create the report.

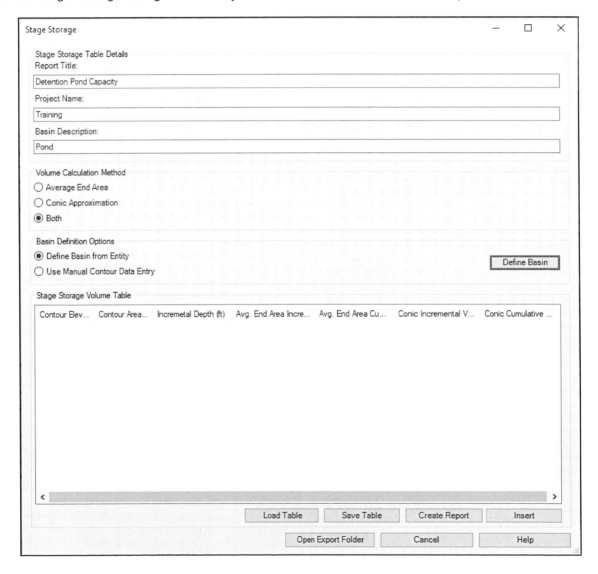

2. Enter **Detention Pond Capacity** for the **Report Title.**

3. Enter **Training** for the **Project Name.**

4. Enter **Pond** for the **Basin Description.**

5. Confirm the **Volume Calculation Method** is set to **Both**.

6. Confirm the **Basin Definition Options** is set to **Define Basin from Entity.**

7. Click **<<Define Basin>>** to open the *Define Basin from Entities* dialog box.

8. Enter **Pond** for the **Basin Name.**

9. Select **Define Basin from Surface Contours**.

10. Click **<<Define>>.**

11. Select the surface by picking one of the contours that represents the pond.

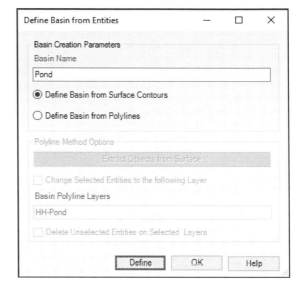

The *Stage Storage* dialog box will open again, now with the volume calculations complete in the table at the bottom of the dialog box.

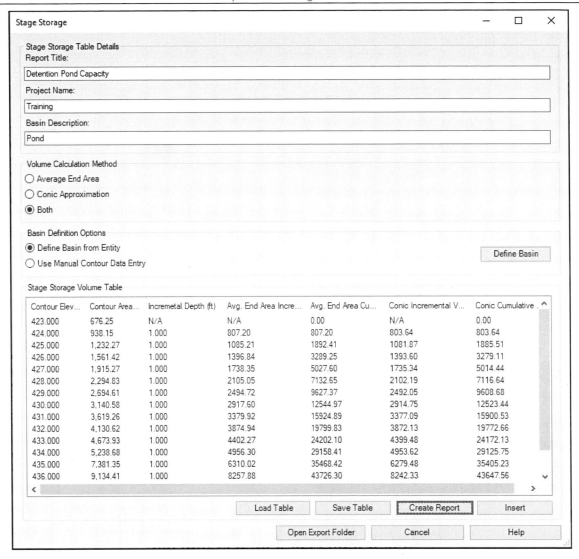

12. Review the volume calculations showing the capacity of the pond at each contour elevation.

13. Click **<<Create Report>>** to select the location you would like to save the exported report. Browse to the path: **C:\A Practical Guide\Civil 3D 2020\**

14. Enter a file name of **Pond Storage** and click **<<Save>>** to create the report.

The report is opened in Notepad for you to review.

15. Close Notepad when you are done reviewing the report.

16. Click **<<Cancel>>** to close the *Stage Storage* dialog box.

# 10.2 Lesson: Volume Calculations

## Introduction

In this lesson, you will use the *Volumes Dashboard* calculate the earthwork volumes between two surfaces by creating a volume surface. Using multiple methods to calculate volumes is a good way to verify and confirm your results. The volume surface can then be used to display the depth of cut and fill.

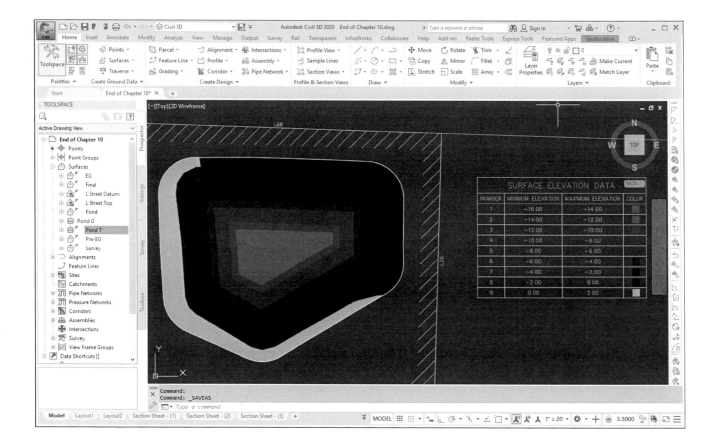

## Key Concepts

Concepts and key terms covered in this lesson are:

- Volumes Dashboard
- Grid Volume Surfaces
- TIN Volume Surfaces
- Surface Styles
- Surface Legend Tables

## Objectives

After completing this lesson, you will be able to:

- Describe the difference between Grid Volumes and TIN Volumes.
- Create a Grid Volume Surface and find its Volume.
- Create a TIN Volume Surface and find its Volume.

## Volumes Dashboard

The *Volumes Dashboard* panorama allows you to analyze the volumes for volume surfaces and bounded areas within volume surfaces.

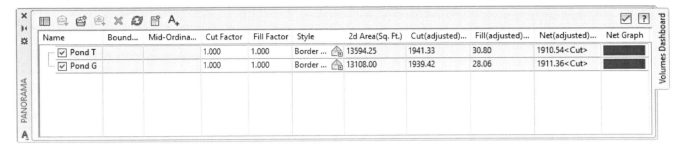

## Grid Volume Surfaces

Grid Volume Surfaces compare two surfaces and calculate a volume based on a user defined grid. In this type of a volume calculation the elevation difference is measured between the two surfaces at the grid points. This means that the accuracy is dependent on the grid size.

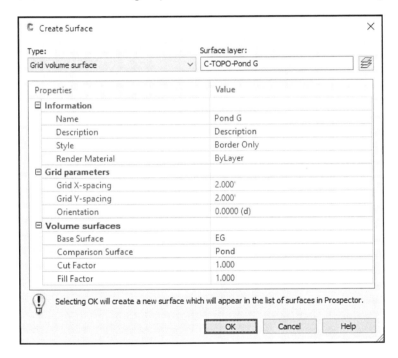

## TIN Volume Surfaces

TIN Volume Surfaces compare two surfaces and calculate a volume. This is a true surface comparison volume where all the points from each surface are used to calculate elevation differences that are used to create the Volume Surface and calculate volumes.

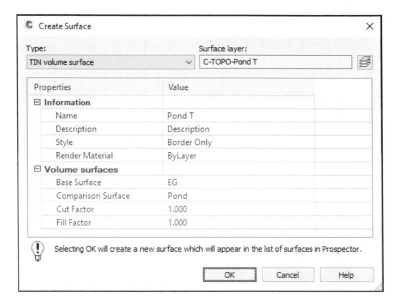

## Displaying Cut and Fill Depths

Volume Surfaces are displayed with styles just like TIN Surfaces. You can use a surface style that has been set up for elevation banding and run an elevation analysis on the volume surface to display colored bands representing the depth of cut and fill.

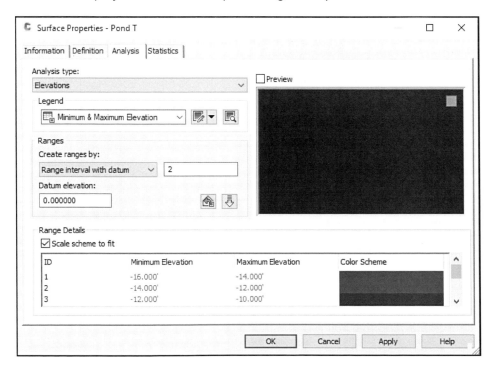

## Exercises: Calculate Volumes

In these exercises, you create grid volume and TIN surfaces to calculate the earthwork volume of the pond. You then display a volume surface with elevation bands to represent the depth of cut and fill in different areas.

You do the following:

- Create a Grid Volume Surface.
- Create a TIN Volume Surface.
- Display a Volume Surface showing the depths of cut and fill.
- Create a Legend.

### 10.2.1   Creating a Grid Volume Surface

1.   Continue working in the drawing **Design.dwg**.

*Reminder:*  You can also open the drawing with this exercise number in the *Chapter Drawings* folder of the dataset if you prefer a fresh start at this point.

2.   Select **Ribbon: Analyze ⇒ Volumes and Materials ⇒ Volumes Dashboard.**

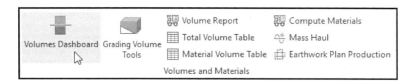

This opens the *Volumes Dashboard* panorama. Here you can analyze the volumes for volume surfaces and bounded areas within volume surfaces.

3.   Click the *Create New Volume Surface* button.

This opens the Create Surface dialog box. You could also get to this dialog box by right-clicking on *Surfaces* in the *Prospector* and selecting ⇒ *Create Surface*.

4. Select **Grid Volume surface** as the **Type**.

5. Click the **Surface Layer** 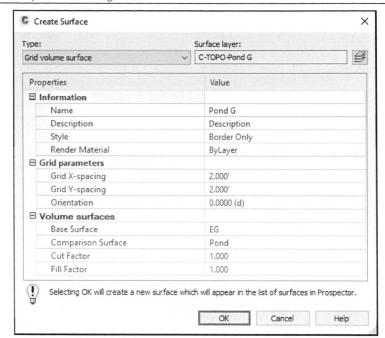 button to open the *Object Layer* dialog box.

6. Set the **Modifier** to **Suffix**.

7. Enter **-*** as the **Modifier value**.

8. Click **<<OK>>** to close the *Object Layer* dialog box.

9. Enter **Pond G** for the **Name**.

10. Set the surface **Style** to **Border Only**.

11. Set the **Grid X-spacing** to **2**.

12. Set the **Grid Y-spacing** to **2**.

13. Set the **Base Surface** to **EG**.

14. Set the **Comparison Surface** to **Pond**.

15. Click **<<OK>>** to create the *Volume Surface* and calculate the volume.

Notice the jagged edge of the new grid volume surface that is displayed around the edge of the pond. This is showing the size of the grid used for the volume calculation. The smaller grid that you use the more accurate the volume calculation will be, within reason. You will not gain anything by using a microscopic grid; however, the calculation will take longer.

16. Review the volume results in the *Volumes Dashboard*.

The volume results can also be viewed in the *Surface Properties*.

17. On the *Prospector* tab of the *Toolspace*, right-click on the *Surface* **Pond G** and select ⇒ **Surface Properties**.

18. Select the **Statistics** tab of the *Surface Properties* dialog box.

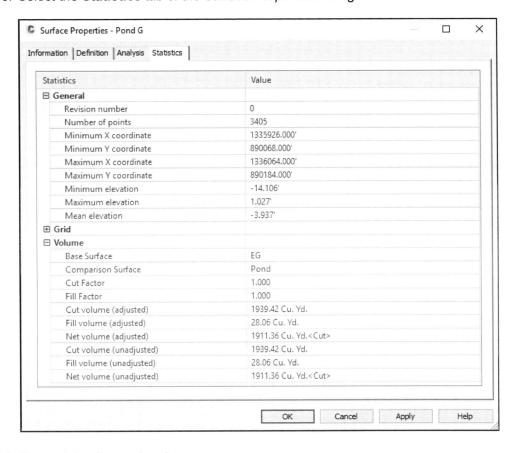

19. Expand the **General** node.

Here you can review the minimum and maximum elevations of the surface. For a volume surface that is the maximum depth of cut and fill.

20. Expand the **Volume** node.

Here you can review the surfaces used to calculate the volume and the volume results.

21. Click **<<OK>>** to close the **Surface Properties** dialog box.

### 10.2.2 Creating a TIN Volume Surface

1. Continue working in the drawing **Design.dwg**.

2. If the Volumes Dashboard is not already open, select **Ribbon: Analyze ⇒ Volumes and Materials ⇒ Volumes Dashboard.**

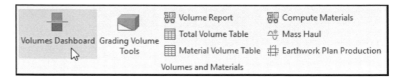

3. Click the *Create New Volume Surface* button.

This opens the Create Surface dialog box. You could also get to this dialog box by right-clicking on *Surfaces* in the *Prospector* and selecting ⇒ *Create Surface*.

4. Select **TIN Volume surface** as the **Type**.

5. Enter **Pond T** for the **Name**.

6. Set the surface **Style** to **Border Only**.

7. Set the **Base Surface** to **EG**.

8. Set the **Comparison Surface** to **Pond**.

9. Click **<<OK>>** to create the *Volume Surface* and calculate the volume.

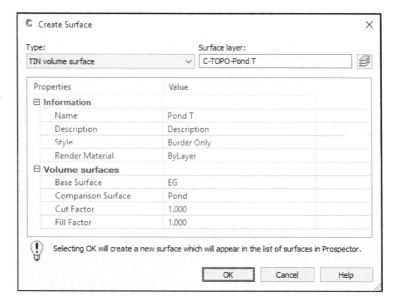

10. Review the volume results in the *Volumes Dashboard*.

11. Close the *Volumes Dashboard*.

The volume results can also be viewed in the *Surface Properties*.

12. On the *Prospector* tab of the *Toolspace*, right-click on the *Surface* **Pond T** and select ⇒ **Surface Properties**.

13. Select the **Statistics** tab of the *Surface Properties* dialog box.

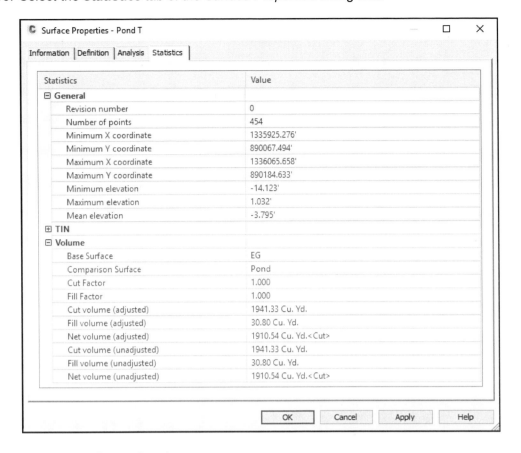

14. Expand the **General** node.

Here you can review the minimum and maximum elevations of the surface. For a volume surface that is the maximum depth of cut and fill.

15. Expand the **Volume** node.

Here you can review the surfaces used to calculate the volume and the volume results.

16. Click **<<OK>>** to close the *Surface Properties* dialog box.

### 10.2.3  Displaying Cut and Fill with Surface Styles

In this exercise, you will use the style *Border & Elevations* that you created in *Chapter 5* for elevation banding to display depths of cut and fill.

1. On the *Prospector* tab of the *Toolspace,* right-click on the *Surface* **Pond T** and select ⇒ **Surface Properties**.

2. Change the surface style to **Border & Elevations**.

This is the surface style you created in *Chapter 5* for elevation banding.

3. Select the **Analysis** tab of the *Surface Properties* dialog box.

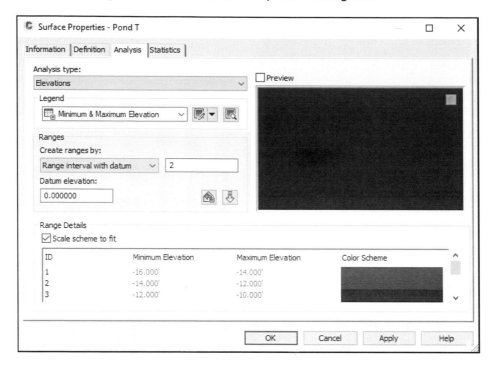

4. Confirm that the **Analysis type** is set to **Elevations**.

5. Set the **Create ranges by** option to **Range interval with datum**.

6. Set the **Interval** to **2**.

7. Set the **Datum Elevation** to **0**.

8. Click the **Run Analysis** button to analyze the surface.

The Range Details table at the bottom of the dialog box will now show different colors assigned to each 2' depth of cut or fill, with reds for cut and greens for fill. You can change the colors or ranges if you want to highlight certain depths of cut or fill.

9. Click **<<OK>>** to display the elevation bands representing the depth of cut and fill in the volume surface.

This is a great way to check your volume results. If you examine the depth bands and find an area that is displaying more or less cut or fill than you expect, then you know there is a problem with your volumes. You should then examine that area closely in the two surfaces used to create the volume surface, the existing and proposed surfaces, to find and correct the error.

## 10.2.4 Creating a Legend for Cut and Fill Depths

1. Select **Ribbon: Annotate** ⇒ **Labels & Tables** ⇒ **Add Tables** ⇒ **Add Surface Legend Table.**

2. At the command line prompt Select a surface, **[Enter]** to select it from a list.

You also have the option to pick it graphically from the screen. However, this can be difficult if there are several surfaces displayed that all overlap each other.

3. Select the surface **Pond T**.

4. Click **<<OK>>**.

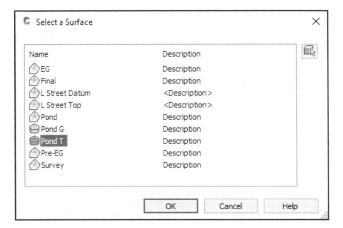

5. At the command line prompt **[Enter]** to select the default option of **Elevations**.

6. At the command line prompt **[Enter]** to select the default option of **Dynamic**.

7. Pick a point in a blank area to the right of the pond for the location of the upper left corner of the legend.

A legend table will be created for the elevation bands displaying the depth of cut and fill. This table is a single object so you can easily move it to another location if it is overlapping anything. The display of the table is controlled by the table style as selected on the *Analysis* tab of the *Surface Properties* dialog box.

8. Save the drawing.

# 11 - Data Shortcuts

In this chapter, you will learn to share data with other drawings in a project by using *Data Shortcuts*. This allows you to work with smaller drawings and give access to other users so multiple people can work on the same project at the same time.

### Lesson: Sharing Project Data with Data Shortcuts

In this lesson, you will learn the concepts and procedures for creating and managing *Data Shortcuts* to efficiently work with large data sets and share project data with other team members.

## 11.1 Lesson: Sharing Project Data with Data Shortcuts

### Introduction

*Data Shortcuts* allow you to share certain *Civil 3D* objects between drawings. This allows you to work with smaller drawings while at the same time sharing project data with others. These shortcuts are managed through the *Prospector* and are stored in a *Data Shortcut Project Folder*.

### Key Concepts

Concepts and key terms covered in this lesson are:

- Working Folder
- Data Shortcut Project Folder
- Data Shortcuts
- Creating References

### Objectives

After completing this lesson, you will be able to:

- Describe what a Data Shortcut is.
- List the types of data that can be shared through Data Shortcuts.
- Understand the Working Folder.
- Create and Manage the Data Shortcut Project Folder.

## Managing Data in Civil 3D

There are four methods of managing data in Civil 3D:

- Single Drawing
- External References
- Data Shortcuts
- Vault

## Single Drawing

This is the simplest method of managing data in *Civil 3D* where you keep all the information related to the project in one single drawing. Using this method, drawings can become large and performance can drop. In addition, only one person can access the project data at a time. However, for small projects that will only be worked on by one person, this method can work fine.

## External References

*External References* are an *AutoCAD* feature and can be used to reference drawings and display *AutoCAD* objects. In addition to this you can label *Civil 3D* objects that have been displayed through an external reference. Finally, you can use external references to reference corridors into drawings to sample cross sections.

## Data Shortcuts

*Data Shortcuts* provide complete reference copies of objects that you can insert into one or more other drawings. *Data Shortcuts* can be created only for surfaces, alignments, profiles, pipe networks, and view frame groups. They provide reference links between drawings without the use of a database. When you create data shortcuts from a drawing, they appear on the *Data Shortcuts* node of the *Prospector*. From this location, you can insert a reference object into another open drawing by right-clicking its shortcut.

## Vault

*Autodesk Vault* is a document management system that allows you to check in drawing files as well as share certain Civil 3D object between drawings. This system requires a Vault Server and someone to manage it. It also requires additional training and commitment from the entire organization.

## The Working Folder

Projects with data shortcut references use the concept of a working folder for storing all projects. For data shortcut projects, the working folder contains the actual project documents. This is similar to the Project Root Directory in Land Desktop.

The working folder will typically reside on your network. You can use a single working folder that contains many projects, or you can have a new working folder for each project. This is up to you and depends on your directory structure and file management standards.

On the *Prospector* tab of the *Toolspace*, right-click **Data Shortcuts** and select ⇒ **Set Working Folder**.

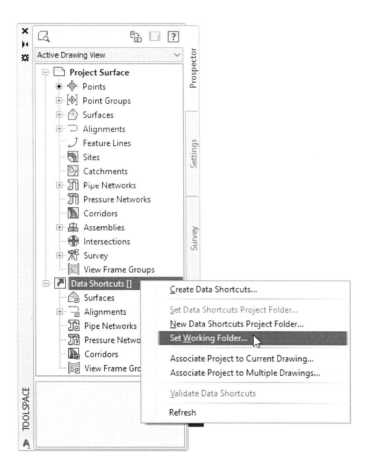

## The Data Shortcuts Project Folder

411

The Data Shortcuts Project Folder contains the data shortcuts. It can also contain the drawings referenced in the data shortcuts and any other project data that you desire.

To switch between Data Shortcut Project Folders:

On the *Prospector* tab of the *Toolspace*, right-click **Data Shortcuts** and select ⇒ **Set Data Shortcuts Project Folder**.

To create a new Data Shortcut Project Folder:

On the *Prospector* tab of the *Toolspace*, right-click **Data Shortcuts** and select ⇒ **New Data Shortcuts Project Folder**.

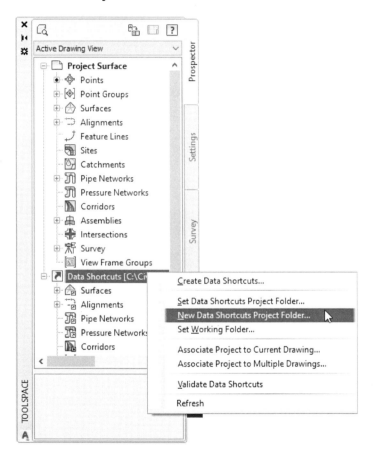

## Data Structure

The *Data Shortcut Project Folder*, or project folder, is a subdirectory of the *Working Folder*. When you create a new *Data Shortcut Project Folder* it will automatically have one subdirectory called "_Shortcuts". You can also use a Project Template when creating a new *Data Shortcut Project Folder*. You can add folders to a Project Template by simply creating new folders in windows explorer. These new folders will automatically be copied to each new *Data Shortcut Project Folder* when new projects are created and the project template is selected.

This new type of project, or *Data Shortcut Project Folder*, is much more flexible than the old Land Desktop project. You can add or edit any additional folders residing under the *Data Shortcut Project Folder*, with the exception of the one subdirectory called "_Shortcuts". This is automatically created and managed by Civil 3D and contains the information for the data shortcuts.

## Process

1. Set the working folder.

2. Set or create the data shortcut project folder.

3. Create data shortcuts.

4. Create references to objects using data shortcuts.

5. Any changes to referenced objects will be updated if there are changes to the source object.

The process for creating data shortcuts for Surfaces, Alignments, Profiles, Pipe Networks, and View Frame Groups is the same. Referenced objects can be used for design purposes, assigned different styles, and labeled. They cannot be edited; this must be done in the original or master drawing.

If the original object is modified in the master drawing, then the drawings containing the reference objects are updated. If a drawing containing the reference object is open then you will receive a balloon notification that the Data Shortcut definitions have changed and need to be Synchronized.

## Exercises: Share Project Data with Data Shortcuts

In these exercises, you create a data shortcut project. Then you create data shortcuts to make certain objects available in the project to other drawings. Finally, you create references to data in the project.

You do the following:

- Set the Working Folder.
- Create a Data Shortcut Project.
- Create a Data Shortcut.
- Create a reference to a Data Shortcut.

## 11.1.1  Setting the Working Folder

In this exercise, you will set the Working Folder.  This is the folder that will contain one or more projects.

    1.   Open the drawing **Project Surface.dwg**.

    2.   On the *Prospector* tab of the *Toolspace*, right-click **Data Shortcuts** and **select** ⇒ **Set Working Folder**.

The working folder will typically reside on your network. You can use a single working folder that contains many projects, or you can have a new working folder for each project. This is up to you and depends on your directory structure and file management standards.

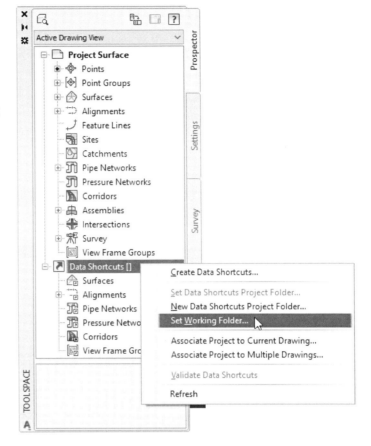

    3.   In the *Browse For Folder* dialog box, the confirm the location **C:\Civil 3D Projects\** is selected.

In this dialog box, you may browse the file system and place the working folder at your desired location either on a local drive or on your network.  You may also create new folders. For this exercise, you will keep the working folder set locally.

    4.   Click **<<OK>>**.

### 11.1.2 Creating a Data Shortcut Project

In this exercise, you create a *Data Shortcut Project Folder*. This project folder resides in the *Working Folder* and will contain the data shortcuts. It can also contain any other file or files that you wish to save there, including drawings.

1. Continue working in the drawing **Project Surface.dwg**.

2. On the *Prospector* tab of the *Toolspace*, right-click **Data Shortcuts** and select ⇒ **New Data Shortcuts Project Folder.**

3. Enter **Training** for the **Name** of the new project.

4. Click **<<OK>>** to create the new *Data Shortcut Project Folder*.

The new Data Shortcut Project Folder along with its path will be displayed in the Prospector as part of the Data Shortcut collection.

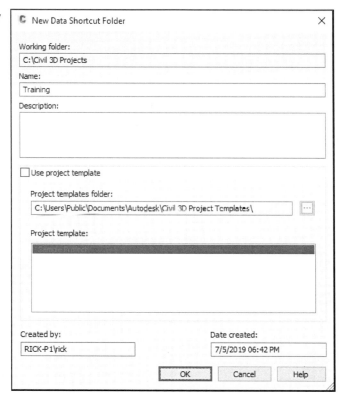

### 11.1.3 Creating Data Shortcuts

In this exercise, you will share a surface from the current drawing and make it available for use in other drawings in this project by creating a *Data Shortcut*.

1. Continue working in the drawing **Project Surface.dwg**.

2. On the *Prospector* tab of the *Toolspace*, right-click **Data Shortcuts** and select ⇒ **Create Data Shortcuts**.

The *Create Data Shortcuts* dialog box is displayed. Here you select the objects (Surfaces, Alignments, Profiles, Pipe Networks, and View Frame Groups) that you would like to share with other drawings.

3. Enable the *Surface* **EG**.

This drawing only contains one surface so that is all that is shown in the *Create Data Shortcuts* dialog box. If your drawing contains additional surfaces, alignments, profiles, pipe networks, or view frame groups they will be displayed here.

4. Click **<<OK>>** to add this surface to the project.

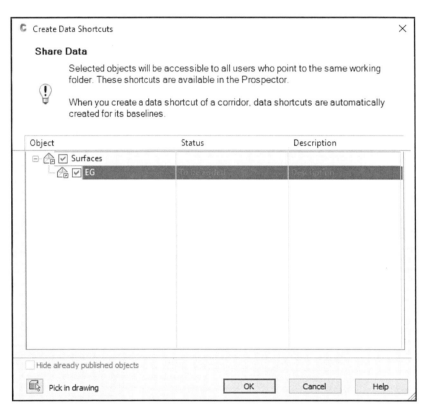

The new Data Shortcuts are now displayed in the *Prospector* under the appropriate object type of the Data Shortcut collection. This data is now available to be referenced into other drawings.

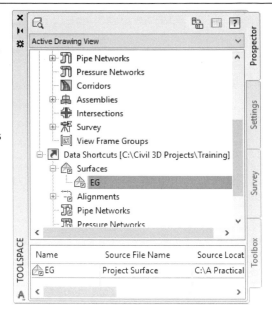

For larger or more complex projects Data Shortcuts can be organized into folders under each collection. For example, you could right click on the Surfaces collection under Data Shortcuts and select Create Folder to create folders for Existing and Proposed surfaces. Then drag and drop the desired surfaces into each folder.

    5.  **Save** the drawing.

### 11.1.4 Creating Data Shortcut References

In this exercise, you will create a new drawing and reference the surface *EG* into it. Then you will create an alignment and profile through that referenced surface. Finally, you will create new data shortcuts that share the alignment and profile with the project.

    1.  Press **Ctrl + N** and select the template **_Practical Guide Training by Style.dwt** to start a new drawing.

    2.  Save the drawing as **Project Alignment.dwg**, in the folder **C:\A Practical Guide\Civil 3D 2020\**

    3.  In the *Prospector*, expand **Data Shortcuts ⇒ Surfaces**.

    4.  Right-click the surface **EG** and select ⇒ **Create Reference**.

This opens the *Create Surface Reference* dialog box. Notice how this is similar to the *Create Surface* dialog box, with the exception that Source Surface replaces Surface Type in the upper left corner.

5. Set the **Style** to **Border & Contours**.

The style can be set differently than the style used in the source drawing where the object was created.

6. Click **<<OK>>** to create the reference.

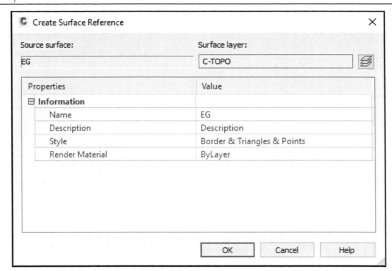

The surface reference is now created in the current drawing. This surface will now display in the *Prospector* as data in the current drawing. However, it is a read only link to the surface in the original drawing. So the original data is protected from any edits or changes. Notice that the surface definition, including editing commands, is not available in the *Prospector* under the surface reference.

7. **Zoom Extents** to review the surface.

You will now create a new alignment across the referenced surface.

8. Select **Ribbon: Home ⇒ Create Design ⇒ Alignment ⇒ Alignment Creation Tools**.

This opens the *Create Alignment - Layout* dialog box where you can name and setup your alignment.

9.  Change the **Name** to **Main Street**.

10. Confirm the *Alignment Type* is set to **Centerline**.

11. Confirm the **Site** is set to **None**.

12. Confirm that the **Alignment Style** is set to **Design Style**.

13. Confirm that the Alignment label set is set to **Major Minor & Geometry Point**.

14. Click **<<OK>>** to create the alignment and open the *Alignment Layout* toolbar.

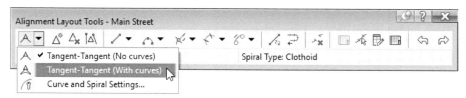

15. Click the **down arrow** next to the *Tangent-Tangent (No curves)* button on the *Alignment Layout* toolbar, to display the other creation commands.

16. Select ⇒ **Tangent-Tangent (With curves)**.

17. Enter **1336096.7,891291.3** for the start point.

18. Enter **1336818.1,891253.4** for the second point.

19. Enter **1336810.4,890868.2** for the third point.

20. **[Enter]** to end the command.

21. Close the **Alignment Layout Tools** toolbar.

Next you will sample a profile through the referenced surface.

22. Select **Ribbon: Home** ⇒ **Create Design** ⇒ **Profile** ⇒ **Create Surface Profile**.

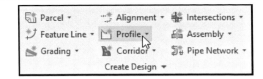

This opens the *Create Profile from Surface* dialog box where you can select the alignment, surface(s), and offsets that you would like to use to sample the profile(s).

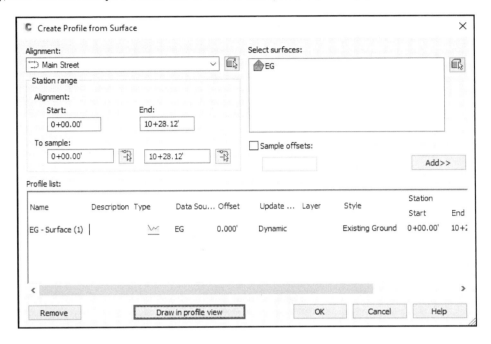

23. Set the **Alignment** to **Main Street**.

24. Select the *Surface* **EG**.

25. Click **<<Add>>**.

26. Click **<<Draw in profile view>>**.

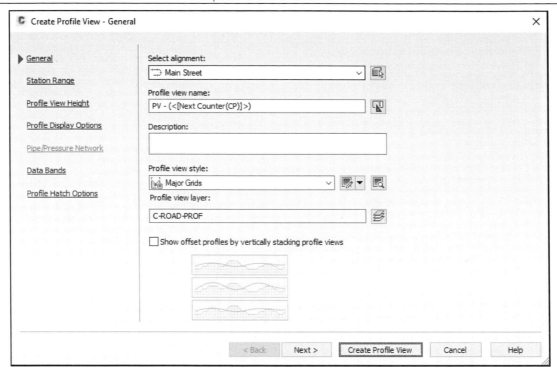

27. Confirm that the **Profile view style** is set to **Major Grids**.

28. Click **<<Create Profile View>>** to complete the wizard and add the new *Profile View* to the drawing.

29. Select a blank area in the drawing to create the *Profile View*.

The profile is created using the surface data from the data reference. The surface is available in this drawing in a read only mode. It can be used for operations like creating profiles and volume calculations; however it cannot be edited in this drawing. The surface can only be edited in the drawing it was created in.

30. **Save** the drawing.

Now you will create *Data Shortcuts* for the new alignment and profile to share them in the project.

31. On the *Prospector* tab of the *Toolspace*, right-click **Data Shortcuts** and select ⇒ **Create Data Shortcuts**.

32. Enable the **Alignments** collection.

This will include all the alignments and profiles below it.

Notice the surface *EG* is not shown in this dialog box. It is a reference and a Data Shortcut to it can only be created in the source drawing.

33. Click **<<OK>>** to add the new alignment and profile to the project.

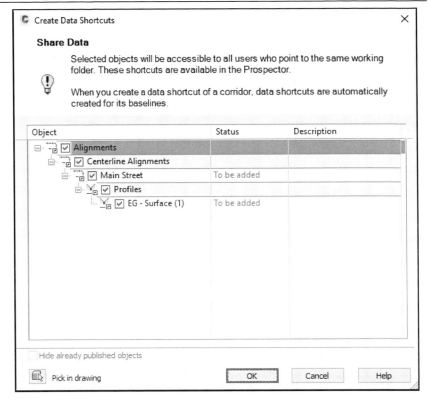

The new Data Shortcuts are now displayed in the *Prospector* under the appropriate object type of the Data Shortcut collection. This data is now available to be referenced into other drawings.

34. **Save** the drawing.

If you go back to the drawing *Project Surface.dwg* and make a change to the surface, like adding surface data, deleting TIN lines or swapping triangle edges, once you save the drawing with those changes, the data reference in the drawing *Project Alignment.dwg* will be shown as *Out of Date*. You can right click on the surface and select ⇒ *Synchronize* to update the surface. There will also be a balloon notification on the status bar where you can select *Synchronize*.

# Index